Y0-AAA-724

# Linguistic Analysis of Mathematics

*By the*

Same Author

The Process of Government

(University of Chicago Press, 1908)

Relativity in Man and Society

(G. P. Putnam's Sons, 1926)

**$*54{\cdot}42$.** $\vdash :: \alpha \in 2 \,.\supset :. \beta \subset \alpha \,.\, \exists ! \beta \,.\, \beta \neq \alpha \,.\equiv.\, \beta \in \iota``\alpha$

*Dem.*

$\vdash .\, *54{\cdot}4 \,.\quad \supset \vdash :: \alpha = \iota`x \cup \iota`y \,.\supset :.$

$\beta \subset \alpha \,.\, \exists ! \beta \,.\equiv : \beta = \Lambda \,.\vee.\, \beta = \iota`x \,.\vee.\, \beta = \iota`y \,.\vee.\, \beta = \alpha : \exists ! \beta :$

$[*24{\cdot}53{\cdot}56 \,.\, *51{\cdot}161] \qquad \equiv : \beta = \iota`x \,.\vee.\, \beta = \iota`y \,.\vee.\, \beta = \alpha \qquad (1)$

$\vdash .\, *54{\cdot}25 \,.\, \text{Transp} \,.\, *52{\cdot}22 \,.\supset \vdash : x \neq y \,.\supset.\, \iota`x \cup \iota`y \neq \iota`x \,.\, \iota`x \cup \iota`y \neq \iota`y :$

$[*13{\cdot}12] \qquad \supset \vdash : \alpha = \iota`x \cup \iota`y \,.\, x \neq y \,.\supset.\, \alpha \neq \iota`x \,.\, \alpha \neq \iota`y \qquad (2)$

$\vdash .\, (1) \,.\, (2) \,.\supset \vdash :: \alpha = \iota`x \cup \iota`y \,.\, x \neq y \,.\supset :.$

$\beta \subset \alpha \,.\, \exists ! \beta \,.\, \beta \neq \alpha \,.\equiv : \beta = \iota`x \,.\vee.\, \beta = \iota`y :$

$[*51{\cdot}235] \qquad \equiv : (\exists z) \,.\, z \in \alpha \,.\, \beta = \iota`z :$

$[*37{\cdot}6] \qquad \equiv : \beta \in \iota``\alpha \qquad (3)$

$\vdash .\, (3) \,.\, *11{\cdot}11{\cdot}35 \,.\, *54{\cdot}101 \,.\supset \vdash .\, \text{Prop}$

**$*54{\cdot}43$.** $\vdash :. \alpha, \beta \in 1 \,.\supset : \alpha \cap \beta = \Lambda \,.\equiv.\, \alpha \cup \beta \in 2$

*Dem.*

$\vdash .\, *54{\cdot}26 \,.\supset \vdash :. \alpha = \iota`x \,.\, \beta = \iota`y \,.\supset : \alpha \cup \beta \in 2 \,.\equiv.\, x \neq y \,.$

$[*51{\cdot}231] \qquad \equiv .\, \iota`x \cap \iota`y = \Lambda \,.$

$[*13{\cdot}12] \qquad \equiv .\, \alpha \cap \beta = \Lambda \qquad (1)$

$\vdash .\, (1) \,.\, *11{\cdot}11{\cdot}35 \,.\supset$

$\vdash :. (\exists x, y) \,.\, \alpha = \iota`x \,.\, \beta = \iota`y \,.\supset : \alpha \cup \beta \in 2 \,.\equiv.\, \alpha \cap \beta = \Lambda \qquad (2)$

$\vdash .\, (2) \,.\, *11{\cdot}54 \,.\, *52{\cdot}1 \,.\supset \vdash .\, \text{Prop}$

From this proposition it will follow, when arithmetical addition has been defined, that $1 + 1 = 2$.

**$*54{\cdot}44$.** $\vdash :. z, w \in \iota`x \cup \iota`y \,.\supset_{z,w} .\, \phi(z, w) : \equiv .\, \phi(x, x) \,.\, \phi(x, y) \,.\, \phi(y, x) \,.\, \phi(y, y)$

*Dem.*

$\vdash .\, *51{\cdot}234 \,.\, *11{\cdot}62 \,.\supset \vdash :. z, w \in \iota`x \cup \iota`y \,.\supset_{z,w} .\, \phi(z, w) : \equiv :$

$z \in \iota`x \cup \iota`y \,.\supset_z .\, \phi(z, x) \,.\, \phi(z, y) :$

$[*51{\cdot}234 \,.\, *10{\cdot}29] \equiv : \phi(x, x) \,.\, \phi(x, y) \,.\, \phi(y, x) \,.\, \phi(y, y) :. \supset \vdash .\, \text{Prop}$

**$*54{\cdot}441$.** $\vdash :: z, w \in \iota`x \cup \iota`y \,.\, z \neq w \,.\supset_{z,w} .\, \phi(z, w) : \equiv :. x = y : \vee : \phi(x, y) \,.\, \phi(y, x)$

*Dem.*

$\vdash .\, *5{\cdot}6 \,.\supset \vdash :: z, w \in \iota`x \cup \iota`y \,.\, z \neq w \,.\supset_{z,w} .\, \phi(z, w) : \equiv :.$

$z, w \in \iota`x \cup \iota`y \,.\supset_{z,w} : z = w \,.\vee.\, \phi(z, w) :.$

$[*54{\cdot}44] \qquad \equiv : x = x \,.\vee.\, \phi(x, x) : x = y \,.\vee.\, \phi(x, y) :$

$y = x \,.\vee.\, \phi(y, x) : y = y \,.\vee.\, \phi(y, y) :$

$[*13{\cdot}15 \qquad \equiv : x = y \,.\vee.\, \phi(x, y) : y = x \,.\vee.\, \phi(y, x) :$

$[*13{\cdot}16 \,.\, *4{\cdot}41] \equiv : x = y \,.\vee.\, \phi(x, y) \,.\, \phi(y, x)$

This proposition is used in $*163{\cdot}42$, in the theory of relations of mutually exclusive relations.

---

FROM WHITEHEAD AND RUSSELL: PRINCIPIA MATHEMATICA.

FROM

WHITEHEAD AND RUSSELL: PRINCIPIA MATHEMATICA.

# LINGUISTIC ANALYSIS OF MATHEMATICS

*By*

ARTHUR F. BENTLEY

THE PRINCIPIA PRESS, INC.
Bloomington, Indiana
1932

To Those Whose Words I Criticize:

This Recognition of My Debt.

# FOREWORD

This essay deals with the language of mathematics, including not merely the mathematical symbols, but also those immediately surrounding forms of expressions and assertion through which the symbols are developed, communicated and interpreted.

The writer seeks to establish a firm construction for this embedding language. This construction is, in effect, a purification of that language: and the purification is presented as one under the control of mathematical consistency itself, a procedure brought forward as in sharp contrast to the many efforts to obtain the consistent organization of mathematics under the control of Aristotelian logic. The influence of Hilbert will be recognized at once in these statements, however far the proposed construction may depart from Hilbert's own manner of attack. There is no contribution here offered to the symbolic organization of mathematics itself. Let it be understood that if the construction of the embedding language has value for mathematics, it will remain for mathematicians themselves to develop it.

In our every-day life we take words as pointing to things. We separate sharply between *words* as the tools of men, and *things* as the actualities to which the words are supposed to point. We take the best words to be those of sharpest definition and greatest precision as pointers.

In mathematics the symbols, the words of its peculiar language, have a different status. Their bond is consistency among themselves. They are not appraised primarily for their service as pointers.

To embalm the mathematical symbols in the "terms" of logic, itself a distillate of every-day language, is not to heighten their validity. Neither, fortunately, is it to lessen it.

The every-day language reeks with philosophies—the absolutisms of pointing. It shatters at every touch of advancing knowledge. At its heart lies paradox.

The language of mathematics, on the contrary, stands and grows in firmness. It gives service to men beyond all other language.

The every-day language asks "what kind of thing" consistency "is." But mathematics is consistency itself.

Mathematicians know this. Yet they feel ever the compulsion to interpret their mathematics in terms of the every-day language. So proceeding, their harvest is super-paradox.

It is a strange but obvious fact that when we wish to extend the standards of symbolic consistency into the regions of the embedding language, we have, still, no way to proceed, save through the medium of that very corruption of language for which purification is being sought. For every-day language is the basal medium of communication between men. Development must therefore be precarious: it must be in part impressionistic: it must be subject at every point to the perils of mis-reading. Only as an island in this sea of linguistic confusion may a small region of precision be established.

This caution, then, must be given the reader: that he read the poorer language which we must use by the light of the better: that he deny himself the specious security of factual definition: that he strive to improve the expression by understanding, rather than degrade it by convention. This requirement is not easy: it is not simple. But its neglect means failure to read at all.

The student of the records of life still writes "animal" and "man." Tennessee still reads "brute" and "human." And with that reading all the message of comparative anatomy and embryology is lost.

For the many well-aimed darts they have let fly against my construction during the course of its development, I wish to thank my friends, Professors J. R. Kantor and H. T. Davis, of Indiana University. Such opponents bring welcome gifts. I have to thank them further, and with them Professor K. P. Williams of Indiana University and Count Alfred Korzybski of New York City, for their kindness in reading the proof sheets and for the many valued suggestions each of them has made.

# CONTENTS

## ABBREVIATIONS

| | |
|---|---|
| Amer. J. | American Journal of Mathematics. |
| Amer. Math. Monthly | American Mathematical Monthly. |
| Amer. M. S. Bull. | Bulletin of the American Mathematical Society. |
| Amer. M. S. Trans. | Transactions of the American Mathematical Society. |
| Annals of Math. | Annals of Mathematics. |
| Deutsche Math.-Ver. | Jahresbericht der Deutschen Mathematiker-Vereinigung. |
| Hamb. Abh. | Abhandlungen aus dem Mathematischen Seminar der Hamburgischen Universität. |
| J. für Math. | Journal für die reine und angewandte Mathematik. |
| Lond. M. S. Proc. | Proceedings of the London Mathematical Society. |
| Math. Ann. | Mathematische Annalen. |
| Math. Zeitschr. | Mathematische Zeitschrift. |
| Rev. de métaph et de mor. | Revue de métaphysique et de morale. |

# INTRODUCTION

"Foundations of Mathematics" is a name adopted within the last generation for a group of problems in mathematical borderlands. They are all problems of consistency. Their investigator takes mathematical symbols as his immediate materials of examination, his direct data or "phenomena." These symbols present themselves to him with consistent meanings held together in various organizations. Making his start with the accepted consistencies of symbolic procedure in these definite algebraic, geometric and analytic organizations, he then endeavors to extend these consistencies across all of mathematics taken as in one system. He is involved thereby, directly or indirectly, clearly or confusedly, in the broadest problems of the appraisal of knowledge in its many forms and in its entanglement in the practical living of mankind.

Within the ranges of his accepted consistencies the mathematician has long been accustomed to stress the word "logic" as indicative of that aspect or phase of his procedure under which the consistency is secured. It has been easy and natural, then, and it has become conventional, to identify the logic of mathematics with Aristotelian logic in its historical development. And thus we have witnessed the rise of mathematical foundation structures in which logic plays the rôle of the foundations.

The logical constructions lead, however, to paradox: and this, not merely in the cruder forms in which they first appeared, where the outcome at times shocked the originators to recantation, but likewise in the most subtle and powerful developments which the most competent thinkers of the past generation have been able to attain. Russell presents the culmination of this line of progress. He uncovered fresh paradoxes, was driven to his theory of types, and stimulated much important thought, but his system still stands defective at a point which is crucial for its validity in whole as well as in part. Brouwer compromised by placing a restriction upon one of the Aristotelian canons, that of the excluded middle, and sought his guarantees of consistency in a mystic power of Intuition, to which he gives so much devotion that the inconsistencies of his own cumbrous development, under the truncated Aristotelian canon, worry him not at all. For the every-day purposes of mathematical work in branches in which the use of some connective foundation doctrine is essential, it is still today the custom to rely upon arbitrary dicta, such as Fraenkel's "Beschränktheitsaxiom" for the "Mengenlehre."

Hilbert represents a further stage of progress. Developing the investigation of Russell's types, he has shown that the strictly logical constructions within mathematics offer a series of separate logical stages or "Stufen," themselves not logically coherent with one another: and he has centered his own program of investigation upon the establishment of a mathematical consistency in its own mathematical right—his well-known construction of "Widerspruchsfreiheit"—although for this he still lacks one essential proof leading back from the more complex to the more simple mathematical presentations.

To distinguish it from the logical foundation structures proper, Hilbert's form of attack is sometimes, and more particularly by his opponents, called linguistic. This is appropriate, though not necessarily in a derogatory sense. The Aristotelian logic itself is, of course, a technique of language; but the term Logic is most commonly regarded as designating an intellectual procedure, with respect to which the linguistic elements appear rather in a subordinated instrumental capacity: whereas, in contrast, Hilbert proposes to convert the whole of mathematics into linguistic materials—symbols, "Zeichen," "Zeichen als Objekte"—and to establish the system of consistency directly by and between these "Zeichen." Not only does he present the ordinary mathematical "objects," such as the natural numbers in the form of "Zeichen," but also the operations of mathematics, such as "+": and then, beyond these, the primary logical elements which mathematics uses, such as "and" and "or": so that finally "some" and "all" must themselves appear as symbols of this kind: it being understood that the very locus of consistency is in the symbols themselves, and not in some other region of fact for which the symbols are merely representative, and that all of the symbols are "objects." It is, then, through the very reduction of all of his materials to one common system of "Zeichen" that Hilbert proposes to secure full consistency for all branches of mathematics in one.

What Hilbert does not do, however, is to carry his analysis linguistically back of the mathematical "Zeichen" into the full system of linguistic materials within which he has in effect made of his "Zeichen" a specialized division. He takes these "Zeichen," each for itself, as if individually, concretely and discretely, before him: he investigates them as thus discretely presented: but as for their very characteristic of being "before him"—"dagegeben" is his term—he merely posits a certain conventional psychological status—an "inner" power or faculty or condition—which he calls the "Anschauung": and when the "Anschauung" has reached its limit as a container for the development of his symbols, he posits an additional psychological factor as further realistic background for his construction. Describing the distinction between his construction and the logical foundation theories by the aid of words of slight accuracy but of easy current application, one may say that for him it is not the laws of intellect or of any other form of mentality that he proposes to study, but the laws of the "Zeichen" themselves: and that the mentality he uses is posited merely as background and basis for his work.

Now, however, this "Anschauung" and all similar presentations are themselves "words," members of that great linguistic field within which the Hilbertian "Zeichen" form one section. The factual reference and validity of these words can hardly be regarded as so definite and certain as to furnish off-hand and without further examination a firm basis for mathematical foundations. What it is that they themselves mean, and more particularly what it is that they mean for the purposes of mathematical construction, has never been directly established by adequately complete study of the situations they describe, and it cannot be inferred from their conventional employment, nor by appealing to some inner power of appraisal: it must be established by studying them in the very systems of presentations which they contain or offer, including, above all, that very system of mathematical "Zeichen," for which Hilbert posits them as bail and bond: and it is Hilbert's very assertion of the individuated concreteness and discreteness of the "Zeichen" which is at issue in this respect.

If Hilbert does not succeed to the satisfaction of himself and his professional colleagues in establishing the much-needed consistency, then the next step that is indicated for investigation is the further analysis of those very linguistic situations which furnish the basis, in the way indicated, for Hilbert's procedure. It is the investigation of that very linguistic region in which the "Anschauung" and the "Zeichen" are posited as together: this, however, not for philosophical, psychological or other wider purposes, but solely for the purposes of the investigation of mathematical consistency itself: and always under that full postulatory construction which is the sign-manual of mathematical validity. Nor is it necessary to wait until Hilbert's success or failure is established for the making of such investigations. Hilbert's own great step in advance over the previous forms of attack contains within itself the germ of the suggestion that experiment should be made to push it one stage further, so as to cover the full system of linguistic materials used in the search for mathematical consistency as well as the system of specifically mathematical "Zeichen."[1]

What has been said above is equivalent to asserting that the "foundations" of mathematics must be sought within mathematics itself. It is equivalent to asserting that the very word "foundations" uses a defective analogy drawn from regions far remote from mathematical procedure: that it is a bad word, containing implications which, so far from furthering the search for consistency, are destructive of its possibilities. Let me display again the existing situation in foundation studies with special attention to this aspect.

The issue of full consistency for mathematics is no mere decorative embellishment of the great structure of the science. That much, at least, the bad word, "foundations," attests. In certain borderland regions of development investigators are compelled, implicitly or explicitly, to take position with respect to it in order to handle their problems. More and more for the

[1]Hilbert entered the field of foundation studies with his system of axioms for geometry, first published in book form in 1899, and now in its seventh edition. This is briefly described in Chap. X. Since 1918 he has given almost continuous study to the more general foundation problems, working with the aid of a group of collaborators, most prominent among whom have been Bernays and Ackermann. Assuming—perhaps too hopefully—a wide familiarity with his work, I have nowhere given it systematic treatment in its full range. In addition to the many minor references in the text, an important citation is made towards the end of Chap. II, and a critical inspection of the materials from which he constructs his postulations will be found in Chap. V, Pars. 25 to 28, where also a chronologically arranged list of his papers is given. His logical and mathematical techniques, which are beyond doubt a permanent contribution to knowledge, I nowhere discuss in detail. These will doubtless retain their power and usefulness within ranges which future investigation will establish, despite any flaw in their basic linguistic specification.

whole science it becomes essential that unremitting attack upon it be made, no matter how many backs be broken in the struggle. It was Georg Cantor who forced it upon the present generation of mathematicians with his system of transfinites, a system which at first seemed so bizarre that publication was refused it by his own colleagues: which later led to the creation of a new and extremely interesting and useful branch of mathematical investigation: which has become for many workers dogma or creed: but which in the end has brought into prominence elements which challenge the coherence and meaning of all mathematical knowledge whatsoever. The issue was indeed close to the surface prior to Cantor's work, in the warring possible interpretations for the more general constructions of Weierstrass. At one of its critical points Dedekind gave it sharp definition. Of the two horns of the dilemma as it then showed itself—they may provisionally be called "relational" or "realistic" on the one side and "operational" on the other—Russell chose the one, and Poincaré and Kronecker chose the other. Brouwer's status has been that merely of a tentative following of Poincaré and Kronecker, a fright, a withdrawal, and a mystical recourse or solace. Hilbert's status, on the contrary, is that of one who has made most emphatic progress towards cutting beneath the roots of the dilemma itself.

In all of the existing constructions, sometimes in greater degree, sometimes in less—in Hilbert least of all—reliance is had upon one or another type of "foundation" materials taken as "known" or "dependable" outside of the range of mathematics itself.

And this despite the fact that mathematics is the safest and most certain knowledge the world possesses or thus far has had prospect of possessing.

Now mathematicians are everywhere aware that their science has a most pronounced habit of producing its most important results without seeking permission anywhere else, without ever asking "by your leave." Indeed so striking is this characteristic that at least once in a generation something is produced by their science which causes mathematicians themselves to view with alarm what is happening. It was true in the days of Pythagoras: and whether we consider the appearance of minus, zero and the imaginaries, the appearance of the non-Euclidean geometries of the last century, or that of the non-Riemannian geometries of this century, it is always the algebraic, the geometric, the analytic, in its own right that is found forcing its way forward, and coming to prevail despite all clamor.

The question now presents itself: Must mathematics in its struggle with its own "foundation" problems seek always a helping hand from without, or may it not be possible that it can proceed under its own power through the extension of its own most rigorous analytic methods? Here at least should be a reasonable field for experimentation.

It was the custom of one great mathematician in his moments of professorial sadness to explain, or at least to attempt to explain, to his students that all there was to mathematics was being definite about something and sticking to it. His remark covers the three great characteristics of mathematical method: it must be postulational: it must have consistency: it must, in the end, take full symbolic formulation.

In the first two of these characteristics, though not, as yet, in the third, this essay seeks to hold fully to the mathematical standard. It is throughout postulational. Where consistency fails, it seeks progress through further analysis of its postulational materials: given inconclusiveness or paradox in the symbolic development, it seeks solution, not by the use of external scaffolding, but by the analysis of the symbols themselves and their meanings. The deeper these difficulties run into the regions of the so-called "foundations," the more essential I regard it to pursue the analysis of symbols and meanings in system,[2] directly and wholly within their presented mathematical settings.

It is just because the analysis now reaches this very issue of symbols and meanings in system, that as a first stage it may not itself be developed in full symbolic formulation. If the symbols are misread, then of what use the symbols? "Quis custodiet ipsos custodes?" First duty of all is to guard the guardian symbols. We have a problem of things, relations and operations: of mathematical things, mathematical

---

[2]The use of the word "meanings" in the phrase "analysis of symbols and meanings in system" enables us to give fluent and reasonably indicative expression to the situation before us in the above passage. Therefore I have employed it and allowed it to stand. The word itself, however, is one that is highly indefinite; subject to many shadings of interpretation; apt in many cases to be dogmatically understood; and certain to convey to some readers the opposite of what I intend. It is the kind of word which, as I shall shortly point out, I will cause to be printed in the style "*meanings*" wherever special danger of misreading exists. In the present case if any dogmatic "meanings" are understood to be in control of the "system" the reading is wrong: whereas, if "meanings in system" is understood as one expression, the reading is correct.

relations, and mathematical operations. If the symbols are "things" for our "Anschauung" as Hilbert holds, if the whole procedure is logically relational as Russell holds, if mystic intuitional genius operates as Brouwer holds, then the vital region of analysis is closed by fiat before the real issue of interpretation has been attacked.

The use of non-symbolic language is, however, always accompanied by great difficulties of understanding. It is all very well to say that a clear thought should be capable of direct, simple and clear expression. That is true, given an unambiguous medium of expression. Here our problem is to develop the beginnings of a method of clear expression within a confused, ambiguous, and variously distorted, linguistic medium. Communication between men is two-sided. Each "word" is not merely what the writer intends it to be, but also what the reader "takes" it to be. In an ambiguous linguistic medium the key-words of communication are "taken" by various readers in various ways, and sometimes with such confusion that the various sets of implications, connections and constructions of meaning may be even as numerous as the individual readers themselves. The case is that which Poincaré remarked in the well-known passage cited at the beginning of Chapter III that men fail of mutual understanding because they speak different idioms which they do not study to translate into one another's terms.[3]

[3]Where intelligent transfer of meanings (here the word meanings is a harmless casual description) as between one Frenchman and another,

When I have sought to convey the thought of this book and its technique of linguistic values to any single individual I have found that I must first learn his idiom, and then modify my expression and perhaps even my detail of construction so as to reach him without undergoing distortion through his particular personal understanding of the words I am using. Manifestly when I address jointly even two men who use different idioms of the type Poincaré observed, there must be a compromise. With as many as three or four such men compromise becomes impracticable. To address a wide audience the possible procedures are either to prepare an extremely complex and voluminous treatise, or to append one after the other a series of typical constructions, or to choose my own preferred approach and safeguard the reading of the text as far as is practicable by explanatory matter. It is the last of these possibilities which I have chosen as the simplest and most compact, though not, indeed, the most thorough-going from the point of view of full intercommunication. And it is this which will explain the presence of so much subordinated matter in the text, and of so many footnotes, designed in great part

---

or as between one Englishman or German and another, is so difficult, what is our problem when we must secure understanding as between users of one language and those of another? We are concerned with analysis and discriminations of meanings, not with approximations and agglutinations. The rough methods of "translation" are of little use. I have therefore at times, as in Chapters IX and XII, employed foreign phrasings directly in my text without attempt to transfer them into English. At other places I have given transcriptions of implication, or more rarely, offered reasonably direct translation. The result is far from elegant, but I offer no apology, because the inquiry before us is one that cannot be carried through—perhaps, in some respects, cannot even be grasped—within the limits of a single language, of German, of French or of English, alone.

to prevent the threatening misreadings of the text.

One special protective device I have made use of with respect to many words which cannot be avoided altogether, however dangerous they are in their manifold implications. In passages in which the danger of misreading is greatest, such words have been placed at once in italics and in quotation marks: thus, "*foundation,*" "*real,*" "*intuition,*" "*concept.*" These are to be read as conventional names for situations which, although presented as within our general knowledge or expectation of knowledge, are as yet but crudely comprehended: and they thus have the value in the text of mere initial indications of regions within which it is necessary most thoroughly to apply that postulatory form of approach which I shall proceed to establish under the name Semantic.

# PART I

## Problem and Postulation

# I

## THE PROBLEM

Algebra, Geometry and Analysis possess their separate constructions, each consistent within its own ranges.

Their technical organization with respect to one another has been achieved: but it remains an organization of convenient practical devices rather than of full theoretical system.

Lacking still is a comprehensively consistent construction for the union of all three: and involved in the search to establish it are difficulties which mathematicians have come to call *"foundation"*[1] problems, and which they commonly regard as entangling them in regions of knowledge *"deeper"* and more intricate even than those of mathematics itself. The paradoxes from Zeno to Cantor and Russell testify to the failure to attain success.

The search for consistency in this field involves in all of the outstanding attempts, such as those of Russell, Hilbert, Brouwer and Weyl, a dependence upon linguistic tools (words, sentences, paragraphs, *"concepts," "ideas," "theories"*) which are much inferior

[1]The word *"foundations"* is especially dangerous because it implies much tacit philosophizing as to what foundations are and why mathematics should need them. In the present paper the problems commonly referred to as *"foundation problems"* are approached strictly as border or contact investigations of (or, one may say *"within"*) the range of the three great mathematical constructions.

in precision to mathematical symbols. Hilbert's "minimum of presupposition" involving objects and their perception, and Russell's propositions, classes and relations are of this order.[2]

From the mathematical standpoint it is always desirable, and in the limit compulsory, to eradicate all such inferior forms of expression. The technique of eradication is that of fully clarified postulation, such as that which Hilbert seeks, but has not yet attained, in his construction for complete consistency—"Widerspruchsfreiheit."

A fully clarified postulation is, however, not attained until all alternative postulates are explored. Illustrative of this is the Euclidean parallel axiom.[3]

To describe the status of any linguistic situation prior to any direct use of postulation a term is needed. For this term I shall here choose Realism, and shall understand that when any system or any element of a system is taken naïvely and immediately as *"manifest," "intuitive," "true"* or *"necessary,"* then that system is to be called a Realism.

The choice of the word "Realism" for this use carries with it no significance beyond that of its immediate specification and development. It is not to be read with any form of philosophical or

---

[2]Knopp, who proclaims the vital need of a dogma of real numbers as a necessary footing for the success of even the most purely technical investigation of infinite series, and for whom the word "real" has implications running far beyond a mere distinction from "complex," is characteristic with his "System von begrifflich wohl unterschiedenen Dingen" (Theorie und Anwendung der unendlichen Reihen, p. 8), this phrase containing no term ever fully precise except "System," and that term precise only in its technical mathematical uses, and with specific limitation of its range.

[3]Until alternative axioms were brought to light and studied a century ago, there was a defect in Euclidean geometry yet waiting to be revealed. This defect was realistic, under the distinctions of the text.

psychological implication. It may readily be suggested that some other word might have been better for the purpose: but, short of an hitherto unused, and therefore blank, symbol, equally serious objections have risen to the various alternatives that have been considered.

We may regard all the mathematical disciplines, all the constructions to unite them in consistency, all of the special linguistic devices used in such constructions, and all of the embedding language and knowledge in which disciplines, constructions and special devices are alike interpreted, as one great field spread out before us in historical time as well as in contemporaneous civilization. The Realisms in that field are with us always. With them, in this essay, we have no direct concern. It is solely with their irruptions into postulatory procedure, and with their implicit survivals in such procedure that we shall have to deal.

When the realisms cease to be naïve, and enter into a postulation which takes them up for inspection, but still continues to proclaim their necessity, we may regard the situation as one of Realistic Postulation.

We shall make practical use later on of a distinction, though without introducing it in schematic form, between implicitly realistic postulations, and explicitly realistic postulations; the word-clusters III and IV, as set forth in Chapters III and V, being of the former type; the clusters V-VIII, of the latter. The difference lies in the extent to which antecedent realism still lurks unsuspected in the postulatory materials, and the extent to which specific attention has been directed to this characteristic of the materials and specific use of it made.

When progress goes beyond this so far as to get rid of all assertions of necessity save those of complete consistency, and when, along with every set of postulates put forth, search is made for, and construction is undertaken under, all alternative postulates that can be identified, then we have a fully clarified postulatory system:[4] and we may call such postulation Semantic, or fully analytic, as opposed to Realistic.

The word semantic may be taken most broadly to designate any direct study of language as a system of connected meanings, where it is conducted with that directness of observation and with that freedom of inquiry which we call scientific. This usage dates from the "Essai de sémantique," (1897) of Michel Bréal, who concentrated attention upon evolutions of linguistic meaning as contrasted with the prevalent philologies specializing upon linguistic form. Since then the word has been variously employed in many languages, but always in senses connected with the meanings of words taken in systems and thus held close to the Greek root from which it was derived. In its specific use in the present book it designates a theoretical construction for scientific knowledge erected in the general linguistic field. Mathematicians are perhaps most familiar with the word as it has been used in recent years by Chwistek and Korzybski. For the former it serves to express an interest in the linguistic basis of logic and mathematics, without, however, as yet transcending the special limitations of a logistic.[5] For the latter it stands for a full functional interpretation of language—styled by Korzybski "non-elementalistic," "non-aristotelian"—within which "logic," as that word is commonly used, would become a special case: and it is thus very close indeed to the meaning adopted for the present essay, although constructed under a different form of approach.[6]

In a fully clarified postulatory system the only "*reality*" or "*existence*" examined is that of the separately inspected elements within the system with respect to one another. The procedure is free from all control "*external*" to the system, and the trend is towards the sharpest and most detailed and exact analysis of all elements with respect to one another.

[4]Barring, of course, the ever present possibility—due to the fact that we have no criterion by which to set a term to human progress—that further alternatives will later reveal themselves. See Chap. III, Rule II.

[5]See Chap. V, Par. 21, and Chap. XIV.

[6]See Chap. XIV.

In a realistic postulation *"reality"* is imposed from without to some specified extent: the procedure is therefore not wholly free: and the trend, instead of being towards maximum sharpness of analysis is towards the clotting of meanings among the realistically-taken elements in such a way as, presumably, or in *"belief,"* to heighten their realistic value to the system. "Reelle Zahl," real number, exhibits this trend in such marked degree that the characterization, which lies primarily, and should be held technically, within the bounds of an organization of real and complex numbers, becomes realistically dominant in *"foundation"* regions. Systems resting in *"truth,"* or in the logical distillations of "truth" such as Russell's, have realistic aspects in their construction, despite all protestation. The "Ding" (thing, or object) of the Mengenlehre, and of other abstract expositions of the theory of aggregates, classes or sets, is realistically postulated: and is helped in no way by being labelled *"abstract."* Hilbert's symbols taken as objects immediately given in knowledge ("Zeichen"—"Objekte"—"Vorstellung"), are realistically postulated. But Hilbert's postulation makes this progress that, while still realistic in its initiation, it nevertheless brings its elements under tests whereby their very realism—their consistency as thus realistic—may hope ultimately to be appraised, and either established or rejected.

## II

## SEMANTIC POSTULATION

Behind all realistic postulation there is an assumption which may be expressed by saying that certain members of the linguistic system (certain words or "*ideas*") stand in a one-to-one to a reality or realities outside of the system. Avoiding the expression "one-to-one," which has an established definition for cardinal numbers (and which here does service merely as a metaphor), we may set up x and X, and differentiate between the two types of postulation.

The term postulation is selected to cover the most general form of linguistic control which we may establish. It is true that there has been a recent tendency, especially in America, to use this term for cases of specific definition, but such usage seems justified only on the assumption that the accompanying analysis is basic. If the analysis goes deeper, the term postulate must go deeper with it. Newton could proudly say that he did not hypothesize—"Hypotheses non fingo"—but that was in a specific sense for hypothesis: and the analysis of today has made it clear to everyone that his whole scientific activity was carried on within the limits of certain hypotheses which in after time could not be ignored in the extension and evaluation of his work. As between the three terms, postulate, axiom and definition—including the use of the expression "undefined" in connection with the postulatory materials of geometry—I have been able in the examination of many cases to find no structural consistency of usage, the choice as between them seeming to depend on incidental factors such as private philosophical views, or on considerations of practical convenience, often peculiar to the particular investigator. The present usage may seem to violate a local and temporal convention, but it is nevertheless the choice that seems indicated, given our available terminological equipment.[1]

Let the word "system" be used to indicate any organization of meanings, implications, or references, whether in terms of fact, or knowledge, or experience, or words, that comes before us.

Let the word "member" be used to indicate any specification whatever within such a system.

Let x be any member of a system, the definition of which is secured within the system and in terms of other members of the system, so that—if either phrase proves to have any valid meaning—its field of applicability is that of the "full system" or the *"system as a whole."*

Let X be any member of a system defined in independence (explicit or implicit, partial or complete) of the system, so that the construction of the full system, or the *"system as a whole"* is explicitly or implicitly dependent upon it.

In the above paragraphs we meet full front the difficulties of expression in the field we are entering, difficulties to which attention has been called in Foreword and Introduction. Under ordinary standards for precision in the conveyance of information, the sentences we have used will appear to some readers vague, to others

[1]One may consider Huntington's distinction between axioms as statements of fact and postulates as statements of conditions to be satisfied. (Fundamental Propositions of Algebra, in Monographs in Modern Mathematics, J. W. A. Young, editor, p. 172). Sheffer's use of the term postulate in his privately issued General Theory of Notational Relativity is of the more specific type, but he makes his postulates rest in a "language function" or "base," which at once becomes a field for further analysis and further postulation. One may consider also Hilbert's construction of formal and material axioms (Hilbert und Ackermann, Grundzüge der theoretischen Logik, p. 22) and the considerations which, after the extension of the axiom system, lead to the construction of the "Stufenkalkul" (op. cit. p. 68, p. 82, p. 98:) to certain aspects of which we will give mention in Chap. V, Par. 25.

perhaps trivial or indeed irritating. The writer is as fully aware of this as any reader. But he does not stop with this mere awareness. He goes perhaps much farther in his recognition of it than his reader will be willing to go. He holds that at the present day, and under the current conceptions of linguistic construction and employment, it is impossible to frame any sentences whatever with precision in this field. That is why he does not himself attempt it at the start. We possess, indeed, many special, limited precisions of construction and definition. They hold within limited ranges and for special purposes, but they will not admit of generalization. Their appearance of exactness is specious, for the very reason that their underlying postulation remains unclear and unacknowledged. The man who believes he has established a basic certainty or precision—who has satisfied himself thoroughly with his own results—soon discovers that at the best he may be able to found a "school" of thought—one school among many: he does not succeed in establishing—at least no one has yet established—a form of accepted expression adequate for the general development of knowledge, and providing for it a technical language of the type we call scientific. "Logic" served well in its day, but the problem of this book is before us solely because logic, with respect to it, has always failed.

The sentences we have used for the specification of x and X have the value, therefore, merely of preliminary empirical indications. We use them frankly in this way, and prefer them to differently formed sentences which make pretenses to precision where precision is not yet available. The test is what progress we can make by their use, not whether they do, or do not, look imposing at the start. They serve to indicate, under the designations "x" and "X" certain phenomena or situations, as yet not fully analyzed, with which all of us are in a general way acquainted, but with which no one of us is precisely acquainted. It is to their credit, rather than to their discredit, that they avoid any attempt to commit us in advance. Many of their problems lie, indeed, far beyond the range of this essay. In the Rules to be set up in the next chapter, the linguistic construction is presented under which we may approach empirically, instead of dogmatically, the special aspects of these problems with which we have concern in our investigation.

In especial, the term "system" is used in the preliminary way, despite all its known, and despite all its possibilities of still unknown, defects. This term will be examined further in Chap. IV, Par. 7. For the phrase "system as a whole," the case is even worse:

since it is clear that, if it is to have sharp meaning, that meaning must be gained for it through its complete consistent development: and, further, that in any such development the particular man who employs it occupies in his own life-time a transitional and indeed equivocal position. Weyl employs the phrase frequently, as when he insists that it is the full theoretical system of physics, or the full system of mathematics, which must be brought into confrontation with experience for interpretative purposes, and never this or that isolated construction or report.[2] Weyl's view involves, however, a sharp separation between phenomenal knowledge and theoretical construction, a separation which he takes as self-evident and fundamental. No such dogmatic separation is involved or implied in the present postulation: and we approach the problem, instead, somewhat in the spirit of the saying of Descartes that "geometrical truths are in a way asymptotes to physical truths, that is to say, the latter approach indefinitely near without ever reaching them."[3]

THE REALISTIC POSTULATE. Given materials x and materials X, a system $S_r$ is constructed, so that "*in its last analysis*" or "*as its foundation,*" all orderings of the form x-to-x are dependent on certain postulated orderings of the form x-to-X.

THE SEMANTIC POSTULATE. Given materials x and materials X, a system $S_s$ of x-to-x is constructed, so that no postulated ordering of members x-to-X is involved, but that the materials commonly regarded as X, if they are taken into account, and in any way in which they are taken into account, are controlled wholly within the field of the "full system" of x-to-x.

---

[2] "Eine Konfrontation mit der Erfahrung vertragen, prinzipiell gesprochen, nicht die isoliert genommenen Aussagen der Physik, sondern nur das theoretische System als Ganzes"; Hamb. Abh., vol. VI, p. 88. Compare also Math. Zeitschr., vol. 20, p. 149: Rice Institute Pamphlets, vol. XVI, p. 252: and Philosophie der Mathematik und Naturwissenschaft, p. 49. See also our discussion of Weyl's development in Chap. X.

[3] Cited by Shaw, Philosophy of Mathematics, p. 37.

The Realistic Postulate may be read as follows: Given a world of facts, X, we have before us systems of language, x, which contain terms such that *"by common expression or belief," "in perception," "in intuition"* or *"as concepts"* they point directly, "one-to-one," to *"facts"* X:[4] the linguistic systems of x-to-x, therefore, being dependent for their *"value"* or *"truth"* on members of the form x-to-X: the whole construction therefore being a system $S_r$.

The Semantic Postulate, on the other hand, may be read thus: Disregarding all realistic interpretations of the type x-to-X for any specific terms in the language, we seek all of our coherency in the language systems x, absorbing all their references, meanings and implications of whatsoever nature, whether as knowledge or experience or fact, into a fully developed analytic system of linguistic connectivities, and postponing, as a further and separate procedure, till the end of the full postulatory inquiry, any question as to the realistic interpretation of linguistic references of the type $S_r$ either (a) as over against a realistically factual world, or (b) in terms of any necessity, or compulsion of *"thought"* or of any substitute or alternative for the word "thought."

We raise in these sentences a flood of questions as to the physical world, whether as fact or as construct, and as to mathematics, whether as abstractly representative of a world or as a psychological approach:—there are endless ways of framing these questions, none of deep significance to knowledge. The reader who wishes to appraise the existing status of their discussion—not in philosophy, but, what is of much greater importance, in mathematical *"founda-*

---

[4]For illustration see Weyl's "Sonderwesen" and "Definitionen," referred to in Chap. X.

*tion*" theory,—may wisely consult the recent book by R. D. Carmichael, The Logic of Discovery, where they are surveyed with ripened and balanced judgment and without dogma, but, on the other hand, without any postulational clue to their treatment. Professor Carmichael regards language as instrumental and necessary, but as nevertheless incapable of conveying the "fullness" of "psychological reality." He sees "fact," on the one side, as test and control for theory; but, nevertheless, at the same time, on the other side, as itself developed and framed in theory. He sees both oppositions and correlations of mind and nature, of man and fact, of logical constructions and connectivities of experience. And he discusses these situations in terms of such possibilities as "conformability," "consonance," "paraphrase," "construct" and "authority." The present status, he holds, justifies us in, and indeed almost requires of us, a belief in consonance, though yielding us no test case, no proof, in support.[5] It is now from the starting point of such a status as Carmichael presents that we here propose to investigate whether postulation and system can be introduced into the discussion of these problems, not however with respect to any of their "philosophical" aspects, but solely for the organization of the language of mathematics, of science, and of knowledge.

Carmichael is much too careful in his procedure to use that term of mathematical analogy, isomorphism, for the correspondence he discusses. Nevertheless this is a term which is only too often used in this region, even by mathematicians themselves. I suggest to any mathematician inclined so to use it that he ask himself these questions. Does he set up "fact" on the one side in "*radical*" separation from the "construct" on the other, whether this latter is in terms of mind, logic or language? If he does, what exactly can he mean by an isomorphism, either between components of two such systems, or between them "as wholes"? Must there not be some

[5]For Carmichael's attitude towards language, see The Logic of Discovery, p. 130. For his relativity of fact, see pp. 182-188. For the issue in terms of consonance between logical connectivities and the relations of phenomena in the natural world of experience, see pp. 135-146. For the issue in terms of the conformability of laws of the spirit to those of the physical world, see p. 89. For the constructs of mind as a possible paraphrase of nature and for alternative views, see p. 191. For the issue of authority as between men and fact, see p. 223. The contributions of Rueff, Keyser and Korzybski are all given careful examination in the course of his discussion. He employs the term "isomorphism," but only for the preliminary construction of a logical pattern, and not in the elaboration of his interpretations.

underlying "system" holding the two together if he is to use the presentation of an isomorphism? When he takes presentations from two different systems in mathematics and establishes an isomorphism between them, does he not by that very act establish a wider system to which those two first systems now belong? If he proposes to present an isomorphism between fact (in any formulation) on the one side and knowledge (in any formulation) on the other, does he not at once introduce system, and at once abandon his original idea of radical separation? And if he does so abandon it, is it not then incumbent on him, if possible, to secure further postulation or knowledge concerning such a system?

For simple illustration of the two forms of postulation, the Realistic and the Semantic, we may consider the paradox of the Cretan liar. "Epimenides, the Cretan, says all Cretans are liars. But Epimenides is himself a Cretan. Therefore he is a liar himself." From this, the conclusion is drawn that Epimenides lied when he said all Cretans were liars: and the logical squirrel cage goes round.

The matter-of-fact avoidance of such a logical difficulty by "common sense," for any particular case, and under definite local understandings of meaning, is easy: and it is all very well as far as it goes. But we are here concerned with the generalized case of knowledge, and of language, and of fact: and this generalized case is no far-away hyper-meticulous splitting of hairs: it is a case that is with us in every-day life, in every moment of speculative brooding, in every mystery of life and universe we contemplate, in every difficult problem we are forced to solve or attempt to solve.

Given interpretation in x-to-X, then the word liar (x) must identify an absolute or real liar (X) in exact connection of the type described as "one-to-one" for the x-to-X. That is to say, if the word liar is used in a system of words of realistic reference, and if the particular word liar is one that is taken with such realistic reference, then there must be no equivocation and no uncertainty as between x, the word liar, and X, the fact liar. The paradox follows.

The objection may, of course, be raised, that this particular word, liar, is not itself one of those words of our language which possess realistic reference. What the proponent of such an objection does, in effect, is to give the word liar interpretation of the type we have called x-to-x: while at the same time maintaining that the particular case before us is trivial, and that its x-to-x interpretation is subordinate and auxiliary to the basic and fundamental system x-to-X which he assumes as control and guarantee for our knowledge. It is now, however, manifestly incumbent upon him to produce, if not all, or even many such words, at least one that is fundamental, and dependably available for use in x-to-X. It is exactly because no such basic and fundamental word has ever thus far been produced, not even in the realm of mathematics, the best and safest of all our knowledge: and further because exactly in mathematics every attempt to establish such words has had vivid paradox for its outcome: that we in this essay distinguish the two forms of postulation, Realistic and Semantic, and assert our right to proceed under experimentation with the latter.

It is clear that when the word liar is transferred to the system x-to-x, whether by the intervention of "common sense" or by the establishment of our semantic postulate, then the paradox of the Cretan is abolished. If "common sense" is the solution for the verbal-logical paradox of the small and local situation, it may be, under our generalized procedure, that we shall not have departed so far from common sense in the end, no matter what unkind remarks that very common sense may take occasion to make about us while we are under way.

If illustrations from logic are displeasing, one may readily note the distinctions between Realistic and Semantic approach in the science of physics as it is before us today.[6] Examine both as words and as facts,—both as dogmatically realistic determination and as tentative construction of knowledge,—the matter, ether, molecule, atom, electron, corpuscle and ray which the physicists use. Note what matter used to mean, what ether for a time tried to mean in imitation of that older meaning of matter, what ether came to mean in the stage when it was defined as a mathematical construction, and what the trends of meanings have become for all of these terms, as information has accumulated from the rapid heaping of one astounding experiment and test upon another. Do this in deliberate freedom, if merely momentary and provisional, from the ancient dogmas, prejudices and conventions of language: and the possibilities of postulation in the semantic field will at once be clear. Attempt it under the ancient dogmas, and it may then well be that the procedure will be so blindly realistic that neither its own postulation nor the possibility of any other postulation can be recognized.

To illustrate, not realistic postulation, but rather those underlying realisms in which the assets of our knowledge become "frozen"—if the use of a metaphor current in the years of the great depression will be permitted—reference may be made to Chapter XI in which the interesting construction of Cantorian non-denumerability is discussed from varying points of approach. The realist, whose existence is intimated in a passage in the smaller type towards the end of that chapter, has arrived at a fixation with respect to his con-

[6]The approach of this essay to its own group of problems is in full sympathy with that of P. W. Bridgman to his physical problems in his Logic of Modern Physics: barring only the makeshift construction of "*concepts*" which Bridgman perforce had to employ as his linguistic background.

struction which is so rigid that his very vision seems to him to confirm his personal conventions of language. He is wholly blind to any possibility of semantic or other alternative postulation beyond the confines of his own certainty, and for him all else is folly.

It should be at once evident that under any realistic postulation questions of metaphysics as distinct from science arise: whereas under semantic postulation no such questions of metaphysics arise within or affecting the systems of postulations themselves, however they may flourish in other fields.

I can very gladly adopt the following passage from Hilbert[7] (barring provisional opinions as to the Cantorian paradise and as to the essential nature of the infinite) as a manifesto upon the needs of the existing situation in foundation theory:

"Aber es gibt einen völlig befriedigenden Weg, den Paradoxien zu entgehen, ohne Verrat an unserer Wissenschaft zu üben. Die Gesichtspunkte zur Auffindung dieses Weges und die Wünsche, die uns Richtung weisen, sind diese:

"1. Fruchtbaren Begriffsbildungen und Schlussweisen wollen wir, wo immer nur die gerinsgte Aussicht sich bietet, sorgfältig nachspüren und sie pflegen, stützen und gebrauchsfähig machen. Aus dem Paradies, das Cantor uns geschaffen, soll uns niemand vertreiben können:

"2. Es ist nötig, durchweg diesselbe Sicherheit des Schliessens herzustellen, wie sie in der gewöhnlichen niederen Zahlentheorie vorhanden ist, an der niemand zweifelt und wo Widersprüche und Paradoxien nur durch unsere Unaufmerksamkeit entstehen.

"Die Erreichung dieser Ziele ist offenbar nur möglich, wenn uns die volle Aufklärung uber das Wesen des Unendlichen gelingt."

I have cited these paragraphs from Hilbert in full, because quotation from them has often been made, and because it too frequently has happened that certain turns of phrasing they contain are flippantly taken as embodying Hilbert's thought. In condensed paraphrase, what Hilbert tells us is that (1) we must carefully search out, cherish, develope and utilize all possible verbal specifications and all possible manners of conducting proof, wherever even the slightest prospect of fruitfulness is indicated: (2) we must establish throughout our search that same security of proof which we possess in simpler work with numbers, where inconsistencies and paradoxes never occur except as the results of our temporary inattention: and (3) we must secure full disclosure of what it is that we have before us when we speak of infinity. Avoiding as it does any translation

[7]Über das Unendliche: Math. Ann., vol. 95, p. 170.

of the immediate atmosphere of discussion in the article in which the passage appeared, this paraphrase all the more truly, I believe, conforms to Hilbert's own line of investigation and development.

As early as 1904 Pringsheim had written that the truth the mathematician seeks is neither more nor less than consistency: "Die Wahrheit die der Mathematiker erstrebt, ist freilich nicht mehr und nicht weniger als Widerspruchslosigkeit."[8]

Geometry today is both explored and appraised semantically. Arithmetic and Algebra are explored semantically, but not commonly so appraised. Analysis is explored semantically, but with an insistent demand for realistic appraisal, which always fails. Geometry and Algebra combine in Analytic Geometry with practical success, but under common appraisal as mere technique, though with implicitly semantic characteristics. Mathematical *"foundation"* theories are all sought and developed under realistic postulation, but as yet with failure to attain full consistency and avoid paradox.

Appraisals such as the above take curiously conflicting forms under the varieties of current "logical" renderings. I recently listened to an address by a mathematician whose work in fully algorithmic procedure has been exceptionally brilliant, and who never, so far as I know, has occupied himself with the technically logical constructions. He nevertheless presented number-theory under the Peano-Russell axioms as his ideal of a "pure" mathematics: while the geometries appeared to him as "applied" mathematics, since he envisaged the geometrical "point" that he put on the blackboard, not as a linguistic element or symbol, but as an extensional presentation. The outcome, to me most strange, was that number-theory, garbed in a "logical" rendering of the separately and discretely taken "thing" of every-day speech (and with all its remaining paradoxes) was "pure" theory: while the developments of quantum mechanics, which have passed from the Bohr atomic "thing" by way of the Schrödinger wave to the Heisenberg and

[8]Deutsche Math.-Ver., vol. 13, p. 381.

Dirac matrices, and in which the discrete separateness of the conventional "thing" is, if not wholly lost, at least no longer apparent, were regarded as in the realm of mathematical "application."

Our task is to place before us as data,—as phenomena for investigation,—as field of research,—or as region of knowledge in which better knowledge is sought (I use all of these manners of phrasing as equivalents in order to avoid misinterpretation by readers who perhaps indulge themselves in *"beliefs"* about any one of them) the systems of geometry, algebra and analysis, and the numerous endeavors to unite them in a common consistency by the construction of *"foundation"* theory. Let us then explore these materials by the aid of the two contrasting forms of postulation, the realistic and the semantic.

Let it be understood that from the point of view of the mathematician our procedure will not pass beyond the regions of the critical: however well from the point of view of the investigator of language and of society it may prove to be constructive: and that whatever specialized mathematical construction may be indicated, it remains for the mathematician to develop it.

## III

## LINGUISTIC MATERIALS AND CONTROL

Language may be studied in terms of printed page, writing hand, reading eye, hearing ear or speaking voice. In such specialized studies we have here no technical interest.

Language may be regarded as a tool of "*minds*" with which to communicate with other "*minds*" about "*things*." Such a view may be before us as a Realism, in naïve line of ascent from sub-human immediacies of expression, through word-magics, which still survive among us here and there, and on into logics. As a Realism this point of view may still have its utility for special purposes. For use, however, in the generalized investigations, which we approach, a Realism would not suffice and a Realistic Postulate would have to be constructed to represent it. This Realistic Postulate would manifestly require correspondences, x-to-X, between such words as "*mind*," "*communicate*" and "*thing*" on the one side, and those "*actual facts*" or "*realities*," X, on the other, which are taken as the references or objective deliveries of the words, x. This procedure, again, though of much usefulness for many special purposes of investigation, is nevertheless crude, still in part naïve, full of obscurities and confusions, and wholly excluded under the Semantic Postulate, which we here propose to employ.

We shall here inspect language as a great system of

connected expressions (words with meanings) consisting of a nexus of smaller systems: some consistent and some inconsistent: some sharply outlined and some "almost everywhere" (often quite in the sense of "fast alle") vague: some rabidly dogmatic, and some freely open to reformatory organization. It contains terms such as Experience, Knowledge and Fact, which, when realistically set up within it, claim to control it. By the same token, however, Experience and Knowledge and Fact, as established and developed in language, are analytically within its scope. With respect to these rival claims we take no position, but specify:[1]

Language is a functional of Experience, of Knowledge and of Fact: and Experience, Knowledge and Fact are functionals of it, and of one another.

This specification serves notice that the word "Language," as it is used in this book, is not to be specialized or degraded to some minor

[1] I deliberately avoid the term "define," because of its great confusion of meaning in logical, and, still more, in mathematical, systems. It could here be employed in an ordinary conventional way, except for the certainty that such a use would meet with criticism: and this, not merely from a single but more probably from dozens of different constructions which would be set up for it. In place of the term "definition," I shall occasionally employ "specification," not because it has any precision of its own, but to avoid specious appearances of precision. The word "functional" as employed in the specification immediately before us in the text will serve to illustrate. It is there used in its mathematical meaning, which is closely indicative of the characteristics of the linguistic situation to be specified, but still with recognition of regions of remaining vagueness. Had I used the word "functional" as an adjective instead of as a noun, the specification would have been at most loosely descriptive. Had I used the noun "function" instead of "functional," a semblance of precision would have been given, which would have falsified the statement, since the term "function" itself is still deeply involved in those confusions of mathematical meaning hereafter to be examined under the specification, M-T. The discussion of functionals by Volterra, Leçons sur les fonctions de lignes, Chap. I, 1913, may be referred to.

meaning under some dictionary phrasing or under some special attitude of interpretation; but that, wherever and whenever the linguistic implication or involvement is found, there and then Language is to be recognized and acknowledged as a phase or aspect of the phenomena to be examined.

I assemble here a few citations which serve to bring out something of the breadth of the linguistic problem, something of its meaning in and for mathematics, and something of its status with respect to the special situations which we shall have before us for analysis:

"Les hommes ne s'entendent pas parce qu'ils ne parlent pas la même langue, et qu'il y a des langues qui ne s'apprennent pas." Poincaré, Dernières Pensées, p. 161.

"To attain clearness of conception the first condition is *language,* the second *language,* the third *language*—Protean speech, the child and parent of thought." Sylvester, Mathematical Papers, II, p. 567.

"Wobei es fast aussieht, als ob die Menschen von den Buchstaben gelernt hätten." Klein, Elementarmathematik vom höheren Standpunkte aus, 3d ed. I, p. 29.

"When the illustrious Willard Gibbs remarked: 'Mathematics is a language,' I cannot feel that he meant that mathematics is merely a dry assemblage of symbols (for to him mathematics was no formal thing) but rather that in some respects language has the properties of mathematics." G. N. Lewis, The Anatomy of Science, p. 21.

"To say, therefore, that thought cannot happen in an instant, but requires a time, is but another way of saying that every thought must be interpreted in another, or that all thought is in signs." C. S. Peirce, Journal of Speculative Philosophy, 1868, vol. 2, p. 112.

"Dabei möchte ich betonen, dass ich das Wort 'Konstruktivität,' für ein wenn überhaupt, so vermutlich auf verschiedene Arten und in verschiedenen Abstufungen präzisierbares (bisher noch nicht präzisiertes) Wort halte." Karl Menger, Bemerkungen zu Grundlagenfragen I. Deutsche Math.-Ver., vol. 37, p. 225.

"Es ist ja in geistigen Dingen nichts ganz Seltenes—ja auf den allgemeinsten und tiefsten Problemgebieten etwas Durchgehendes—dass dasjenige was wir mit einem unvermeidlichen Gleichniss das Fundament nennen müssen, nicht so fest steht, wie der darauf errichtete Oberbau." Georg Simmel, Soziologie, p. 13.

"The development of Symbolism as a Science . . . must provide both what has been covered by the title Philosophy of Mathematics, and what has hitherto been regarded as *Meta*-physics—supplementing the work of the scientist at either end of his inquiry." Ogden and Richards, The Meaning of Meaning, p. 390.

Language subdivides most generally into

(a) Inchoate Implication.
(b) Words-common.
(c) Terms.
(d) Symbols.

We may understand the organization of language in these subdivisions as follows:

(d) Given full consistency in x-to-x we have Symbols, and we call our procedure Mathematics.[2]

(c) Enveloping the mathematical systems of consistent symbols, we have Terms of the Aristotelian type. These are built together in logical connectivities, and involve implications of X, and implicit or explicit uses of the x-to-X.[3]

(b) It is in a great sea of Words-Common of practical daily life that the terms are found, and it is out of this sea of Words-Common that they emerge.

(a) Around all is a chaos of Inchoate Implication, cries, slogans, preachments, emotional utterances, ignorances, verbal intolerances.

This is the linguistic field in which we shall examine the systems of mathematical symbols. We begin with these symbols directly, and take them and their consistency as our subject-matter. But we at once find

---

[2]In this we have a fair preliminary standard for testing whether the "*foundation*" theories of mathematics are, or are not, themselves to be regarded as a part of mathematics, and what the conditions are under which any such theories can so be regarded.

[3]The "logic" upon which the mathematician relies in his proofs is itself the consistency of (d) and not a derivative from (c). See Rule II.

that they are dragging implications of meaning from the regions (c), (b) and (a) along with them: and we find these implications surrounding and coloring and confusing our interpretation of the symbols and all our work with them. We shall range backwards into the (c), the (b), and the (a) only so far as is necessary to enable us to clear away these confused implications, and we shall treat the (c), the (b) and the (a) always and only as raw material awaiting consistent analysis, and never as controls of our procedure.

From either the typographical or the pedagogical-declamatory standpoints, it may seem a crudity for us to set up our subdivisions of language in the order from (a) to (d), and then give specification to them in the reverse order from (d) to (a). This procedure may, however, be taken as symbolic—in the casually conventional sense of that term—for the whole course of the investigation we are undertaking. We begin by organizing roughly, empirically; and then by the aid of the more sharply outlined presentations we attain, we work backwards towards the less sharply defined presentations.

For general orientation, to aid us in our inspection and use of language as we proceed with the work, the following rules may be formulated. These rules are in no sense to be taken as in control of our investigation, but rather as provisional descriptions, offered in advance, of that which the procedure will in the outcome involve.

These rules are derived from a series of investigations such as that carried on in Chapters IV and V following.[4] They are sum-

---

[4]Papers thus far published in this field are:

L'Individuel et le social: les termes et les faits. Revue internationale de sociologie, vol. 37, pp. 243-270, 1929.

New Ways and Old to Talk About Men. The Sociological Review, vol. 21, pp. 300-314, 1929.

maries of experience, hints for future guidance, but not yet offered as adequately organized generalizations. The present investigation must stand or fall by its own results, and not by the right of the rules. The rules then become merely such an expression of the nature of the linguistic-knowledge situation as we have gained by this and other investigations up to date.

It is, however, to be noted that neither the rules, nor the investigations from which they are derived, nor the semantic postulation itself, could be set up under the dominance of any of the older forms of conventional *"psychology."* As opposed to "psychological" the approach of this paper could be called sociological: but that again only in a very special sense of sociological, the sense, that is, of methodological emancipation from tribal dogma. I have refrained from developing the work from this point of view in the text for two reasons. The first is that the investigation *must* stand on its own feet, and be valued by its own results. The second is that to discuss the psychologies and sociologies directly in the present stage of development of our technical terminologies would be tantamount to philosophizing, and the vagueness of philosophizing is the one thing to avoid. Practically all the psychologies as we know them are dogmatically realistic. Many realistic sociologies have been set up. The paradoxes as between these realistic psychologies and sociologies are more vicious than those of number and the continuum. It is not through preliminary attack on the sociological paradox that the paradox of the continuum is to be solved, but quite the contrary: the former awaits relief from the latter. The sociological approach, as here used, is solely methodological and critical. It is in this sense alone that I depend upon it. We can summarize its import thus: "The moment that one studies individual *"minds"* socially, that moment the individualistic psychological theories collapse into incoherence. The moment that one studies dogmatic social constructions in individual presentations, that moment the dogmatic sociology collapses." One has then the choice of arbitrary blind belief or of the open mind—the full postulatory approach. We choose the open mind and apply the linguistic solvent. Freed, thus, from dogma, psychological or other, we bring to our work no "content" from sociology or psychology, but inspect our present problem as one which must be solved before sociological

---

A Sociological Critique of Behaviorism. Archiv für systematische Philosophie und Soziologie, vol. 31, pp. 234-40, 1928.

Sociology and Mathematics; I, Their Common Problem of Analysis; II, Mathematical and Sociological Spaces. The Sociological Review, vol. 23, pp. 85-107 and 149-172, 1931.

investigation can hope to yield us any dependable scientific "content." The reader who thinks that his private or conventional views as to *"minds"* and *"mental process"* are *"right"* or at least sufficiently "sound" to control all his development and appraisal of knowledge, and this in the face of the existing chaos among the psychological constructions, will make little progress with our present form of reasoning. He must first seek to gain release from dogma. It is an approach to such release that these rules represent.

**Rule I. Every exact analysis, in, of, or by means of language, rests in preliminary provisional dissection and organization of linguistic materials.**

This is the region of investigation commonly called "empirical." It is itself analysis, but from the present approach it is the cruder portion of analysis, and is given the special descriptive name "dissection" merely to avoid confusion with respect to Mathematical Analysis and Semantic Analysis, to both of which the term analysis must be applied. An excellent illustration in this region is offered by Hilbert. When he sets up his minimal presupposition—his "geringste Mass von Voraussetzung"—(see the passage cited in Chap. V, Par. 25), he is in effect making use of a crude preliminary dissection, and making his whole system dependent upon it. He does not devote space in his writings to this dissection, but accepts it in conventional or quasi-philosophical form, and uses it dogmatically. Nevertheless crude provisional dissection is all that it is. The procedure of the present paper consists substantially in carrying analysis from within the Hilbertian system itself back into these regions of crude dissection, in order to gain greater control. One may compare Poincaré's remark upon Hilbert's early axiomatization of geometry[5] to the effect that Hilbert was successful only because he presupposes analysis already constituted and that he can use it for his demonstration. An analysis that gives a successful system for geometry may, however, not be one that similarly succeeds with algebra. And always we must remember that many analyses are possible, and that the choice among them is to be determined by their consistency and range combined: much as Poincaré proved that if one mechanical explanation is possible then an infinity of such explanations is possible.

---

[5]Dernières Pensées, p. 122.

RULE II. Maximum linguistic agreement of experts in investigation, historically and contemporarily, is final court of appeal for maximum certainty of analysis. Constructions in consistency[6] themselves stand or fall in the end by the same test.

One may inspect Rule II in connection with any form of discrimination one may conventionally make between the three kinds of *"facts"*: (a) the mathematicians at work as *"persons"*: (b) the historically-developing mathematics incorporated in its symbolic systems: and (c) the technique of logical proof within mathematics. Conventionally we find the (a) facts using the (c) facts to justify the development of the (b): whereby the (c)—which is, indeed, itself taken to be a "capacity" or "power" of the (a)—somehow acquires a super-authority over the (a) and the (b) both. This is little more than a muddle of words of incoherent value. The present approach—and this is what Rule II especially presents—rejects this artificial, conventional severance, and inspects the whole procedure of mathematicians-at-work-with-mathematics-in-language: wherein the "logic" becomes rather special attention to the procedure of proof, than the substance of proof itself. In particular the word "agreement" in Rule II is to be read, not as an expression of individualistic psychology, but in the sense of the preceding remarks on the rules in general and of Rule VI in particular.

How chaotic the existing system of expression remains in its mathematical applications is most strikingly shown in Professor E. T. Bell's vice-presidential address at the 1930 meeting of the Mathematical Section of the American Association for the Advancement of Science.[7] He frames his discussion, it is true, by the aid of such word as concept, idea, faculty and insight—all of them words which are participants in and contributors to the very confusion he exhibits: but his entire paper may aptly be read into a criticism of such words wherever they intrude into mathematical interpretations. "The simplest and most obvious of all the sciences," he writes, "has not yet agreed with itself as to what is provable,

---

[6]It will be observed that consistency is nowhere defined in this essay. It is taken throughout as fact or field of investigation. The essay itself ranks as preliminary empirical investigation: and it does not presume to go far enough to establish definition under fully explicit postulation.

[7]The Scientific Monthly, March, 1931.

what not provable, what is sense, what nonsense, and what the provinces of meaning and inference are for the most rudimentary abstractions of which the reasoning mind has thus far shown itself capable."[8] He suggests the compilation, in the form of a spectrum, without comment or interpretation, of the characteristic views of leading mathematicians of the present time upon the subject of the theoretical justification of their own activity, and says: "The bald exhibition of the facts should suffice to establish the one point of human significance, namely, that equally competent experts have disagreed and do now disagree on the simplest aspects of any reasoning which makes the slightest claim, implicit or explicit, to universality, generality or cogency."[9] And as to the notoriously glaring contrasts of "cold scepticism and emotional belief . . . respecting the sober propositions of every-day classical mathematics," he adds: "The sane middle road which some would wish to travel has not yet been proven to exist, and those who try to take it in the prevailing darkness may find themselves falling down an abyss."[10]

For an attitude towards language and mathematics most sharply opposed to that of the text, one may refer to Edmund Landau's admirably constructed little work "Grundlagen der Analysis" (1930). In his "preface for the learner" Landau tells us that he presupposes or takes for granted "logical thinking" and "the German language"—just these and nothing more. Then, to avert scepticism, he assures us that *"one* number (Zahl), *no* number, *two* instances, *all* things of a given aggregate (alle Dinge aus einer gegebenen Gesamtheit) are clear word-forms (klare Wortgebilde) of the German language." In his "preface for the expert"—a preface which wisely he implores the learner not to read—he remarks that he had long regarded his development as logically perfected, but that his assistant, Dr. Grandjot, reading his manuscript, pointed out to him that it was not: so that he had made a material change with respect to the Peano development. This, it may be remarked, is our perfect illustration of the strictly "logical" procedures: they are ever being declared "perfect," whereupon they are ever being remodelled to "make them perfect."

RULE III. Meanings, references, implications and connectivities of all types are taken as in system.

---

[8]Idem, p. 197.
[9]Idem, p. 205.
[10]Idem, p. 208.

This is to say: the distinction of "things" and "words," if and when it is made, is made within one system, which system may, or may not, ultimately be called knowledge, or experience, or fact, or language, according as the results of continuing analysis do, or do not, justify any such description. Our present investigation is in no way involved, either explicitly or implicitly, with problems of this last type.[11]

Rule IV. Any meaning, reference, implication or connectivity may be taken as the starting point or base from which to study any other.

Rule V. All correspondences within language shall be of the form x-to-x. Purported correspondences x-to-X (implications, references) shall under the semantic approach be analyzed into x-to-x. In its sharpened form the x-to-x shall require expression in symbols.

*Specification.* A Word-Cluster is a section of language (symbols, terms, words-common or inchoate implications) obtained by empirical dissection, whether its members are assembled under definition, purported definition, or implication of discussion.

*Specification.* Connectivities are the forms of organization of word-clusters. They are the "systems of meanings" of words, taken in the widest range of meaning for the word "*meaning,*" and ranging all fields of knowledge, experience, fact and language.

Rule VI. Word-clusters and connectivities shall not be taken as if established under Aristotelian logic, nor in the general form of dichotomies, but shall be

[11]See Chap. IV, Par. 7: and compare the phrasing of the Semantic Postulate and of its colloquial rendering in Chapter II.

regarded primarily as empirical arrangements and organizations, awaiting identification of exact connectivity and of consistency of symbol, to be sharpened where possible and so far as possible into analytic differentiations of full consistency in the form $S_s$, and under continuous suspicion where not so sharpened.

Our attitude towards language is not "logical," but rather that of an empirical scientific investigator with phenomena spread out before him to dig into. I do not discuss logic directly in this inquiry and in the formal sense do not employ it. In the broader sense of the term, consistency under semantic postulation may be called "logical" if one will, but all of the age-long implications of the word-clusters in which logic is prominent make such a course undesirable. Mathematical consistency is treated here as semantically sufficient unto itself; and what logic, in any particular definition of the term, has to do with it is an inquiry which any one may undertake for himself in accordance with his special needs. Under realistic postulation, of course, the case is very different, since there logic is both the necessary reliance and the source of paradox—though reservation must be made with respect to the Hilbertian consistency, if one calls it logic, since this aims to become a mathematized component of the Hilbertian system. Related to logic is the realistic rendering of the verb "to be," and the discussion of the various implications of the *"realities"* contained in the whole or in the details of any system. These also fall entirely outside of the scope of this paper, and are referred to in footnote or incidental comment, but nowhere developed in systematic construction.[12] I see no reason why anyone should be required to exhibit solemnity

[12]The confusions in the many recent efforts looking towards the reconstruction of logic are, however, sketched in Chapter XIV, which is in the nature of an appendix to the main investigation which concerns us. No attempt at systematic development is there made, and apparently no systematic development which will do justice to all of the varied forms of attack is practicable at the present time. Minor references to the status of logic in mathematics will be found in Chap. IV, Note 16 and Chap. X, Note 50. In especial with respect to logical definition, see Chap. III, Note 1 and Chap. X, Note 24. For the use of the verb "to be" see the introductory pages of Chaps. VIII and XII, the linguistic examination of the sentence "Are decimals denumerable?" near the beginning of Chap. XI: also Chap. IV, Par. 8 and Chap. V, Par. 19.

towards the poorer parts of our knowledge as a condition for proceeding with investigation of the better organized parts: nor do I see any reason why any one else's construction of the poorer parts should furnish any criterion for the criticism of someone's procedure in the better parts.

The manner in which the poorest parts of our knowledge have arrogantly taken power over the better parts—that is to say, the manner in which language, naïvely and superstitiously accepted, has throttled the development of consistency in language—was the life-long interest of the great German investigator, Fritz Mauthner, whose writings are to be found all too rarely in American libraries. Especially did he concern himself with the psychological and logical superstitions. Of Aristotle he says that "he made the extant forms of speech the objects of a superstitious cult as though they had been actual deities"[13] and he charges that it is "precisely due to this linguistic servility" that the language of science has so long "remained under the bondage of the logical terminology"[14] "an influence which has been wholly pernicious in its results."[15] "If Aristotle had spoken Chinese or Dacotan, he would have had to adopt an entirely different Logic."[16]

Our approach to these problems of logic and language, I believe I may safely say, is in the broadest and most general sympathy with that of John Dewey, as he has developed it especially in his Essays in Experimental Logic, 1916. While sharp divergences of verbal formulation can readily be noted, and while Dewey's range of inquiry and his method of analysis are very different from the present, transformation from the one manner of construction to the other can readily be effected. The importance of Dewey's work in advancing our understanding of all of these problems must everywhere be recognized.

*Specification.* Common-Reference Description is a name we shall apply to certain crude terms, usually appearing in couples which purport to carry logical defi-

[13]Aristotle, translated by Charles D. Gordon, p. 84.

[14]Idem, p. 104.

[15]Idem, p. 19.

[16]Kritik der Sprache, III, p. 4. These and other remarks of Mauthner's can be found cited by Ogden and Richards, The Meaning of Meaning, p. 50, et al. See also citations in my book, Relativity in Man and Society, pp. 249-251 and p. 254.

nition; having roots for the most part in inchoate implication; simulating or resembling symbolic form only in the detached procedures of isolated workers; never in universal use as firm channels of technical communication; and tending always to embody dogma and to distort analysis. They appear here as current crude, though pretentious, expressions, which we employ for convenience in indicating locus of difficulties.

I present now, on pages 46-47, for preliminary inspection and orientation in tabular form, a list of the word-clusters which we shall need to isolate and study within the field of our materials of investigation as specified at the close of Chapter II. In naming these word-clusters and in illustrating them, I have made use to great extent of German vocabularies in place of English. This is in part because the German language is in many cases richer and more specialized in the use of such terms than English (consider the group, "Ziffer," "Zeichen," "Nummer," "Zahl," along with others less precise, such as "Anzahl"). It is, however, even more because I wish to use the terms, not with dictionary definitions, whether German, English or German-English, but as specialized names for word-clusters,—for situations in language,—which we must identify and discriminate: and the German terms in an English context can be held freer from slippage, and from undesired variations of conventional implication, than could the English terms; just as the same might be true for English terms in a German context.

In my own preliminary development of these word-clusters, and indeed up to the final preparation of the manuscript for publication, I have known the first four word-clusters by the German names "Ziffer," Zeichen," "Nummer" and "Strecke": and it is with some reluctance that I change to English nomenclature: though, indeed, the German terms in their own linguistic setting have perhaps as many defects for our particular purposes as have the English. Attention should be given to the linguistic dissection, and to the resulting analysis: and the names applied to the word-clusters should be taken rather as aids to memory than as guides to understanding.

Word-Cluster I, "Character," serves to present the linguistic embodiment of our materials. It is taken, not as instrumental to any special constructions of convention or of psychology, but in full semantic rendering.

Word-Cluster II, "Symbol," presents the symbolic consistencies of mathematics as they have established themselves historically in their own right of development. We specify consistencies from the three branches of mathematics, Algebra, Geometry and Analysis: but the presentation "Symbol" is not specified as limited to them in this arrangement.[17] If a mathematician sees an additional consistency as pres-

[17]It may be observed, however, that the three consistencies discussed correspond to three general situations in knowledge. There is the situation of things discretely taken. There is the situation of things taken as capable of subdivision, yet without reaching discretely elemental components. There is the situation of change, transition, motion. In addition to these we have other situations in knowledge, for which no type of mathematical consistency has ever been developed. These are situations such as those of soul, mind, behavior, and of all the subordinated terms, the virtues, the instincts, the feelings, the purposes. Comment upon this set of facts is easy, but also it is multifarious, quarrelsome and equivocal.

## WORD-CLUSTERS

(Obtained through dissection of the materials of investigation)

| CLUSTER NAME | POSTULATION (See Chap. II) | ILLUSTRATIONS (In the main, each with current *"meanings"* under many word-clusters.) |
|---|---|---|
| I. "CHARACTER" | $S_s$ | In general: letter, word, phrase, book: mark, sign, ideogram. For mathematics: Ziffer, Ziffernkomplex, figure (arithmetical or geometrical), cypher, graph, digit, numeral, counter. |
| II. "SYMBOL" | $S_s$ | Zeichen: sequence, series, algorithm, operation, rule of combination, curvature. |
| II*A | | |
| II*Aa | | 1, 9, n, 13, 1000, $10^{10}$, MC. |
| II*Ab | | $=$, $>$, $+$, $-$, $\surd$, 0, $\infty$. |
| II*$Ac_a$ | | —3, ¾, 1.2, $3.\dot{3}$. |
| II*$Ac_b$ | | $\sqrt{2}$, 3.14159 . . ., e. |
| II*B | | |
| II*Ba | | Line-segment, plane, point, line. |
| II*Bb | | Congruence, translation, rotation, cross-ratio, coordinates. |
| II*Bc | | Asymptotes, mathematical "spaces." |
| II*C | | |
| II*Ca | | $\frac{dy}{dx}$ |
| II*Cb | | $\frac{d}{dx}$ |

## WORD-CLUSTERS
(Continued)

| CLUSTER NAME | POSTULATION (See Chap. II) | ILLUSTRATIONS (In the main, each with current *"meanings"* under many word-clusters.) |
|---|---|---|
| III. "NUMBER" | $S_r$ | Nummer: natural, rational, irrational, transcendental: quantity. |
| IV. "EXTENSION" | $S_r$ | Strecke: length, area, surface, solid: relation. |
| V. "ZAHL" | $S_r$ | Kardinal, Null, "reelle," Aleph, Omega, Zahlenfolge, Punktmenge. |
| VI. "MENGE" | $S_r$ | Element, Eigenschaft, Enthaltensein: Spezies: class, set, law. |
| VII. "AUSWAHL" | $S_r$ | |
| VII*A | | Ding, Objekt, Gegenstand, Begriff. |
| VII*B | | Anschauung, Intuition, Wahl, "die schöpferische Definition," Auswahlaxiom, Medium freien Werdens, Urteilsschema, Gesetz des ausgeschlossenen Drittens, axiom of reducibility. |
| VIII. "DAS HILBERTSCHE OBJEKT" | $S_r$ | 3, $=$, Z, $\epsilon$, $\rightarrow$, $\sim$, V, (x), $\tau$, $\Sigma$, $\Pi$. |

ent or in the making, he may add it: or if he feels able to combine two of them in full symbolic consistency, as the case stands today and without appeal to "*external*" aids, he is free to take that step. If language presents or may sometime develop consistencies beyond those of the mathematical disciplines—and whether these, then, are themselves called mathematical or not—place remains open for them: though they are beyond our present concern.

Word-Clusters III and IV, "Number" and "Extension," present systems of implicitly realistic organization: the quantitative and yet presumably discrete "numbers" of arithmetic; and the concretely "real" areas and solids implied in, and influencing, geometries which, with respect to them, profess to work "abstractly."

Word-Clusters V-VIII present systems developed in explicitly realistic postulation.

The arrangement of the Table is devised solely for the purpose of bringing the materials we need in this essay before us in the most convenient form for inspection. It is a mere listing, one after the other, of the situations we shall have specially to examine. A full schematic arrangement might easily be set up, but it would involve attitudes and decisions upon issues which are much better left out of account at the start because they are much more debatable and certain to distract attention from the main object of pursuit. For example all of the clusters III-VIII might be made members of a third group of the table, this group to have two sub-divisions, the first to include III and IV, the second V-VIII. On the other hand there might be sound schematic reasons for placing III-VII in a third group, and placing the Hilbert system, VIII, in a fourth. We have not advanced far enough as yet for pedagogical arrangement, and we have no need of it at this time.

It should be observed that the table is not an exhibition of consistency, either in its organization or in its illustration. Quite the reverse. It is an exhibit of raw materials, some embodying consistencies, but others reeking with inconsistencies. And in particular it must be recognized that no single one of the illustrative terms used in the table, whether symbol or common word, can, as the case stands today, maintain the right to exclusive allocation to the position in which it appears. Here is the modern Babel, a Babel of meanings, not of tongues. Consider the "1" used as an illustration of the II*Aa, and presenting there an algorithmic value. It could also be used for III, where conventionally quantitative arithmetic is found: while in a differently symbolic presentation it is an Hilbertian "object" of VIII: and with still different implications it could be used in or for each of the other word-clusters.[18]

The reader whose habits of work require him to commence with firm definition and classification will find herein nothing but disappointment. We commence, instead, empirically. We start with the confusions, displaying them as we find them, identifying and organizing them as fully as is possible to us under present knowledge. In these confusions what is a single word or "the same word"[19] as an appearance

---

[18]Thus the terms, law, relation and rule of combination, may be variously placed depending on the different systems of meaning in which they are used. See Chap. IV, Pars. 7 and 10: the discussion of Brouwer's "diskret" in Chapter IX: the last part of Chap. X: and Chap. XI. The symbol, 0, placed here in illustration of the II*Ab, would by the most general usage of specialists of the present day, be assigned rather to the II*Aa, where in the development hereafter to be given it would exhibit a pronounced inconsistency. See Chap V, Par. 13, and Chaps. VIII and XII. The word quantity is another which could be variously assigned. See Chap. V, Par. 16.

[19]See Chap. V, Par. 21.

on paper or as a sound in the ear enters into many organizations of meaning, many connectivities: and it enters in such a way that even the most definite conventional usage or prescription for any one of the illustrations which we may present for any one of the word-clusters before us has implications of meaning from other clusters still clinging to it. If this were not so—if any fully clarified system of meanings had as yet been attained—then the "*foundation*" problems of mathematics would not still be causing us concern.

Given such confusion, our position for the purposes of this essay is that we have no justification for setting up at the beginning some one set of meanings—let us say those of the denumerable number sequence—*as if* they were already fully clarified, hoping then to proceed upon their firm support towards further clarifications. Our first problem is to find out whether unclear implications from other word-clusters, other connectivities, do not still cling to the interpretations of our most fully clarified algorithmic procedures. And, indeed, just such a lack of clarity in the specification of numerical things and numerical operations is one of the problems with which we shall be concerned.

Supplementing the table of word-clusters to be examined in our materials, I add for convenience of reference, and again on a basis of empirical observation, rather than of organized system, first a list of connectivities to be examined in these word-clusters: then a list of common-reference descriptions which we shall from time to time employ for purposes of orientation with respect to theories developed out of conventional linguistic materials: and finally names for two aspects of analysis upon which our attention will more and more come to center, and to which we shall in the end entrust ourselves for guidance.

## CONNECTIVITIES

(In need of analysis, one with respect to another)

| NAME | TYPE OF POSTULATION | INDICATIVE REMARK |
|---|---|---|
| Dk | $S_s$ | Deriving from "diskret." |
| D | $S_s$ | Deriving from "dasselbe." |
| W | $S_s$ | Equational consistency: algebraic value: Wert. |
| G | $S_s$ | Geometrical consistency (in expansion from Euclid). |
| A | $S_s$ | Analytic consistency. |
| Dk-?-W | $S_r$ | Realistically discrete value. |
| Dk-?-G | $S_r$ | Realistically extensional value. |
| B | $S_r$ | Bedeutung (in realistic significance). |
| BB | $S_r$ | Die Hilbertsche Widerspruchsfreiheit. |

## COMMON-REFERENCE DESCRIPTIONS

(Unreliable, conventional devices for orientation and discussion)

| | |
|---|---|
| Objective-Subjective | Abstract-Concrete. |
| Inner-Outer | Discrete-Continuous. |
| Mind-Matter | Structure-Function. |
| Particular-General | Existence-Transition. |
| Part-Whole[20] | Individual-Collective. |
| Finite-Infinite[21] | Instantaneity(temporal)-Duration. |
| Thing-Operation | Instantaneity(spatial)-Extension. |

[20]See Chap. V, Par. 16.

[21]See Chap. IV, Par. 5: Chap. V, Pars. 14, 17 and 19: and Chap. XI. The "infinite" is before us in this essay, not as a matter of "*belief*," nor as a problem of "*truth*," but as the indication, reference or meaning of a word, for which consistency must be secured through the use of other words, and can in no other way be attained.

ASPECTS OF ANALYSIS

(For guidance in research)

M-T The "mathematical-thing."

M-O The "mathematical-operation."

Just as the list of word-clusters was arranged for the immediate empirical uses of this essay, and with entire disregard of the possibilities of schematic organization, so the list of connectivities is arranged in the most convenient way to bring into relief the outstanding features of the recent literature of discussion. Not only is it incomplete, but its entries do not even exhibit definite correspondences with the word-clusters.

Putting the two tables together, which I do here merely for convenience and to prevent probable but wholly unnecessary misinterpretations, we have the following arrangement:

| POSTULATION | WORD-CLUSTERS | CONNECTIVITIES |
|---|---|---|
| SEMANTIC | I | Dk |
| | II | D (with W, G and A singled out for examination.) |
| REALISTIC | III | Dk-?-W |
| | IV | Dk-?-G |
| | V-VI-VII | B (for specializations, see Chap. V, Par. 21.) |
| | VIII | BB |

In any ultimate schematic organization, each fully established word-cluster would be presented along with its peculiar connectivity, and the analysis that gave the word-cluster would give also the connectivity at the same time; word-cluster and connectivity becoming merely two different ways of speaking of one linguistic procedure: while combination, rearrangement and subdivision would result in accordance with the practical schematic purpose in view. This would be possible, however, only so far as the various realistic systems could be forced to bring their present obscurities into open analysis and take definite stand with respect to the essential issues involved.

The two names for aspects of analysis, M-T and M-O, are given description in words-common as "mathematical-thing" and "mathematical-operation." This description is for convenience at the start, and serves merely to direct attention to the region of investigation. It can have no positive value for us under the existing status of linguistic knowledge, because nowhere in any of the regions of knowledge can we find positive and consistent meanings for the words "thing" and "operation," which meanings we can import into mathematics in a way that will yield definition for M-T and M-O in any of the types or forms of definition. Our problem is to investigate M-T and M-O in mathematics. If, then, we can gain a consistent construction in mathematics for certain situations which we call M-T, in organization with other situations which we call M-O: if, in other words, we can advance M-T and M-O to symbolic value in mathematics, or even make the beginnings towards such an advance; then we may hope that the words "thing" and "operation" in their many wider uses will gain some increment of meaning from the phrases "mathematical-thing" and "mathematical-operation" as used to describe the symbolized M-T and M-O: whereas we have no right whatever to hold in the present status of linguistic knowledge that the situations M-T and M-O in mathematics will gain any increment of meaning from the use of the current words "thing" and "operation" as mediated through the phrases "mathematical-thing" and "mathematical-operation." The line of progress in which we may have hope will be from mathematical language to other language, and not from other language to the mathematical.

Nevertheless it will be well to indicate roughly in advance the general background of knowledge in which those words *"thing"* and *"operation"* are used, both in mathematics and in wider ranges. It is common in elementary arithmetic to regard cardinals as in some sense things and ordinals as in some sense operations. Just what sense, of course, one hardly knows: and the less one knows the more dogmatic in his expression he probably is. In the more recent *"foundation"* studies of mathematics, culminating in Hilbert, this use of the "mathematical thing"—"Ding, "Objekt," "Gegenstand"—has come ever more sharply to the front. The term is used, it is true, with increasing *"abstractness,"* but that does not necessarily mean progress; at least not till we know what *"abstract"* means, and we know next to nothing about it as yet: it is just another crude term. The historical quarrels about zero, about minus quantities, about incommensurables, and later about imaginaries, have all involved presuppositions in regard to *"thing"* and *"operation"*: and the issue as between them is as vital today as ever, and indeed more importunate in its generalized form than it ever has been before.

Now this issue in mathematics, unclear as it is, is matched by a similar unclear issue in other sciences and in practical life. Formerly the physicist had firm hold of *"matter"* as thing, the operations of which he could study: but when he had to add ether as another thing, he found by painful experience that the construction would not work. He came over, therefore, more and more to an operational point of view. Today in the problems of radiation and the corpuscle, what is the *"thing"* and what the *"operation"* is simply not known at all.[22] The biologist struggles with structure and function: the psychologists are confused with mind and behavior: the sociologists, with institutions, minds and societies. The mathematician cannot go out into other sciences, or into philosophy, or into practical every-day life, and there secure a firm foundation for his distinction of *"thing"* and *"operation."* He must proceed by analysis in his own field, if he is to make progress. He must in the end view his mathematics as itself a subject-matter of objective interest, to which he must apply scientific analysis.

After the mathematician has thus made sure of his own *"thing"* and *"operation"* he can join his knowledge of his own procedures with knowledge of other scientific procedures, if he wishes, in any way he wishes, and for any purpose he wishes: but that will be a development in a different realm from the one now before us.

---

[22]For a full and interesting discussion of the many aspects of these problems, see Harold T. Davis, Philosophy and Modern Science, 1931. Still more recent is Charles G. Darwin's New Conceptions of Matter, developing the difficulties under a physicist's own interpretation of his most critical experiments.

# PART II

## Examination of Mathematics as Language

# IV

## CHARACTER AND SYMBOL

Language without meanings is a corpse. Meanings without language are as unknown as life without a body. The simile will serve, though built out of words no one can define, and subject to endless varieties of misinterpretation. Disregarding corpses and ghosts, except for occasional uses in ancillary interpretation, we proceed to examine linguistic phenomena in full play.

The first step of analysis, using the word-cluster I, "Character," and the connectivity Dk, is established for all language. The second step, using the word-cluster II, "Symbol," and the connectivity D, is presented in mathematical specimens. This latter is the linguistic region in which we investigate systems of symbolic consistency: and how far it may ultimately be found to extend beyond what is now known as mathematics—how far, that is to say, other knowledge may some day come to be "mathematicized"—is an inquiry well beyond our present purpose. Here our concern is with the mathematical symbols and with a special problem of consistency as between the several consistent systems of such symbols.

The exhibit of the materials of the problem of mathematical consistency under full linguistic inspection is to be made in this and the next succeeding chapter. To hold these materials together, while under examination, as a separate division of the book, and for convenience of reference, numbered paragraphs are used running consecutively through the two chapters. It is to be understood that my arrangement of these materials is merely that which seems best adapted to emphasize the distinctions which are most important for present purposes. Nor am I seeking to give satisfaction to the mathematician either in arrangement or in organization. Rather I am seeking to disturb him—and that in an especial way. His disturbance is indeed great enough already in this field of his activity: but thus far it has been too often infertile. The effort here is to uncover possible seeds of fertility.

1. We may begin by considering a piece of paper containing a pencil mark thus: 7.

Should we ask someone, any one, to make a report on what we have before us, we may expect roughly and conventionally, some such answer as follows: "The piece of paper and the mark on it and the form of the mark are physical objects: however, the mark has meanings which latter are not physical, but rather inner or psychical: and what we have is, from the physical point of view, a figure, while from the psychical point of view it is a sign or symbol."

In such an answer, and in the vision and understanding behind it, reliance is had upon the common-reference descriptions, subjective-objective, mind-matter and inner-outer, or upon others of their type—there are endless varieties of pretense in this field. These common-reference descriptions are not merely accepted for speculation or theory in the background. They are present, implicitly or explicitly, in direct control of eyesight and observation and "report of fact": that is to say, in report of what conventionally and dogmatically is asserted to be *"fact."* The reliance is confident and serene, despite the defective technical status of all such common- reference descriptions, no one of which has ever secured a recognized consistency of usage throughout specialized investigation, psychological or other.

We here strip off all such common-reference formulations and presentations, and all physical and physiological as well as psychological investigations connected with them.[1] We shall find distinctions we shall label "Character" and "Symbol," but they are not those of physical object and psychic meaning.

We identify our marking on paper, "7," in the most general way as datum or phenomenon—i. e., something that arouses interest,—in the general field, Language. Its immediate history, in the form in which we have it before us, is in terms of human motor phenomena: and its immediate reception is ocular.[2] These immediate aspects are, however, incidental to our inquiry, as are the correlated vocal and aural aspects. Essential to it is its identification, i. e., its discrimination from other markings on paper. We have no way, however, in such a presentation, or identification, to determine dogmatically, "*necessarily*" or by "*external*" tests what the particular "it" in question "is." We could, but do not, inspect it in atoms of paper or graphite, or in microscopically distinguishable fragments of graphite. On the other

---

[1]Such physical and physiological, and with them behavioristic, psychological and sociological investigations, may, or may not, in the long run prove to be more "*fundamental*" than the investigations we are here making. We take no position as to that, but merely note that even those investigations, and with them all investigations as to what is meant by, or what *is*, "*fundamental,*" are carried on through language and are developed functionally within language. See Rule III.

[2]Or, if the 7 happened to be Braille, then tactual.

hand, if the 7 were written, as in German script, with a cross-bar, the fact of the broken line would not necessarily make it two separate "its." Should we have before us, instead of the 7, a certain 387, there is no compulsion to make this 387 either one single, or three separate, presentations or identifications: and in fact mathematics examines it in both ways. Or, again, if we have $4 + 3$ before us, this can be taken as "one" presentation in identity with 7, or it can be taken differently, say as several presentations in equation.[3] The same is true of 1,000 or of $10^3$. If we call each spatially detached marking a "Character," we may, if we desire, inspect several of such markings as a "Character-Complex," (so, "Ziffer" and "Ziffernkomplex") but we have no dominant control for the choice between "Character" and "Complex," the selection being manifestly determined by minor, and provisional, practical purposes. Nevertheless the selection of "a Character," and its discrimination among "Characters," is involved in whatever we do with the materials.

Now, in mathematics, our 7, and all other numerical Characters, are variously before us in the contexts, or word-clusters, which we have listed separately as "Character," "Symbol," "Number," "Zahl," "Menge" and "Auswahl." Aim of our study is, as has been indicated above, not to clot these various contexts into some one realistic presentation, such as "Zahl," under a postulate x-to-X for the word "Zahl,"

[3]The importance of clarity here will be illustrated in the examination of Caratheodory's axioms in Chap. XII. One may compare Lewis' suggestions of "strings of marks," and of types of order in terms of quids and quods: (A Survey of Symbolic Logic, pp. 355-60).

and in a system $S_r$, but instead to analyze these clusters as fully as possible under a postulation x-to-x in a system $S_s$.

We begin with the word-cluster, I, "Character." We inspect distinguishable components of language, and we describe as follows:

"Character" I offers materials of investigation with the connectivity Dk. None of the other listed connectivities are required for their specification.

*Specification.* Dk is the connectivity which discriminates and organizes Character among Characters.

As such it is before us as a matter of observation. It presents the singular-plural situation of grammar. It also embodies, or contains the possibility of embodying, the mathematical situation of numeration, here preliminary and undeveloped.

We hold firmly to this specification, and do not go beyond it. To present it we have indeed been using a background of linguistic implications, which include separations we call facts, separations and comprehensions we call experience, and comprehensions we call knowledge: the obscurity of which is evident in whatever phrases we may use in which to refer to it. But to analyze or interpret, to deal in any way with this background, we must proceed by the use of language. Instead of dogmatically establishing the background in language, as if language were not participant in that dogmatic establishment, we present Word-Cluster I and Connectivity Dk as primary observation for whatever development may follow.

We proceed, thus, under a full linguistic-semantic inspection. In such inspection Language, in its widest sense, in which it covers the full field of words, meanings, implications and constructions, finds itself under the necessity of investigating, among other phenomena, the phenomenon of itself. Such investigation yields Word-Cluster I, "Character" ("Ziffer") as the embodiment of many other procedures. If we so take it, and if we assign to it the connectivity Dk, our procedure, both as to Word-Cluster I and as to Connectivity Dk, is semantic, under postulation $S_s$. We indicate, indeed, the derivation of Dk from "discrete," but what we set before us is no realistic discreteness, but exactly that separableness of mark, sign and figure, letter and word, which is before us empirically as the linguistic frame.

The word Character was suggested to me by Professor J. R. Kantor for the present use after I had appraised and abandoned many other proposed replacements for the German word "Ziffer," which I had myself long used as an aid to construction. It is a striking fact that our languages have no close term for the presentation of linguistic elements of all types as embodiment for all forms of connectivities in the ranges of the words *"thought," "meaning," "theory,"* etc. The name Character has however, little about it that can be misleading: since it presents to us the pertinent implications of "Ziffer," figure (in the arithmetical sense, if we include therewith sign of operation), cypher, mark and graph; without involving as these all do, many varied opportunities of alternative understanding: and since it presents equally well the wider linguistic situation of letter, word and sentence. The word "sign," which, in one of its renderings, would be exactly right for our purposes, becomes hopeless because of its dozens of other meanings, and because certain of these meanings overlap the region of the word "Symbol" in the application we shall shortly give it. In a broader study where I could have offered a much more detailed analysis and construction of the full linguistic situation, this word-cluster might, perhaps, itself have been styled "Language"; but in the present essay the technical use of the word in that way would only cause needless confusion.

If this analysis is to be followed into later stages, this first step in it *must* be cleared of the many possible and probable misreadings it can have. Therefore I repeat and emphasize:

We have before us a discreteness we may call linguistic.

We do *not* know in what way such linguistic discreteness is involved with what we may call factual or experiential discreteness.

We do *not* know in what way language is organized with respect to fact and experience.

We have *nowhere* in the world for our dependence any consistent theory of this organization.

We *do* know, however,—that is, we find, and always find, and seemingly cannot avoid finding—that language is functional in investigation: which is to say, it is functional in knowledge and in experience of or in fact.

We recognize that every approach we have to the special problems before us for investigation is linguistic.

We therefore begin by stripping our material down to a skeleton, and this skeleton is linguistic.

We do not even pretend that the linguistic skeleton is "the" skeleton of our problem: we treat it as very possibly one among many, but nevertheless as the one which we can here and now most profitably use.

We proceed, that is to say, in postulation and without dogma: and we postpone, without prejudice, the problem of the interpretation of our results in terms of experience, or of knowledge, or of fact.

To employ a different figure of speech, we use a postulatory reagent to precipitate something that we may hope intelligently to study; instead of making confusion worse confounded with dogma, creed, convention or belief.

2. We face next situations in which the report comes to use that "every Character 7, or Character =, or Character 17, is the same Symbol 7, or =, or 17": and we describe as follows:

"Symbol," II, presents Characters with the connectivity D.

*Specification*: D is that connectivity between Symbols which gives linguistic fixation to Characters as

Symbols, organizing many Characters as one[4] Symbol.

We do not convey detail of information in the wording of this specification. So much the better: so much less the probability of conventional misreadings. The meaning (in the loose conventional sense of "meaning") is present, and will make itself plain in the development. That meaning is throughout one of semantic postulation.

Just as the name for the connectivity Dk was taken from the word "diskret," that for D is taken from "dasselbe." The names might be anything we wish: it is the system we build which matters. Nevertheless, so far as my studies have gone I find these names apposite. Significance grows for them: and there are many indications of further growth. The suggestion for their use lay, no doubt, in the casual manner in which Hilbert remarks in a footnote[5] to his first systematic paper on general mathematical *"foundations"*: "In diesem Sinne nenne ich Zeichen von derselben Gestalt auch kurz 'dasselbe Zeichen' " ("in this sense I speak of Zeichen of the same form briefly as 'the same Zeichen.' "): a footnote which manifestly challenges much further thought. The name Dk is valuable because it holds "discreteness," source of so much mathematical and philosophical, not to mention physical, trouble, closely to the linguistic frame, where it has the minimum of harmfulness, along with the maximum possibility of consistent development in whatever direction proves needful. In much the same way the name D is valuable because it holds all the tangled presentations of sameness, unity and identity under semantic organization, as starting point for their interpretation in whatever way sound interpretation opens up as knowledge advances.

The connectivity Dk is present between symbols as it was present in the preceding word-cluster between Characters. It is present likewise in all other word-

---

[4]For the use of the word "one" in this specification, as for the use of the word "it" and "a" in the preceding text, interpretation can be sought nowhere except in the full analysis of the full system of language in which it occurs. See also Chap. V, Par. 21.

[5]Hamb. Abh., Vol. I, p. 163.

clusters, and is taken up into every connectivity, becoming a verbal component of each word-cluster, and securing varying specification and import in each.

Compare in the next chapter the appearance of the Dk in the inconsistent connectivities Dk-?-W and Dk-?-G: and its sharpened form in the Hilbertian BB. One might, if it were of immediate advantage, for any purpose of study, give a special name to each such specification of Dk for each other connectivity—thus Dk-D, perhaps for its appearance among Symbols. It is not of importance to us here. Connectivities overlie one another and are entangled throughout all our material. Pictorially we may look upon the consistent overlapping connectivities within the whole field of language as akin to the five intersecting cubes with summits coinciding in pairs within the pentagon-dodekahedron: but still overlaid and obscured by innumerable inconsistent connectivities presented in convention and dogma, and distracting our vision from the consistencies.

3. Recalling that I and II, with Dk and D, are of general linguistic application, though presented here in mathematical illustration, we now proceed to consider specifically mathematical word-clusters and connectivities, starting with sub-clusters within "Symbol." Reference to the table in Chapter III, and to the accompanying text, will show that the name II*A is used for materials from Arithmetic and Algebra, II*B for those from Geometry, and II*C for those from Analysis: and that these three groups are not herein set forth under any fixed principle of classification, but rather empirically as three commonly recognized ranges of consistency. We shall now proceed to consider these in turn, indicating subdivisions to be found among them: and treating them always as "Symbols" in the sense in which we have brought "Symbols" before us; disregarding thus for the

moment all involvement with "*meanings*" and implications which involve realistic postulation, and leaving the consideration of the realistic word-clusters and their forms of connectivity to the next succeeding chapter.

Symbols II*A, inspected on the basis of many centuries of discussion and development,[6] present themselves in four groups. The II*Aa are primarily those commonly called natural numbers. The II*Ab are operative signs.[7] The II*$Ac_a$ are expressions combining II*Aa and II*Ab, which, through renderings of one form of transcription into another—as with rationals, periodic decimals, and even algebraics, under the use of certain devices of the language of denumerability[8]—can be presented in series, eliminating the II*Ab. The II*$Ac_b$ are similar to the II*$Ac_a$—and in the system of the II*A have no radical difference—except that no immediately recognizable mathematical or linguistic technique, device or trick is available for the elimination of the II*Ab and for the display of conventionally realistic, or mathematically erudite, terminate expression in forms II*Aa.[9]

*Specification.* W is the mathematical connectivity in full consistency of the II*A.

4. The subdivisions of the II*A exhibit, within the mathematical material itself, a preliminary distinction of the nature of M-T and M-O. This distinction, as

---

[6]See Rule II.

[7]As to the inclusion of zero in the II*Ab see Chap. V, Par. 13 and Chaps. VIII and XII.

[8]See Chaps. VIII and XI.

[9]Except, of course, through the use of "individual" names, such as pi and e.

we have it before us at this stage, is one of analysis, but of analysis on that early empirical level we have called dissection in Rule I. On this level we may use M-T and M-O as names, which are as yet no more than candidates for possible status as symbols. We will recognize provisionally the II*Aa as M-T and the II*Ab as M-O. Whatever may be determinately transformed or transcribed into II*Aa we may also recognize as M-T. Whatever cannot be so transformed or transcribed,—in other words, in this case, the II*$Ac_b$,—remains then a problem for investigation, awaiting further analysis and the establishment of symbolic value for the M-T and M-O.

Decimals are a form of transcription developed within the system W. Cantorian denumerability and non-denumerability is read over upon decimals as real numbers, the set being taken as non-denumerable. The analysis of the text even in this early stage is sufficient to show that there are problems of language and of consistency still awaiting analysis, which run far wider than the arbitrary impaction of numbers into "reals," and which may have solutions of vital import for this narrower dogma.[10]

5. The statements thus far made must be read in full freedom from the obscure implications of any and all of the common-reference descriptions listed in the table, and from all similar forms of adulteration and degradation of meaning. One of these common-reference descriptions, that of finite-infinite, has been taken up and developed consistently within the system W, under the symbol ∞, commonly described as "operational infinity." Another, that of whole-part, including quantity, has been developed in later interpretations of this system to be examined in word-clusters

[10]See Chaps. VIII and XI.

III to VIII. The construction with the former leaves puzzles of implication and further interpretation, despite its consistency within the system. That with the latter has never gained full consistency, and is little more than camouflage for a puzzle. Both are dependent on implicitly or explicitly realistic constructions involving the materials and dissection M-T and M-O, though not as yet their consistent symbolization.

The term "abstract" from the couple "concrete-abstract" gives no help although it has done yeoman service, especially for geometry: but this service has in reality been nothing more than that of holding unpleasant problems off at arm's length, while the mathematician proceeds about his business: and its final contribution to the understanding of the *"foundation"* problem is just nothing at all. Any one of the other common-reference descriptions is apt to be used by any person who accepts it dogmatically to interpret the whole situation, or at least as a sedative during his interpretation. Probably no two investigators use any of these common-reference descriptions with identical implication: which means simply that the common-reference descriptions are not really exact and clear even to the man who uses them, and in the form in which he uses them. Nevertheless they continue to be used implicitly, even where not explicitly acknowledged, in all the *"foundation"* theories. A mathematician would not think today of publishing a report on his technical work until he had attained consistency within its full range, or at least believed that he had: but the *"foundation"* studies are all published without having attained consistency, and the most powerful investigators, such as Hilbert and Russell are the ones who most freely admit it. Our program here requires us, not to pretend to learn about M-T and M-O from the confused common-reference descriptions: but, quite the contrary, to study M-T and M-O in their own situations in the II*Aa, II*Ab, II*$Ac_a$ and II*$Ac_b$,—exercising the greatest care in analysis. It is much more probable that we can learn something about the common-reference descriptions from M-T and M-O than the other way around. No mathematician would depend on common-reference descriptions and implications of finite-infinite and part-whole to control his mathematics: all the less should he depend on any of the other common-reference descriptions. All the while, however, it remains true that even in the case of finite-infinite and part-whole some of the common-reference implication still clings about the mathematical development in its border regions, and with special involvement of the problem of M-T and M-O. The way to get rid of this is the direct mathematical way, and not the mystic, realistic, psychological or philosophical way; and certainly not the way of conventional *"common sense."*

6. PROPOSITION I. The system W of the II*A is a semantic system, $S_s$, and the distinction M-T and M-O is systemic within it.

This is to say that the distinction M-T and M-O is *"internal"* to the consistent system W in this sense, that the II*Aa, when taken as M-T, can be consistently defined as such only in terms of the operations II*Ab, taken as M-O: and that the II*Ab, when taken as M-O, can be consistently defined as such only in terms of the II*Aa: the consistent definition of either requiring a mutual, correlative, cooperative, or, as we may say, a systemic definition of the other for its consistent establishment. If we care to describe the situation in terms of the current, but very vague, word *"meaning"* we may say that the meaning of the II*Aa requires the use of the meaning of the II*Ab for its consistent determination in the system W, and conversely that of the II*Ab requires that of the II*Aa: and that any attributions of *"external"* or *"realistic"* meaning to either the II*Aa or the II*Ab result in flagrant inconsistencies of construction. We are in the realm of algorithm, taking algorithm as we may perhaps venture to do in that broad sense which is not merely the decimal calculation of the high school, nor special devices of calculation, nor calculational procedures in general, but the full symbolic development of number systems in their own right.

Klein, in discussing the great constructional patterns in the evolution of mathematics, identifies one of them by use of the word algorithmic, though with implications not wholly the same as in the passage above. He remarks first upon what he calls the particularizing or logical trend ("sondernde," "logische"), observable in methods and disciplines alike (and observable, also, incidentally in pedagogy, where it divides the field with the next following trend). He then considers the perceptual or commingling trend ("anschauliche," "verschmelzende"). These two however are not sufficient to his mind for full characterization: through and around them we must give attention also to the algorithmic or formal trend ("algorithmische," "formale"). Among the citations concerning language in mathematics in Chapter III, we put Klein's remark that "it almost looked as though men had sat pupils to their alphabets": and here he develops further that thought. "Algorithmic procedure," he says, "has played a great rôle in the development of our science: we may see it as in its way an independently forward-driving force, innate to the mathematical formulas themselves, and independent of, and, indeed, often antagonistic to, the insights and purposes ("Absicht" and "Einsicht") of the mathematician ("der jeweiligen Mathematiker") who on his part seems to be just casually present in what happens."[11]

This direct inspection and tentative analysis by Klein is well worth taking into consideration by any mathematician who is accustomed to consider the *"foundation"* problems under such contrasts as those of intuitional versus formal, or operational versus logical. Contrasts like these, though wholly vague themselves, have a certain philosophical pomposity, by means of which they may readily hypnotize the unwary by-stander. Klein did, indeed, use certain terms belonging to the language of such contrasts: but he did not use them as though they were in control of his knowledge. Instead, with his steady observer's eye, he looked straight at the facts before him when he coupled such words as "sondernde" and "logische"; and likewise when he saw mathematics spread out before him, not as a sort of by-product of man's intellectual activity, but as a great historical-social development, susceptible of empirical presentation and investigation in its own right.

The presence of the $\text{II}^*\text{Ac}_b$ in no sense violates the consistency of the connectivity W, nor the consistency

[11]Elementarmathematik vom höheren Standpunkte aus, I, pp. 82-86.

of the connectivities Dk and D within "Symbols," but instead is evidence of the subordination of the distinction M-T and M-O within and to the full system of the II*A.[12]

Of this proposition we may say: (a) it "proves itself" to anyone who can read it in full freedom from the common-reference descriptions we have listed, since in this case it is a direct statement of the consistent appearance of that which we call the consistent system W:[13] (b) it cannot be "proved" to anyone who interprets its terms under any of the dogmas of the common-reference descriptions: (and this not because of defects in the proposition, but because of a defective understanding of the nature of such proof itself): and it becomes to such persons insignificant or meaningless. The ultimate decision will rest in the general expert agreement as to what is best practice in the region of applicability of Rule II.

7. The word System, as we have introduced it in Chapter II and used it in Rule III of Chapter III, covers the general case of organization in experience, in knowledge and in approximations to knowledge. It at once took specification for us, under the alternative postulations of Chapter II, as systems $S_s$ and $S_r$. Now in mathematics the word System has a technical value which, so far as it goes for the immediate purposes of those who use it, is reasonably exact. A mathematical

---

[12]The word-clusters which involve the inconsistencies in this region will be examined in Chap. V.

[13]Disregarding difference of verbal expression, and of so-called psychology, this is the view which Poincaré took towards reasoning by mathematical induction. See Chap. VII. The long-continued discussion as to the need and as to the possibility of "proof" for induction may be recalled.

system requires the presence, first, of "objects" of a mathematical nature, and next, of "operations" or "relations" of mathematical nature. Mathematicians are apt to take pride in the extreme abstractness with which they characterize their "objects," "relations" and "operations," and to draw confidence therefrom: but from our present point of view the term "abstract" itself, as it is used in mathematics, is a very vague and unsatisfactory word from the regions of the common-reference descriptions. When one carries the usual definition of a mathematical system beyond its immediate uses and into the region of the "*foundation*" problems, then this definition shows itself far from exact, since a consistent and complete analysis of the whole issue of operations and relations is vital to the success of the construction, as will appear plainly enough in the examination of Brouwer and Weyl in Chapters IX and X of this essay. It is of course always easy for the individual investigator to issue a fiat as to how operations and relations stand to one another: just a little extension of the abstractness will usually serve. Bôcher's fiat for example is that the rules of combination as distinct from the relations may be regarded quite simply as relations between three objects.[14] This serves his own purpose, but it has no other value than a formal reduction of operations to relations in a system $S_r$ in which the elements

---

[14]Maxime Bôcher, Introduction to Higher Algebra, p. 80, sq., in defining the System, exhibits, first, Objects in the broadest possible mathematical way, and, next, Sets, in which those Objects are elements. He then defines a System as a Set with its associated Rules of Combination: but he is at once compelled to add that it is desirable to admit, not merely Rules of Combination, but also Relations between the elements of a system.

are defined independently of the operations and relations, and the analysis is carried no deeper than such definition. Historically the geometrical presentations are the ones out of which the relational construction has primarily arisen, while the number presentations have been more manifestly operational: but at the present time neither type holds separate, and each is contaminated by adulterations from the other. It is sufficiently evident that the analysis of the distinctions M-T and M-O within a system $S_s$ is necessary to secure a consistent construction.

A discussion of "systems" from a point of view sharply opposed to that of the present essay may be found in two articles by Paul Weiss in the Monist for 1929 (see especially pp. 451, 460 and 471). It is fortunate that his radical formulation is available for reference and comparison, since in this matter the half-way attitudes are no longer permissible to any one who strives to think clearly and thoroughly. Weiss asserts flatly that without "logic" as a basis we can have no "systems" whatever. "Systems are possible," he tells us, "only because logic has already been assumed." "All parts of systems as well as systems themselves are subject to the three laws of thought." "The heart of systematic development lies in the principle of substitution."

Weiss' reduction in this way of all constructive knowledge to "substitutions" is entirely in line with various recent developments of logical interpretation for mathematical "foundations": and the question the reader should now force himself to answer is the following: "When the ultimate domination of a clarified and contentless procedure of substitution is rigorously established, what is it, precisely, that he has before him?"

8. Let us now pause to appraise again the materials of our work. We have asserted that our "phenomena"—that is, the presentations that are interesting us—appear before us in language. We have said neither that they *are* language in any dogmatic sense

for the word "are", nor that they are dogmatically something other than language, for which the language is a mere frame or embodiment. Instead of presuming to decide such an issue at the start of the investigation, we have taken the position that this is a type of issue to postpone till after the kind of enquiry we are making has been completed. We remain, however, under obligation to examine our phenomena in language, and to develop a form of analysis adequate to handle them in that way. In this analysis we have first identified a general verbal separateness or discreteness, and established the word-cluster, "Character," with the Connectivity Dk. We have then overlaid this with a system of Connectivity D, and identified the word-cluster, "Symbol." The great field of all Symbols includes many systems, mathematical and perhaps others, and we have thus far discussed only the one system which we have named W, and the corresponding word-cluster which we have named II*A. In Chapter V, we shall examine systems of connectivity entangled with the system W, and embedded in word-clusters bearing such names as "Number," "Zahl" and "Menge."

At this point it is reasonably certain that the specialist in this field will make an objection. He will say perhaps: "I follow, as a provisional technique, your presentation in language of the connectivities Dk and D, but the moment that you pass to W, and give it to me as a form of D, so that you present the II*A under the II directly, it seems to me that you are confusing two situations which really lie at far extremes: your construction of "Character" is raw linguistic material: your construction of the connectivity W is in full consistency: you should in your development reach the connectivity W at the end, instead of introducing it at the beginning as you do: it is something very different from the raw material."

Historically his view is plausible, but here we deal not with history but with immediate analysis. The answer is that the consistency W lies actually in the refinement of the Symbols II*A, and is not to be sought outside. It is exactly this that I wish to show.

To take the opposed course would involve us, at least in our intermediate technique in logical-realistic classifications. The alternative presentation, such as the suggested critic might desire, would proceed something as follows. We should first lay out the linguistic field, using the characterizations Dk and D, or some substitutes for them. Here we should have language presented to us somewhat as it is known to philology. We should here not be regarding the Dk and D as themselves connectivities of word-clusters, but as "facts." We should then begin to develop word-clusters within these regions of "fact," beginning perhaps with III, and proceeding through V, VI etc. of the table in Chapter III. If, following this course, we should arrive in the end at the fully consistent system we have already introduced as II*A, connectivity W, we should then have before us a realistic-logical classification as follows:

A. The philological or linguistic materials.
B. The practical-logical word-clusters.
C. The systems of full linguistic connectivity.

Here we would face the alternatives of either reading the full consistencies back into the position in which I have placed them, or, on the other hand, of giving them some psychological or logical or other realistic interpretation. The latter would be the temptation from which we have here cut ourselves off at the start.

This may be stated in a somewhat different way as follows. Under our semantic approach we do not take words as given, and then operate upon or with them. We work wholly within the full linguistic field. The presentations of Word-clusters I and II are as much word-clusters for us as are any of those that follow. They are reports in and by language upon language. Taken in this way, the whole issue of the construction of language with respect to fact, experience and knowledge remains open: there is no chance for other interpretative devices to creep in,—for other word-clusters of implicit rather than explicit value, and of potential distortion. On the same basis it will be noted that the use of the terms word-cluster and connectivity in Rule VI, Chapter III, is broad enough to cover all cases from the most inconsistent to the most consistent and from the most barely philological to the most fully semantic.

9. We turn now to the Symbols II*B, those of the geometries. These are to be inspected just as we inspected the II*A in the status in which they are before us after many centuries of investigation. In this inspection, if we have before us a circle or triangle drawn upon paper, we will not regard it as an incidental "illustration" for some abstract symbolic development, or for some mental creative effort, but rather as itself a linguistic element, a symbol of the II*B. Doing this, we notice at once a manifest incompleteness in the available symbols of the II*Bb. We have many II*Ba corresponding to the II*Aa, but we are far from having a complete set of specialized II*Bb corresponding to the II*Ab: instead we have much of the M-O aspect of the geometries represented by words drawn from general vocabularies. Geometrical proofs are carried on by use of many different types of argumentation, and in the main with very much more use of ordinary linguistic expressions than are algebraic proofs: and so we must supplement such symbols as those for congruence, those of projection and those of the coordinates, with others which are implied in such terms as "rotation."[15]

Should we now start to set before ourselves the fully consistent connectivities of geometry with respect to M-T and M-O, it would seem at once as though the project was to be much easier than for algebra and

[15]See the second part of Chap. X, upon systems of postulation for geometry. The plus and minus signs used to indicate rotations in special forms of attack do not cover the full field in which symbolization is required.

arithmetic, where the difficulty raised by the sharp split in the ordinary conceptions of rational and transcendental numbers draws attention at first glance. The geometries, in the first place, long before Euclid, had made the "point" which they used in their proofs "*abstract*" and had developed a correspondingly "*abstract*" system of lines, surfaces and solids, thus gaining a linguistic coherence of a certain type for their work. In the next place the geometries have yielded to many useful and plausible axiomizations, especially since the outstanding work of Hilbert in the early years of the present century. In the third place, the geometries show great varieties of construction in the way in which alternative sets of objects may be taken as basic in any given system, with the remaining objects derived from these basic objects: and they also show frequent transformations of "operative" elements into "thing" elements and vice versa. The difficulties that arise, however, are great, and there are many intricate problems, long suppressed or speciously evaded, which at once come to clear light under semantic examination, so that it will probably require long labor to penetrate them. Nevertheless we have before us in the characteristics just stated, and under semantic postulation, a basis for proceeding.

*Specification*: G is the mathematical connectivity in full consistency of the II*B.

PROPOSITION II. The system G of the II*B is a semantic system, $S_s$, and the distinction M-T and M-O is systemic within it.

10. The difficulties to be faced in future develop-

ment with respect to the M-T and M-O of the II*B may be briefly sketched.

That the geometries have operational features, no matter in what logical phrasing they are embalmed, is evident to every geometrician. The obscurities of the situation can well be indicated by recalling the long discussions as to whether Euclid did, or did not, implicitly or explicitly, use rotations of figures in his proofs.

That the geometries tend to take the form of collections of objects between which relations are studied, and that these relations tend in turn to appear as objects is well known. Given a geometrical system in which such a presentation seems to have been perfected in objects and relations and nothing further, then semantic analysis shows at once that the operational features have been extruded into some assumed region of logical or psychological capacity, located in some sense in the heads of mathematicians. The M-O aspect has been evaded, therefore, in the geometry, only by positing its presence in an exceedingly obscure region of human ignorance outside of the geometry, where it lurks ever on the point of a return into the geometry with the threat of destroying the coherence of the whole relational method of construction.[16]

---

[16]With respect to this situation Klein remarks that "logic" can only enter after "man ein System gewisser einfacher Grundbegriffe und gewisser einfacher Sätze, der sog, Axiome, besitzt, das den einfachsten Tatsachen unserer Anschauung gerecht wird": Elementarmathematik vom höheren Standpunkte aus, II, p. 172. Compare also Poincaré's comment on Hilbert's axioms, cited in Chap. III. If what we have given us is just a single form of geometry, say the Euclidean, then a development in the form of things and relations seems self-evidently satisfactory, for the whole logical operative procedure can readily be given naive location in the human mind: A Kantian or

We now combine these points with those mentioned in the preceding paragraph, and we find that our analysis must allow for (a) geometries presented wholly as M-T with an "external" or "psychic" M-O; (b) the apparent possibility of starting in any geometry with any specific M-T presentation as basic, and deriving the others from it; (c) the frequent appearance of specific M-O aspects in a geometry having M-T basis; (d) the ready and frequent conversion of M-O aspects into new M-T aspects, with the consequent appearance of other aspects as now in their turn M-O; (e) the possibility of extending the analysis, as this paper proposes to do, so as to take up all of the alleged *"external"* M-O aspects within the geometries themselves. Considering the varieties of the geometries, and the many methods of dealing with them, we have here manifestly a field of investigation which cannot be disposed of in any few pages at any one time.

For illustration of typical situations we may consider the following. A vector appears as an operation, M-O: it very quickly is treated as a thing, M-T. A group, established as a set of objects and a rule of combination (including of course identity and inverse) is spoken of alternatively as M-O to the objects or as itself M-T: in which latter case the original objects appear as operations within it. Invariance is the determination of M-T out of M-O. Cross ratio in projective geometry becomes readily more of M-T to its

---

other construction may be used for background philosophy. If, however, as is the case today, we have given a great variety of geometries, then, under a comparable form of approach in things and relations, the one-pattern mind fails us as operator: its "logic" is in difficulties, and the search for the solution requires extension of analysis.

investigator than the materials by the aid of which he established it.[17]

11. Symbols II*C are those of Analysis. As an organized system of symbols they are of late historical appearance, dating—despite many brilliant prior experiments—only from the enterprise of Newton and Leibnitz. Preceding their organization in time, and underlying it mathematically, had come Analytic Geometry, which we may best describe as a technique that had great "practical" success for the manipulation in immediate contact of the Symbols II*A and II*B. Through Analytic Geometry new types of problems had come to sharper attention and clearer consideration: and it was these problems which the II*C proved themselves competent to handle. Developing swiftly, expanding widely through the following generations, opening up immense new fields of knowledge, the II*C came to be recognized as a third grand division of mathematics, with its own specialized consistency within its own full symbolic organization.

*Specification*: A is the mathematical connectivity in full consistency of the II*C.

The symbols of the II*C include some that take ready inspection as M-T—thus, to many workers, $\frac{dy}{dx}$: and they include others which are characteristically M-O, such as $\frac{d}{dx}$ and the difference symbol $\Delta$. However, this issue as to which of them should be regarded as M-T and which as M-O is before mathe-

[17]For the status of such problems as left by Klein, see the discussion by Pierpont The History of Mathematics in the Nineteenth Century, American M. S. Bull., Vol. 11, p. 144, p. 151.

maticians, not as one of naive realistic requirement, but rather as one of subtle disputation under the impulse to provide them with a realistic garb in imitation of the II*A and the II*B, a garb which they do not at all need for their successful manipulation, and which, if they were given it, would be at best unnecessary luggage for them to carry. Their full power is in x-to-x: and their rendition in x-to-X is superfluous degradation. They are thus before us in a form, and with a history, in which their presentation as fully semantic and in no sense realistic with respect to their M-T and M-O characteristics, can much more readily be appraised and accepted, than can at first glance—at least by many theorists—the corresponding semantic presentations of the II*A and the II*B. We may at once, therefore, set forth:

Proposition III. The system A of the II*C is a semantic system $S_s$, and the distinction M-T and M-O is systemic within it.

Assuming such comparatively ready acceptance for Proposition III, let us use it as a vantage point from which to look back upon Propositions I and II. Taking all three propositions together, what we have done is something as follows. We have said to ourselves: here before us are the symbols of Analysis, magnificently successful and consistent in their own right, but painfully incoherent when muddied with meanings from vulgar speech: here, again, before us are the symbols of Algebra and Geometry, magnificently successful also, except in certain outlying regions which we can now identify as exactly those regions in which certain of the inherited meanings of vulgar speech enter directly into their manipulation—in which, as we may perhaps say, they still attempt to walk upon their "feet of clay." Instead, then, of forcing upon Analysis the one vicious aspect of the other two, let us free the other two from that one vicious aspect which Analysis for itself has never possessed. Let us take the three systems, each in a safe semantic consistency of its own, and see, then, where we stand. If various devices such as the "*real*" number-point, "*intuition*" and other "*mental*" operations, the appraisal of the "abstract," and so forth, are helpful, let us accept them as conveniences, much as we accept a piece of chalk and a blackboard. But let us, once and for all, cease to regard ourselves as cripples compelled to use these devices as our crutches. Let us throw away the crutches and run, full-breathed, in consistency.

For Newton, although he thought in terms of infinitesimals at the start,[18] the new technique became rapidly specialized as Fluxions, as a study of differentiations with respect to time, and so its characterization was largely of an operational nature. For Leibnitz, who saw his mathematics in a particular philosophical setting, the infinitesimals, or rather the relations of the infinitesimals, became the direct objects of attention. Later generations of mathematicians followed "fashion," sometimes period-fashions, some-

---

[18]See Cajori, A History of the Conceptions of Limits and Fluxions in Great Britain from Newton to Woodhouse, p. 33. In 1704, in the Quadratura Curvarum, Newton wrote (translation by John Stewart): "I consider mathematical quantities in this place not as consisting of very small parts, but as described by a continued motion." Cajori, op. cit., p. 17.

times nationality-fashions, swinging sometimes towards one extreme, sometimes towards the other in that least significant, though often busiest of their activities, namely their manner of talking about their work.[19] Not more than a generation ago, when the name Calculus was commonly used, many of the text books made their constructions in terms of infinitesimals, a procedure which still survives for various minor industrial and engineering uses. The construction of Limits, as an extension of the understanding and formulation of the procedures of Analysis, brought enormous gains.[20] But despite that construction, the differences in stress and emphasis with respect to the M-T and M-O of Analysis still remain. On the one side stands, for example Volterra, who sees

---

[19]Cajori, op. cit., gives a most interesting account of such opinions, their origins and their fluctuations.

[20]We may say of the presentation in terms of Limits that it is a notably capable use of language for organizing situations which had formerly been troublesome and for ejecting irrelevant and disorderly elements from attention. I have, however, an observation to make in this respect that has a certain curious interest for me personally, and that may perhaps have some wider significance when taken, as I take it, as a development that just came to pass in the ordinary course of events, and without design or even notice at the time. Of the many references to limits and to discussions in terms of limits which have formed part of the text of this essay at one time or another while it has been under its protracted course of construction, most, and possibly all have disappeared. And this despite the fact that in at least one published paper (Revue internationale de sociologie, Vol. 37, 1929), I had suggested the use of the construction of limits for the development of the meanings of the terms, individual and social, in the as yet unborn science of sociology: while in other papers, still unpublished, I had gone much further in this direction by asserting the operational similarity of such limiting social constructions with the mathematical use of limits. It is apparent that this "similarity" is one of linguistic technique and values: but I already have reason to believe that in my next return to that particular social problem, the construction in the form of limits may be superseded by a still more efficient semantic phraseology. In the separate essay, "Semantic Analysis," incorporated in this book as Chapter XIII, the use of the term "limits" still survives.

the symbols of the II*C as operators: on the other side are various workers in the Cantorian line of development who, when they treat of "Real Analysis" give a significance to the word "real" far beyond that of a simple separation from the "complex."[21]

12. It is again an expression of existing mathematical status that the systems W, G, and A, of Symbols II*A, II*B and II*C, taken without realistic fixation of any M-T are in full working harmony.

PROPOSITION IV. The combined systems, W, G, and A, taken under the postulation x-to-x, and with the rejection of realistic interpretations, x-to-X, for any M-T or for any M-O, form a consistent semantic system $S_s$, and the distinction M-T and M-O is systemic within it.

Having these systems consistently before us in "Symbol," we shall next have to examine other mathematical word-clusters which surround them, out of which they have arisen, and which still claim the right to exercise authority over them. We shall consider first word-clusters of this kind which we shall call implicitly realistic, as contrasted with other systems which in their struggle towards a desired consistency, have become explicitly realistic in their postulation. We shall see that in no case have such systems gained consistency, we shall establish the reasons for their failure, and we shall propose to degrade them to the level of defective linguistic procedures.

---

[21]Weyl, who himself may be cited for his stress on the operational aspects in his work on group theory, notes the requirements for further steps after Cauchy (see Chap. X). For Volterra's operational point of view, see H. T. Davis, The Theory of the Volterra Integral Equation of Second Kind, 1930. Knopp, previously cited, is an illustration of the extreme requirement on the realistic side.

# V

# WORD-CLUSTERS LACKING CONSISTENCY

13. "Number," III, is a word-cluster in which conventional number is taken implicitly as realistic M-T in a system x-to-X as to M-T.

This conventionally realistic attitude towards "Number" in ordinary obscure realistic thought, gains added texture and body, and increased "substantiality," by its confused association with another obscure term, namely Quantity.

Just what numbers conventionally "are" is something that it is difficult to state in terms that will hold validity over long stretches of historical time, since the conventions are only too apt to change their content of reference without any weakening either of their sense of infallibility or of their vehemence. In general we may understand, "Number" to cover the realistic implications or references of Symbols II*Aa and of all "Symbols" which under available techniques of W, are transformable or readily inspected as capable of transformation into II*Aa. The obscurities and confusions, not only of past generations but also of the present, appear vividly in the history of zero as a number. Zero came into use as a practical aid in numerical record and computation. In the course of generations men began to observe that they were treating it "like a number": and from that an advance was easy for the more venturesome spirits who began boldly to call it a number itself. This rashness excited loud outcry from other mathematicians who, whether wittingly or unwittingly, were controlled in their manners of expression by the more stable conventions of "quantity." Time went on, technical considerations prevailed, the "number line" was used even for most elementary purposes of instruction, new zeros were disclosed and accepted, various "'nulls" proved to have great practical utility: and today the proposition that zero "is" a number, with heavy emphasis on the "is," is a standard component of conventional orthodoxy. But all the time "exceptions" with respect to zero persist in all regions of its use; and these most certainly serve to segregate zero, somehow, some way, from other number. In technical procedure such exceptions may readily be accepted in a matter-of-fact way: but in *"foundation"* procedures they destroy full consistency, wherever they persist.[1] Such obscurities and confusions, such matter-of-fact blindnesses and compromises are inherent in the development of Word-Cluster III, but do not have place at all in Word-Cluster II.

*Specification*: Dk-?-W[2] is the connectivity of III in an implicit system $S_r$. It is that attitude of approach, and that scheme of *"understanding,"* which presents discreteness as *"existent"* under a postulate x-to-X in the region of the realistically taken M-T of III. Under it the M-O aspects are translated into, or interpreted by, or, more commonly, evaded by, some form of common-reference description.[3]

14. The system Dk-?-W lacks consistency in two well-known regions, namely, that of the infinite extension in the magnitude series of natural numbers, and that of the decimal table when assumed as statically complete, and brought into correspondence with the continuum. In this implicit system $S_r$ distinctions are made as if *"fundamental"* between naturals, rationals, algebraics and transcendentals, or between certain groups of them: although in the consistent system

[1]For further consideration of the issue of "exceptions" in mathematics see Chap. VIII.

[2]This may be read "Dk-maybe-W": but in much mathematical *"foundation"* work, where a symbol of this kind could be profitably employed, it would more wisely be read in its fuller form, thus: "Dk-maybe-W *and* maybe-not."

[3]See Chap. IV, Par. 5.

$S_s$ of W, no such distinctions are *"fundamental"* but they appear only incidentally for specified provisional purposes.

It is the common remark of workers upon *"foundation"* problems that the difficulties of construction all lie in the two regions above indicated, and that, given solution there, all the rest of the far-reaching mathematical development with all of its intricacy or appearance of intricacy will take care of itself. Thus Weyl insists that in the whole mathematical construction there are just two great gaps, two regions from which we look into what may perhaps be the insoluble, these being the outlying progression of the sequence of natural numbers, and the continuum. For the rest, he says, there is no difficulty.[4] Such a remark, from our present point of view, takes the natural comment that those "more complicated" phenomena are already understood under semantic appraisal, and that what is needed for progress to full consistency is the extension of this existing semantic view into all of the presentations of number and of the continuum from the first beginnings onwards.

15. "Extension," IV, is a word-cluster in which length, surface and solidity are taken implicitly as realistic M-T in a system x-to-X as to M-T.

*Specification*: Dk-?-G is the connectivity of IV in an implicit system $S_r$. It is that attitude or approach, and that scheme of *"understanding,"* which presents discreteness as *"existent"* under a postulate of x-to-X in the region of the realistically taken M-T of IV. Under it, also, the M-O aspects are translated into, or

[4]Die heutige Erkenntnislage in der Mathematik, Symposion, Sonderdruck, Heft 3, p. 12: "Im Aufbau der Mathematik gibt es zwei offene Stellen, wo es möglicherweise ins Unergründliche geht: der Fortgang in der Reihe der natürlichen Zahlen und das Kontinuum. Alles andere, der Übergang von den natürlichen Zahlen zu den negativen und gebrochenen, aber auch die Einführung der imaginären und hyperkomplexen Grössen, ist eine formallogische Angelegenheit, die keine Schwierigkeiten und Rätsel mehr birgt: der mystische Geruch in dem die imaginären Grössen lange Zeit standen, hat sich vollständig verloren."

interpreted by, or, more commonly, evaded by, some form of common-reference description.

In the implicitly realistic word-clusters, III and IV, parts, wholes, finites and infinites all struggle to appear with equal substantiality as M-T. The connectivities Dk-?-W and Dk-?-G fail to attain consistency with respect to them.

16. In the next four word-clusters, V to VIII, we shall examine constructions which, with mounting explicitness, strive to attain refinement of the Dk-?-W and the Dk-?-G, or their subsumption under, or their replacement by, other systems of connectivity. Before examining these directly, it is desirable to survey, in preliminary dissection, the present status of the references whole-part. We may omit a similar survey for finite-infinite, since these terms in various developments are acutely present to the attention of every one interested in the field. This survey will at the same time enable us to sharpen our comments on word-clusters III and IV.

Citations as to Whole-Part. As a general indication of the confusion in the use of these terms, and without any immediate criticism of the constructions from which the citations are taken, we may consider the following: (1) Weyl, in discussing Brouwer, offers the two following remarks close together in the text:[5] (a) "Nicht in der Beziehung von Element zu Menge,

[5]Philosophie der Mathematik und Naturwissenschaft, p. 43. For Weyl's more extended interpretation of the situation in these respects see Math. Zeitschr., vol. 10, p. 77 sq. I allow these and the immediately following citations from Hausdorff to remain in their German form without attempt at English rendering. Certain of the terms used cannot be touched without distorting their implications.

sondern in derjenigen des Teiles zum Ganzen sieht Brouwer im Einklang mit der Anschauung das Wesen des Kontinuums": (b) "In einem Kontinuum kann es nach Brouwer nur stetige Funktionen geben. Das Kontinuum lässt sich nicht aus Teilen zusammensetzen." (2) Hausdorff[6] inspects such statements as, for example; "Eine Menge entsteht durch Zusammenfassung von Einzeldingen zu einem Ganzen"; and "Eine Menge ist eine Vielheit als Einheit gedacht"; and points out their obscurity of meaning: whereupon, nevertheless, he accepts them as manifestations of "einen primitiven, allen Menschen vertrauten Denkakt":[7] specifying further for his own purposes: "Wir wollen uns mit dieser Auffassung begnügen, und es als Grundtatsache hinnehmen, dass ein Ding M in eigentümlicher, nicht definierbarer Weise gewisse andere Dinge, a, b, c, . . ., und diese wiederum jenes bestimmen: eine Beziehung die wir mit den Worten ausdrücken: die Menge M besteht aus den Dingen, a, b, c. . . ." Thus while his development proposes to run under the control of the symbol "epsilon" of Elemente and Eigenschaften, what he is investigating throughout is nevertheless the whole-part situation of Enthalten and Teilmengen, which are seen to persist in the body under the Mengenlehre clothing. (3) Caratheodory, in dealing with Punktmengen, continually shifts his expression between "gehören," "bestehen," "entsprechen" and "enthalten," (belong, consist, correspond, contain) according as the implications of these terms

[6]Mengenlehre, 2d ed., p. 11.

[7]Compare also his much sharper statement in the opening paragraphs of the first edition of the work cited.

may respectively seem most helpful to him at the moment.[8]

Quantity. Quantity is in its way an affair of whole-part. Though popularly regarded as a typically mathematical *"concept,"* and though in the past it was often used by mathematicians in experiments for the definition of their subject-matter, it is now generally abandoned for this purpose. In common use, and in many philosophical schemes, quantity is set up under the common-reference description, concerete-abstract, which is wholly trivial. Peano, in his Introduction to the first edition of his Formulaire (1894) identified it with real number ("Q signifie nombre réel positif (quantité)") as distinguished from rational number. As to the general futility of the term for theoretical purposes one may examine discussions by Russell[9] and Weyl.[10]

Collections, Uniform and Specialized. These, illustrated respectively by a bag of marbles and a deck of cards, are handled by special branches of mathematics, yet without yielding information as to *"fundamentals."* Set up as *"fundamental,"* first by implication and then expressly, in the early constructions of the "Mengenlehre," they were quickly abandoned,[11]

---

[8]Vorlesungen über reelle Funktionen, p. 19, sq.

[9]Introduction to Mathematical Philosophy, p. 195.

[10]Philosophie der Mathematik und Naturwissenschaft, p. 50.

[11]Zermelo, Unterschungen über die Grundlagen der Mengenlehre, I, Math. Ann., vol. 65, p. 261, 1908. "Die urpsrüngliche Cantorsche Definition einer 'Menge' als einer 'Zusammenfassung von bestimmten wohlunterschiedenen Objekten unserer Anschauung oder unseres Denkens zu einem Ganzen' bedarf einer Einschränkung, ohne dass es doch schon gelungen wäre, sie durch eine andere, ebenso einfache, zu ersetzen, welche zu keinen solchen Bedenken mehr Anlass gäbe." For the appraisal of Zermelo's own development with respect to the "Auswahl" and to "well-ordered" series, reference may be made to the paper by Alonzo Church, Alternatives to Zermelo's Assumption, Amer. M. S. Trans., vol. 29, p. 178.

since they proved to be breeding grounds of inconsistency, utterly worthless for mathematical constructions on a broad scale.

Organ and Organism: Psycho-Social Specifications. These, illustrated respectively by the status of brain in body, and by the status of sovereignty in government and of government in society, have not been used for mathematical "*foundation*" purposes, and indeed lack mathematical constructions adequately adapted to their own specialized use.

We shall disregard Quantity, Collections, and Organic, Psychic and Social Constructions, together with all whole-part implications belonging to them, and shall center our attention on the sharply isolated whole-part characteristics of Inductive Number, Geometrical Area and Mengen, reminding ourselves that we are still within the range of preliminary dissection by the aid of low-grade language, while nevertheless our purpose is to build towards exact analysis.

Inductive Number. Very early in the history of mathematics it appeared that, despite all practical quantitative applications, the most effective way to handle rational fractions was not under a construction of whole-part, but under a construction of pairs. This method yielded increasingly successful, results with complex numbers. In conflict with this long historical development, the present generation of mathematicians has been in great part determined, if possible, to handle the infinite series of naturals as a whole, to which the finites are parts. In this it has not been successful to the extent that it can secure full consistency. If we distinguish proper-parts, proper-wholes, mediate-parts and mediate-wholes, the natural number One may be regarded as a proper-part, the natural number Two may then be regarded as a mediate-whole, or alternatively as a proper-part itself, and so forth. Proper-parts are here realistically M-T. Mediate-wholes may also be inspected as M-T, with due caution. For this system, taken as the system W, no proper-whole is found as M-T. What one reaches in progression towards it is the dominance of M-O before the investigating attention. What is required before one can inspect this dominating M-O as M-T is arbitrary intervention from outside the system. Hence the "*foundation*" theories.

Areas. Practical Surveying, with respect to Areas, stands in much the same status that Quantity does to natural number: and it is equally beyond our present interest. The Area, for Geometries of the earlier types, may, in the phrasing of the preceding paragraph, be inspected as a proper-whole. It may be made to yield mediate-parts: while also, larger proper-wholes may be constructed around it, to which it then comes to stand as a mediate-whole. To this particular geometrical approach, the "point," on the one side, and "space" itself on the other present themselves as M-O, and arbitrary intervention from without is necessary to garb them as M-T. But then consistency fails, unless the full postulatory semantic method is adopted.

"Mengen." In "Mengen," the arbitrary interventions, under which M-O aspects in Number and Area are forced into M-T garb, seek a construction under which whole-part and finite-infinite will be provided with a common denominator of the general form, "Element" and "Menge." The "Element," it soon appears, must be a "Menge," and the "Menge" must have itself as "Element." With "Element" and "Menge" a consistent system may be constructed, just as was found possible with theology in the days when the theological interest was sufficiently acute to motivate the labor: and such a system may well be a mathematic among mathematics. Our concern here is not with the detached construction of the abstract "Mengenlehre,"[12] but instead with the common denominator values of the system with respect to the whole-part description for other mathematical construction. In this respect our survey reports that paradoxes appear in every such interpretation, and that these have not yet been removed in full consistency, but are evaded by opportunisms, such as Brouwer's dictum upon the excluded middle, Fraenkel's "Beschränktheitsaxiom."[13] Weyl's "umfangsdefinite Urteile,"[14] and the Russell-Wittgenstein-Ramsey[15] manipulations of the axiom of reducibility. The entire

---

[12]Or, we may put it thus: (1) no objection whatever is raised against any consistent point-set construction: (2) a confused linguistic situation is pointed out, under which workers in point-set theory are apt to "*believe*" that they are dealing in some sense "realistically" with numbers and the continuum: (3) analysis of this situation exhibits the analytic correspondences of the M-T and M-O aspects throughout the field, and clears off the fog of "*belief*": (4) it at once follows that point-set constructions, naively taken, are worthless for mathematical "*foundation*" purposes. See Chaps. XI and XII.

[13]Zehn Vorlesungen über die Grundlegung der Mengenlehre, p. 102.

[14]See Chap. X.

[15]See Ramsey, Lond. M.S. Proc., (2) vol. 25, p. 338, 1925. Ramsey's later essays show a distinct progress away from the logical fixation of infinity and towards a freer interpretation of the problem of mathematical construction. See his posthumously published book: "The Foundations of Mathematics, and Other Essays," 1931.

development in this field tends through Brouwer, Borel and Suslin, back to a specialized "Menge," which is no longer abstract, but analytic, and which finally proves to be just a new manner of speech about the decimal table:[16] and here the issue of the paradoxes, despite all the refinements of investigation, lies as acute between "Häufungspunkt" and "Kondensationspunkt" as it ever did in the simple days of Zeno, or in the towering conceptions of Cantor.

The whole-part situation in mathematics is still full of confused implications from common-reference descriptions. Consistency fails, because analysis of these implications is lacking. Within mathematics the analysis must be made, and nowhere else, since mathematical analysis yields vision, other language by comparison only the blurs and the blind spots.

17. We have now the basis for a fuller orientation of word-clusters III and IV with their connectivities Dk-?-W and Dk-?-G, in respect to word-cluster II with its connectivities, W, G and A.

"Number," III, offers presentations which individually are taken as finite and which when so taken may be regarded as parts, but which, when regarded as infinite, do not furnish wholes.

"Extension," IV, offers presentations which individually are taken as wholes and which when so taken may be regarded as infinite in subdivisibility, but

[16]Compare the trend of development in Hausdorff between his first and second editions (op. cit.). Karl Menger, (Deutsche Math.-Ver., vol. 37, p. 213, sq. and p. 298, sq.) comments on this, and puts special stress on the analytische Verzweigungsmenge. See also his remarks (idem, p. 225) that the word Konstruktivität has never yet received adequate analysis in mathematics.

which, when traced back to their parts, exhibit no finite.

Dk-?-W is that implicitly realistic connectivity which, taking finites in the guise of parts, has never succeeded in understanding its presentations of infinite wholes.

Dk-?-G is that implicitly realistic connectivity which, taking wholes in the guise of infinites has never succeeded in understanding its presentations of finite parts.

The realistic approach is well illustrated by many remarks of Whitehead in his small popular book, An Introduction to Mathematics. For example, he says; "There is necessarily a fundamental distinction between the properties of space and the properties of number—in fact, all the essential difference between space and number. The 'spaciness' of space and the 'numerosity' of number are essentially different things, and must be directly apprehended."[17] In these sentences the expressions "necessarily," "essentially" and "must be" merely register the fact that Whitehead himself had not pushed analysis any further, and that no satisfactory analysis by anyone else had come to his attention in the year of his writing, and that therefore he choose to assert that no further progress ever would be made. In another passage he says: "The axioms of quantity are entirely abstract, just as are the mathematical properties of space. They are the same for all quantities, and they presuppose no special mode of perception."[18] One may compare also Weyl's manner of separating phenomenal knowledge from theoretical construction,[19] and Poincaré's discussion of the distinction between "faits bruts" and "faits scientifiques."[20]

18. We might now, were we proceeding on a schematic basis, set up a special word-cluster for realistic interpretations of Analysis, as a special sub-

[17]An Introduction to Mathematics, p. 240.
[18]Idem, p. 246.
[19]See Chaps II and X.
[20]So La Valeur de la Science, Chap. X.

division of mathematics, and along with it a corresponding connectivity, Dk-?-A. We have no need of this, however, since, for Analysis, such materials have merely the value of speculative embroideries around the body of the consistent technique itself: whereas in the cases of Algebra and Geometry they appear as conventions of language, older than the techniques and arrogating dominance. Being arbitrary and troublesome, these latter materials must be directly investigated and assigned their places in the general language structure.

So far as Analysis is concerned we need not do more than summarize the situation that is before us.

The connectivities W and G organize with semantic consistency in A, but, when interpreted realistically as Dk-?-W and Dk-?-G, they fail to make A either realistic or consistent in some anticipated correlated form, Dk-?-A.

Taking M-T and M-O as systemic, W and G are analytically tolerant, and yield systemic M-T and M-O in A: but when given realistic identifications they lead in A to nothing but puzzlement and paradox.

19. Proposition V. Symbols II*A are[21] neither finites, nor infinites, wholes nor parts. Symbols II*B are neither finites nor infinites, wholes nor parts. Symbols II*C are neither finites nor infinites, wholes nor parts.

---

[21] The word "are" in Proposition V should be read in the semantic sense, that is "are, within consistent language," which means here within connectivity W, within the range of any surrounding consistency of language, or finally within any intelligent meaning of consistently mathematical character. See the introductory paragraphs of Chapters VIII and XII.

These propositions do not apply to the developments of Word-Clusters III, IV, V, VI, VII and VIII. If they are read in terms of the linguistic organization of those word-clusters, they will fail to convey their intended meaning. Even among the Hilbert "Zeichen" of Word-Cluster VIII, under Connectivity BB, the oppositions of finite and infinite retain specifically realistic values, however carefully Hilbert may endeavor to translate them out of the language of the "real" into his language of the "ideal."

20. We proceed now from an inspection of implicitly realistic word-clusters, to an examination of explicitly realistic constructions designed to organize Algebra, Geometry and Analysis in common.

"Zahl," V, is the identification of number and point—"Nummer" and "Punkt,"—each as realistic M-T,[22] in its system, and both as "the same"[23] M-T. This is accomplished by the construction of the continuum in IV and the interval 0, 1 in III, the acceptance of all forms II*$Ac_b$ as realistic M-T, the use of any appropriate system of transcription, such as radix fractions, to present a whole of "Zahlen," the postulate that infinite series reach points, or point-like termini, the implicit postulate that hypothetically completed M-O is M-T, and the glossing of all difficulties M-T and M-O. The historical development is well-known. Wallis, (1696,) identified periodic decimals as rational: algebraics were in due course identified: Liouville showed the existence of classes of transcendentals (1844): the proof was given for e and pi that they could not be algebraic (1873, 1882): and a con-

[22]Dantzig makes passing comment: "Such is the irony of words that the so-called *real* numbers have been attained at the sacrifice of a part of that *reality* which we attribute to the natural numbers": Number, the Language of Science, p. 236.

[23]See the discussion in Par. 21.

struction was provided by Stolz (1885) under which every irrational could readily be taken as represented by a non-periodic decimal.[24] The continuum of "Zahl" now appears commonly in the form of the nested interval, with the postulate that the separation of end-points is null, or alternatively that each interval *contains* or *is* one point. Under "Zahl" we may include the "Punktmenge."

*Specification*: B-Z is the connectivity in a system $S_r$ of word-cluster V, "Zahl."

21. B-Z is a member of a family of connectivities, B. We shall take B ("Bedeutung") as a blanket term[25] covering many connectivities, and let appended letters indicate specially interesting specimens of the family, B.

We have now reached a point in our investigation at which it is futile to attempt to analyze in great detail the various forms of connectivity which will be before us as we go over the literature in which they must be sought and examined, and in which they are, so to speak, embodied. The futility lies in the fact that we never find the connectivities B twice alike. They may sometimes be phrased alike, but the background implications of the phrasings will be found to be, in this or that essential respect, different: and without fully analyzing and clarifying these background implications, we cannot say clearly what the particular B before us actually is.

---

[24]Allgemeine Arithmetik, I, pp. 109-119.

[25]B approaches symbolic value under a sharp offsetting of semantic and realistic postulation.

Such a phrase as "We never find the connectivities twice alike" is to be understood as follows: We may postulate at one end that no two presentations or phenomena whatsoever are dogmatically "alike" (since, indeed, if we identify no other differences, there is always a difference in the conventional, or historical, space and time of occurrence): and, at the other end, we may postulate that in systems of mathematical connectivity, such as W and G, many separate presentations in W and G are "alike" or "the same" in the maximum degree of sameness which we know (therein using our connectivities Dk and D in their full linguistic range). When we take the "Number" and "Extension" connectivities, Dk-?-W and Dk-?-G, we may report that we find cases of each of them so much alike in the works of various mathematicians and for specific purposes that we are justified in characterizing them simply as "the same": in other words, every time such cases are presented or described we can definitely recognize them for the purposes in hand. Of "Zahl," when used in a special technical field, say that of infinite series, we may make a similar report. But the "Zahl" connectivity, B-Z, belongs to a group of B connectivities, and is, by each writer on *"foundations,"* enveloped in further interpretations in such highly individualized—which here merely means uncertain and obscure—ways, that the "alikeness" vanishes as we inspect the various specimens for purposes of careful discrimination: and along with the "alikeness" vanishes also the importance of the theories.

Without attempting further specification, and without being too particular as to the distinction between explicit and implicit characteristics, we may recognize in addition to B-Z the following specimens of the B connectivity:

B-M. The "Ding," "Eigenschaft" and epsilon of abstract "Mengenlehre."

B-Ded The Dedekindian "Schnitt."

B-R The Russell types and reducibility.

B-Br The Brouwer mixture of "Folge ζ," "Spezies," "Eigenschaft" and excluded middle.

B-W Weyl's "Urteilsschema."
B-Fr Fraenkel's "Beschränktheitsaxiom."
B-Car. Caratheodory's form of fluctuation between "Zeichen" and "Zahl."
B-Chw. Chwistek's "Semantik."

When these chapters were written I was not acquainted with Chwistek's theory. I can now do no more than insert a brief statement, the reading of which may best be deferred until after the analysis of Hilbert's construction in paragraphs 25 to 28 has been reached. Chwistek proposes to use "less"—whatever that may mean—"intuition" than Hilbert uses: and he proposes to give language still more of that characteristic which Brouwer calls "deadness" and which the latter so greatly deplores in Hilbert's work. This "intuition," Chwistek specifies, need be barely enough to distinguish one sign from another, to note the presence or absence of a sign, and to obey rules for making substitutions of signs. Language, taken in the form of "expressions," "Ausdrücke" —which we are permitted to call "judgments," "Urteile," when and as we wish—is presented as basic to logic and mathematics: and in such a way that if we are given five letters and one sign of substitution, we have all the equipment that we require. In this way all logic and mathematics is to be "mechanized" in a "Semantik." His envisionment of his materials in a frame of "realistic discreteness" which is in sharp contrast to the semantic analysis used by us for similar materials in Word-Cluster I, "Character," will be plain in even so brief a summary. So splendidly automatic is knowledge to become, according to Chwistek, that even Hilbert's efforts at "Widerspruchsfreiheit" can be casually passed over by him as incidental within his perfect mechanics.

Chwistek's starting point for his development, his interest throughout, and his most significant test at the latest stage he has reached, is the Richard paradox in the linguistic setting given it by Poincaré. His goal, as is the case in all the B systems, is a complete and final settlement, once and for all, of all of our difficulties with respect to logic, language, mathematics and knowledge: and, quite characteristically also for this type of system, we find him announcing repeatedly that he has reached it, only to announce a transformation of his procedure a few years later, with a new decree for the banishment of metaphysics and a new proclamation of "monumental unity" for all science. His latest system is one which offers us a simple type-like ("typenartige") Semantik, under which, we are told, the "Mengenbegriff" is reduced to the "Begriff" of a linguistic expression ("Ausdruck"). We are to concern ourselves merely with "Mengen von Ausdrücken." On the one hand, our "Mengen" are before us as particular "Ausdrücke." On the other hand, any desired "Ausdruck," and therefore any desired "Menge," can be read as a judgment ("Urteil"). True judgments are full "Mengen." False judgments introduce not-full "Mengen": and a false judgment that is not a "Mengenausdruck" is an empty "Menge." We are, in short, to deal solely with aggregates of expression, and our aggregates are before us as themselves expressions: but still, most regrettably, an aggregate of expressions cannot belong within its own field, and the possibilities of the expressional aggregate of all aggregates of expression are such that self-restraint will still remain advisable to the ardent mathematician. Such then is Chwistek's semantic mechanization of knowledge—his perfect solution of the problem of formulation for theoretical science.[26]

22. The naïve presentation of "Zahl" required some form of equally naïve subjective setting from the earlier days of its development. Cantor's construction of "Begriffe" was just sufficient to give him a gentle opiate under which he could proceed with his interesting and powerful development. Dedekind's work had its greatest value in offering a new form of description, but he built in a "Gedankenwelt," and a construction of an existent or basic infinite, the "set of all things": so that his own form of reasoning led

[26]I cite from Chwistek's two latest papers under the title, Neue Grundlagen der Logik und Mathematik, Math. Zeitschr., vol. 30, 1929, and vol. 34, 1932. For his "intuition" see the first of these papers, pp. 704, 708-9, 721: for mechanization, see pp. 707, 721. For the summary of results, see the second paper, especially pp. 533-4. His earlier approach to the problem is to be found in two papers, Math. Zeitschr., vol. 14 and vol. 25. His most general development of his Semantik is contained in two papers which, unfortunately, I have been unable to consult, namely his Theory of Constructive Types, Annales de la société polonaise de mathématique, Krakow, 1925, and Une méthode métamathématique d'analyse, Comptes rendus du 1er congrès des mathématiciens des pays slaves, Warszawa, 1929.

at once to paradox. Peano's symbolism gave incentive to many logistic elaborations, but without reaching the pre-logical linguistic differentiations.

Concerning Dedekind's *"foundation"* construction, Hilbert puts it this way, that, for Dedekind, the "endliche Anzahl" is "nicht der Anschauung zu entnehmen," but must be derived logically from the infinite "Menge."[27] The quick demonstration that this project was a failure brought despair to both Frege and Dedekind, but without destroying for a moment the mathematical value of Dedekind's contribution. It is just one more illustration of the typical situation in mathematics as described by Pierpont: "The consoling feature . . . is this: the results are right although the reasoning is faulty. The intuition of these great men is far in advance of their logic."[28] The solution lies in surrendering dependence on realistic finite as well as infinite, and in developing semantic analysis of the finite-infinite common-reference description.

23. "Menge," VI, is a word-cluster which provides, as described in paragraph 16 above, a broader verbal common denominator, and the hope of a consistent symbolism, for the M-T aspects of "Nummer" and "Punkt," already before it in identification by the word-cluster "Zahl." We may recognize in especial the connectivity B-M of "Ding," "Eigenschaft" and "Enthaltensein," dating in its formal axiomatization from Zermelo. The setting up of the abstract theory, the development within it of analytic "Mengen" and the increasing concentration upon them, and their final appearance as a restatement of the decimal table have already been mentioned.

24. "Auswahl," VII, is a word-cluster which attempts to organize the M-O aspects ejected from the

---

[27]Math. Ann., vol. 95, p. 167.

[28]Amer. M.S. Bull., 1928, p. 32.

realistic M-T system of "Mengen." It involves, with respect to the common-reference description subjective-objective, first an attempt to handle the general requirements for a theory of the subjective as over against the objective aspects of "Mengen": and second, the specific problem of axiomization that arises within the "Mengenlehre" at the place at which the M-T aspect of II*A, and the M-T aspect of II*B come together, i. e., at the place at which selections of series of natural-number-point-things must be made from the continuum of number-point-things. Its components subdivide into VII*A, the more objective expressions it requires, and VII*B, the more subjective expressions it requires. From the point of view of semantic analysis it is futile to spend time on any of its casuistries or compromises.

25. "Das Hilbertsche Objekt," VIII, is a word-cluster which specifically undertakes to make the entire content of mathematics, and presumably of all knowledge in any exact sense, appear under the form M-T, with the reduction of all identifiable M-O aspects to M-T forms. For this purpose it postulates "Zeichen" as "Objekte," starting with the ordinary numerical "Zeichen," but, then including as "Objekte," first all operative mathematical "Zeichen," and next also all operative logical "Zeichen." These "objects" are taken as "discrete" in realistic postulation, so that the Dk connectivity of language is spread realistically over the entire system: and they are coupled with an "Anschauung" in which they appear, and which is to be taken as existent in some sense *"outside of"* the system, and as the locus of all background

M-O, if any, which is not incorporated in the system itself. When the development proceeds into the infinite two new kinds of "Zeichen" or "Objekte" are added, namely variables and integrations.

*Specification.* BB is the Hilbertian connectivity.

BB is the most highly developed and most fully clarified of the B system of realistic *"foundations."* It has proceeded so far in postulatory clarification that it is entitled to be set off by itself, in differentiation from all other forms.[29]

Hilbert's "Zeichen" are not to be confused with "Symbol," as that term is technically developed in this book. His "Zeichen" have a discreteness, a separateness of presentation, an independence in their own right, which is characteristic of Aristotelian definition, but which in our development has been discarded, because of the inconsistencies to which it leads. They are indeed inspected by Hilbert as freed from any immediate, individualized reference to phenomena of a world lying *"beyond"* them, so that they have lost one of the aspects which are found confused in the Aristotelian canon of identity, but they still retain this other aspect which is crucial to the Aristotelian system. Of the Hilbert "Zeichen" Weyl

---

[29]Chronologically Hilbert's development of this construction may be traced through the following publications which are his most important in this field:

Grundlagen der Geometrie, 1st ed., 1899; 7th ed., 1930. (This latest edition includes as appendices reprints of four of the essays next listed.)

Über den Zahlbegriff: Deutsche Math.-Ver., vol. 8, p. 180, 1900.

Über die Grundlagen der Logik und der Arithmetik: Proceedings, Third International Mathematical Congress, 1904. (Translated by George Bruce Halsted, Monist, vol. 15, p. 328, 1905.)

Axiomatisches Denken: Math. Ann., vol. 78, p. 405, 1918.

Neubegründung der Mathematik: Erste Mitteilung: Hamb. Abh., vol. I, p. 157, 1922.

Die logischen Grundlagen der Mathematik: Math. Ann., vol. 88, p. 151, 1923.

Über das Unendliche: Math. Ann., vol. 95, p. 161, 1926.

Die Grundenlagen der Mathematik, II: Hamb. Abh., vol. VI, p. 65, 1928.

Probleme der Grundlegung der Mathematik: Math. Ann., vol. 102, p. 1, 1929.

(With W. Ackermann) Grundzüge der theoretischen Logik, 1928.

says in his Philosophie der Mathematik und Naturwissenschaft (p. 44): "Sie sind nicht gemeint als Zeichen für etwas." Nevertheless the construction of "Anschauung" in which they are offered also includes a construction of "Tatsachen": and herein lies the justification for retaining the Hilbert procedure among the realistically postulated systems, while at the same time separating it under a special characterization, BB, from the other forms of such postulation. For Hilbert's background in this respect the introductory pages of his paper, "Axiomatisches Denken," listed in the bibliographical footnote, may be consulted.

The base from which Hilbert proceeds has been established by him in assertions which I paraphrase as follows:

In 1922; "As necessary condition for our work we must have something set before us in advance, certain extra-logical discrete objects, perceivable as immediate experience and present prior to all thought." And also: "Thus making my stand, I take the mathematical "Zeichen" themselves as objects of that kind for our theory."[30]

In 1927: "In mathematics the concrete "Zeichen" are themselves object of our consideration: their form, as they are before us, being immediately recognizable and unmistakable. This is the very minimum of presupposition, without which no scientific thinker can

[30]Neubegründung der Mathematik: Hamb. Abh., vol. I, p. 163: "Als Vorbedingung. . . . muss . . . etwas in der Vorstellung gegeben sein: gewisse ausserlogische diskrete Objekte, die anschaulich als unmittelbares Erlebnis vor Allem Denken da sind." "Indem ich diesen Standpunkt einnehme, sind mir . . . die Gegenstände der Zahlentheorie die Zeichen selbst."

Compare also Math. Ann., vol. 95, p. 171: "Soll das logische Schliessen sicher sein, so müssen sich diese Objekte vollkommen in allen Teilen überblicken lassen, und ihre Aufweisung, ihre Unterscheidung, ihr Aufeinanderfolgen oder Nebeneinandergereihtsein ist mit den Objekten zugleich unmittelbar anschaulich gegeben als etwas, das sich nicht noch auf etwas anderes reduzieren lässt, oder einer Reduktion bedarf."

proceed, and which every one of us, wittingly or unwittingly, must employ."[31]

Let us consider these, not in terms of the English rendering, but in terms of Hilbert's own language.

In changing his phrasing from the earlier to the later form it will be noted that he substitutes the word "konkret" for "diskret," and that he transfers the stress from "Gegenstände" to "Gegenstand." In these apparently slight verbal changes there lies involved the whole enormous world-wide and time-old range of philosophical and psychological disputation. If the Hilbertian analysis were carried back into the material of its own assumptions, such wavering would be impossible. Further, most of the terms used are, for purposes of exact communication from one investigator to another, meaningless or nearly so. This is true of "Vorstellung," "anschaulich," "Erlebniss," "Denken," "Betrachtung" and "Einstellung": and in certain aspects also of "Vorbedingung," "unmittelbar" and "Voraussetzung."

Now in building up his system Hilbert is compelled to make use of a great apparatus of logical "Zeichen," all presumably after their reduction to the status of "Objekte." It is, however, very soon noticeable that the "Anschauung," as an assumed external operational-subjective, will not hold the full content of Hilbertian development. Another construction has to be added

---

[31]Die Grundlagen der Mathematik, II: Hamb. Abhr., vol. VI, p. 66. "Und insbesondere in der Mathematik sind Gegenstand unserer Betrachtung die konkreten Zeichen selbst, deren Gestalt unserer Einstellung zufolge unmittelbar deutlich und wiedererkennbar ist. Dies ist das geringste Mass von Voraussetzung, das kein wissenschaftlicher Denker entbehren kann, und daher jedermann, sei es bewusst oder unbewusst, inne halten muss."

to it on this external subjective side, namely the capacity of building ideal forms, and Hilbert even sets a fairly definite line in mathematics between the two, as in his illustration of prime numbers.[32] Beyond this with transfinite induction and with all procedures in the region of "Auswahl" one may identify still a third type of subject, which Hilbert has expressly set himself the task of reducing to mathematical formulation.

Still other types of Hilbertian "subjects" which he employs in the hinterland of mathematical *"foundation"* theory were provisionally identified by me in an extensive, but unpublished, study, made prior to the present construction, under the title "The Mathematical Object." These are irrelevant for our purposes here: and indeed that whole earlier scheme of attack in terms of subjects and objects has been abandoned in order to be replaced by the technical devices, M-T and M-O, which make possible a more empirical organization of the materials. How the "Auswahl" takes place as a subject may readily be traced in Hilbert und Ackermann, "Grundzüge der theoretischen Logik" (1928).[33] Consider the simple organization of axioms first set up, the confusions pointed out in their development, and the "Stufenkalkul," or procedure in logical stages, developed under stimulation from the Russell theory of types. For the first "Stufe," we find the following: "Wir denken uns zunächst einen festen Individuenbereich gegeben und darin gewisse Grundprädikate. Man kann sich diese Grundfunktionen etwa als anschaulicher Natur vorstellen." This is the region of the discrete or concrete objects of Hilbert's early procedure, and of safety in the manipulation of the procedure "all." With further "Stufen" we require the axiom of reducibility: we have uncertainties, if not confusions, and we have also futility. Hence, in the last chapter of the "Grundzüge," the authors forecast the further development of Hilbert's own technique of "Widerspruchsfreiheit." In certain earlier essays, Hilbert had asserted the possibility of establishing the "Auswahl" firmly in the mathematical construction.[34] His

---

[32]Math. Ann., vol. 95, p. 172, p. 174.
[33]See p. 22, p. 98, sq., p. 100, and Chap. IV, Sec. 9.
[34]Math. Ann., vol. 88, p. 152: vol. 95, p. 178.

forms of proof should be investigated carefully by persons interested in this problem in terms of the "subjects" that are at work.

The present status of his construction is stated by Hilbert as follows: It has furnished proof of the epsilon-axiom for the "Funktions-variable *f*" to such extent that "die verbleibende Aufgabe nur noch in dem Beweise eines rein-arithmetischen elementaren Endlichkeitssatzes besteht."[35] This, however, from the point of view of semantic analysis may be read as saying that in a system of independent, complete and "widerspruchsfreie" axioms on full postulatory basis, under the powerful Hilbertian procedure, the system still lacks success in the incorporation of the discrete elements out of which it is built as consistent within the system. That Hilbert accepts the arithmetical finite realistically is self-evident: that he is confident he will succeed in the end in securing the desired proofs is clear from his context: that he will fail so long as the remaining aspects of his realism are retained by him, is the expectation of the semantic point of approach: but that his own technique should have concentrated his attention on the weakness of this very feature of his construction where his confidence and belief are greatest, is the finest possible tribute to the power and importance of that technique itself.

26. We may set forth the situation in which Hilbert leaves the mathematical *"foundation"* problem, in the following proposition:

---

[35]Math. Ann., vol. 102, p. 4, 1929. See also Hamb. Abh., vol. VI, p. 84, 1927, and Math. Ann., vol. 95, p. 190, 1925. This point is discussed by Weyl, Consistency in Mathematics, The Rice Institute Pamphlets, XVI, p. 265, 1929.

PROPOSITION VI. The Hilbertian system, as maximal representative of systems x-to-X in M-T, is not only dependent upon unclarified "*external*" M-O, but has failed thus far to establish its own M-T in full consistency.

To this we may add, also in the garb of a proposition, a summing up for the realistic interpretations of mathematics, as follows:

PROPOSITION VII. In any purported mathematical system $S_r$, establishing its M-T aspects in x-to-X, the search for consistency exhibits: (a) ever greater particularization of the M-O aspects: (b) ever greater reduction of these particularized M-O aspects into M-T presentations: and (c) the reference in "*belief*" of the unclarified residuary M-O aspects to some assumed region "*external*" to the system itself, from which region these realistically posited aspects are assumed to exercise control over the system itself and over its construction.

We are now in a position to say that whatever is of any value for mathematics in the common-reference description subjective-objective is brought by semantic analysis and postulation under the control of mathematics itself: and further we are able to say that whatever aspect of this description is taken by any investigator at any given time as not under control of analysis within the system is worthless for the system, and itself needing illumination from the system rather than being a probable source of illumination for it. If the reader who has taken pains to follow the technique of analysis herein used, will inspect the common-reference descriptions of the table (excepting only the last two couples) he will see that every one of them has yielded to valuation within the system of mathematical symbols, where alone there is hope of exact interpretation. By that same token every one of them has broken down hopelessly so far as it makes claim to "*external*" authority or control. This is not for a moment to say that the analysis herein is complete: merely that the technique has been established, first fruits secured, and justification given for a thorough investigation. I have not the slightest interest in metaphysical, philosophical or psychological problems or problem-constructions, and hence I deliberately refrain from further or wider discussions in those directions.[36] Should any one wish to bring them into the reckoning I would hold that the way to make progress was to abandon them entirely in their current vague forms, and proceed by extension of analysis in the regions of precise language.[37]

27. The propositions I to VII are sufficiently established within the postulation which has been used. We next come to a remark which is indicated by the course of development, but which if given propositional form for the sake of emphasis, must be set forth

---

[36]Of the metaphysical aspect of subject-object, however, a word may be desirable. It would be hard indeed to find a philosopher or psychologist who would frankly make flat separation between subject and object under any existential category whatsoever. Nevertheless it is the custom, not only of philosophers and psychologists, but in even greater degree of workers in other fields, to introduce subject and object "as if separate" for the purposes of their work. In this paper the procedure of "as if separate" is abandoned, and instead the use of an analysis much more in accord with the general consensus, is adopted. This, of course, is not undertaken on any basis of "*truth*" or "*reality,*" but solely as advantageous postulation.

[37]"Mathematics is the only true metaphysics." Lord Kelvin, Life, p. 1124.

as provisional, since it requires much more elaborate investigation than we can here attempt to give it. It cannot be regarded as sufficiently established until through it one can handle all situations that arise: or until, at least, one can say that, having handled securely all situations that have been investigated, the remaining situations, under the best judgment that can be given them, are indicated as safely within the scope of the proposition.

PROPOSITION VIII (PROVISIONAL). In the combined systems, W, G and A, and under the systemic construction of M-T and M-O, any aspect isolated in Dk and D may be taken as M-T for specialized purposes of study, and to it other aspects may be organized as M-O.

This procedure, already applied in many specialized fields, may certainly be undertaken in very broad fields: and it is indicated for "the full field" of W, G and A, although what may in the end be meant by such a phrase as "the full field" is beyond human power as yet to specify. The most spectacular recent illustration of this possibility is the introduction of the Alephs as M-T. But we have many more procedures of equal or greater importance. Any existential statement of an equational procedure in simple arithmetic illustrates it. The "great relational certainties" of mathematics, so often appealed to, are of this nature. We have groups and invariance. We have projective geometry. We have above all the endeavor of Hilbert to reduce all mathematics to the M-T form (though this is complicated with other problems), and his use of the logical symbols along with mathematical symbols (including symbols of mathematical operation) as "Objekte." Here we are at the very heart of the developing work in mathematical "*foundations*" with the possibilities and the outcome unknown.

The status of these issues as they appear in logico-mathematical constructions may be illustrated by citations from the well-known work by C. I. Lewis, A. Survey of Symbolic Logic.[38]

"The abstractness and the rigorously deductive method of development," he writes, "have more and more prevailed in the most careful presentations of mathematics. When these are completely achieved a mathematical system becomes nothing more than a complex logical structure."

What this citation tells us is that the Aristotelian "identity" is dominant in such systems with respect to the "*discreteness*" of their presentations, but that, through its "*abstract*" rendering, it frees itself from issues as to objectivity "*outside*" or "*beyond*" the logical system itself, so that the word or symbol becomes the direct "thing" or "object" of the system. Turning next to "operations," Lewis writes:

"A word of caution upon the meaning of "operation" is here necessary. It is exactly by the elimination of all peculiarly mathematical operations that a system comes to have rigorously deductive form. . . . In any rigorously deductive development of arithmetic "plus" and "times" are simply relations. An operation is something *done, performed.* The only things done, performed, in an abstract deductive system are the logical operations—variables are not added or multiplied."

Here we have plainly the deportation of all operation to the "*mind*" of the logician. The requirements for ultimate success are that all "operations" be held firmly there, and there only: and that the system, nevertheless, attain full consistency. (The Hilbert construction in which "operations" are "objects" rather than "relations" is of later date than Professor Lewis' book.)

Finally he tells us that "abstract mathematical systems differ only with respect to the *relations* of their terms, and probably also for certain relations of higher order—relations of relations. And the relations being likewise abstract will differ from system to system only in type, and in distribution in systems: that is, any two systems will differ only in types of logical order."

[38]Pp. 342-3: 1918.

In this last sentence he sets up the goal to be achieved under such logical procedure. It is the failure thus far to achieve it that is incentive for such further investigations as those we have been conducting.

It is to be understood that in the above passages Lewis is describing what he calls the "orthodox" view, and that his own inclinations are towards "heterodoxy." He recognizes that there are operations of the logistic method which are "pre-logical"; and he points out that "symbolic logic . . . must be developed by operations the validity of which is presumed apart from the logic so developed": (Op. cit., pp. 355, 361).

28. We may now bring the Hilbertian system into more definite relation with semantic postulation. Instead of inspecting it in an x-to-X and as working with a "geringste Mass von Voraussetzung," we may take that "geringste Mass" itself up within the system: or, that is to say, we may take it under the semantic connectivities Dk and D. Its M-T is now no longer its fixed necessity, but is systemic with its M-O. But, under Proposition VIII, we will regard it as working with the widest possible application of M-T. It appears before us therefore as a limiting case under semantic construction: and in view of its great successes to date, it may well prove to be the case in which full consistency can best be established. Its final establishment in this respect would leave it no less semantic, and would seem to be contingent on the express abandonment of its remaining realism.

Inspecting the Hilbertian system in this way with reference to the last two of the common-reference descriptions of the table, those namely in which the instantaneities are opposed to durations and extensions, we find now that these two remaining descriptions gain meaning from that system, perhaps; but they certainly have no important meanings of their own to contribute to that system which without them it would lack. If we say that Hilbert's system is a study in maximal instantaneity that phrase merely has the value of orienting it with reference to the crude and conventional terminologies which we are compelled so much of the time to employ: it brings no contribution to the understanding or valuation of the system itself.

## VI

## THE SEMANTIC M-T AND M-O.

At the close of Chapter III we inspected briefly the shadowy linguistic background in which *"thing"* and *"operation"* perform their services as words: and we saw that those words themselves, wherever they are put to use—and therefore wherever knowledge is involved—are affected with linguistic vagueness in varied conventional coloration; a vagueness which inevitably distorts their mathematical application, and the application as well of any of their conventional alternatives. In Chapters IV and V we substituted in their place the conventionally colorless designations M-T and M-O: and we were able to give these terms precision and to establish a semantic organization of M-T and M-O in mathematical consistency; thus differentiating our procedure sharply from the numerous procedures with realistically postulated "mathematical things" and "mathematical operations" which characterize *"foundation"* theory.

In the course of the development it appeared first that all systems which give a realistic value to M-T, whether implicit or explicit, still remain inconsistent: and second that in all of these realistic systems the M-O aspect, never wholly evaded, hovers in the background with threat of destruction of all that has been accomplished.

As against the pretenses of these many realistic systems, all originating in the confused background of human knowledge, let us now give a more general consideration to the existing conditions which indicate the desirability of their abandonment and of the substitution of the semantic approach.

If mathematics is exact knowledge, while other knowledge is inferior to it in exactness——

If the exactness of mathematics is established in the language of mathematics, while the inexactness of other knowledge is similarly established in the very language of that other knowledge——

If exactness in mathematics can be attained both by men with minds which we call the greatest and by men with minds which we call the humblest: while both types of minds perforce fall far short of exactness in all their other knowledge——[1]

If the distinction of "thing" and "operation" (grammatically garbed as noun and verb), the more it is taken realistically, so much the more leads to inexactness and paradox——

If this distinction in induction and in pure geometry tends to lose its realistic colorings just in the degree that consistency increases——

If this distinction, in advancing consistency, is found always more and more appearing as one between "operating thing" and "operation of thing," rather than one of rigidly logical separation——

[1]I call attention again to the address of Professor Bell, from which citations were given in Chap. III, as to the status of the "certainty" which mathematicians at present possess in the regions immediately bordering their specialized investigation.

If mathematical systems aiming at maximum formulation in terms of "thing" show always regions of conventionally posited and still unanalyzed "operation" behind them——

Then—we have a provisional case for the extension of mathematical investigation across this region of "thing" and "operation" by semantically analytic, instead of by rigidly logical, procedure:

Then, also—the mathematical construction that we secure will, if fully consistent, have strength great enough to resist successfully any demand whatever that it undergo degradation to non-mathematical forms.

Such, most generally expressed, is the justification offered in the present status of knowledge for seeking precision with respect to M-T and M-O.

The great obstacle to any such search lies in insistent realisms, understood in the sense of our description in Chapters I and II: and it lies not so much in explicitly realistic postulations, as in the implicit realisms that assert authority over postulations—in the all too common attitude that there must be in some way more "truth" or more "import" in the words we use obscurely than in the words we use exactly. The words we use exactly are humble in their exactness—they know and admit their limitations—but the obscure words are bold and arrogant and rapacious, though all they can show for authority is their presence as tribal fixations.

The basis of solution lies in a postulate to control these dogmatic and obscure realisms: whether that postulate be the one of this paper, or some other and better postulate which may be developed hereafter.

The semantic M-T and M-O that we have secured in our analysis have these characteristics:

They are free from the paradoxes of part-whole and finite-infinite, and as well from the many confusions of particular-general, abstract-concrete, subject-objective and other common-reference descriptions.

They do not restrict any portion of mathematical development, but instead increase freedom for it, by justifying free postulatory selections of any M-T for any desired project whatsoever.

They facilitate the search for consistency by identifying the system of consistency with the consistency itself: so that there is no longer need to show how the consistency can be consistent for a system external to it.

In especial they remove from the investigation of the mutual organizations of Algebra, Geometry and Analysis that conflict which investigation under the control of external realisms has found it impossible to reduce or overcome.

As the right to geometrize needs no "proof," so induction needs no "proof": as the power to construct in either field is given, so also is given the power to order and organize the constructions of both, without insult from particular realisms.

It is neither my intention nor desire to make further use of the semantic postulate for the general constructive purposes of mathematics. The remaining chapters of Part II will offer, instead, merely the records of certain special studies, undertaken either in the course of the development of the postulation, or for the purpose of its test. The presentation in these chapters is cumbersome and long: although their results, such as they are, might have been briefly and compactly stated. It is not these particular results, however, that are here of significance, but rather the workings and possibilities of the postulatory procedure itself. Our requirement is that we pursue the meaning of each term we inspect as fully as we are able to pursue it in the particular context in which it appears. We are permitted no recourse to the short cuts of convention, personal idiosyncracy or dogma.[2] We must hold ourselves within the linguistic development, and adhere to the semantic standards: and it is this which, in such initial studies, requires the wearisome detail.

The material for such studies is empirically taken. It can be found only in the writings of individual men. It must be taken just as it comes, and not in any idealized renderings. So to take it may make us seem at times to overstep the bounds of courtesy. But it is not criticism of the individual that concerns us. It is, instead, analysis of that linguistic medium in which the individual lives and moves and has his being. His particular work is before us as "individual" only in the sense that it is "individualized" within the great linguistic structures, historical and contemporaneous, within which his problems and formulations and solu-

[2]Lapses of this kind are always possible, no matter what pains one may take. They are to be reckoned to defective workmanship: and their cure is to be sought in continuing care of analysis.

tions all arise. It is, indeed, often the case that the thinker who most sharply formulates and most powerfully develops is the one who lays the best foundations for further analysis: and that his constructions, even when superseded, enter more mightily into later knowledge, than the minor efforts which may lay claim to closer accord.

## VII

# KRONECKER AND POINCARÉ

Mathematics has been presented in preceding chapters under full semantic postulation, in which the M-T and M-O aspects are systemic.

Mathematical *"foundation"* theories, on the contrary, have been shown to make use of realistic postulation, and to have footings first in certain implicitly realistic mathematical conventions, and then finally in the conventional realisms of every-day non-mathematical language. The *"foundation"* theories to which we have given most attention are systems $S_r$ as to M-T: and we have observed in Proposition VII that such systems always show some surplusage in the form of M-O, and that, after they have struggled faithfully to envisage as much as possible of this M-O in the garb M-T, they then expel the surplusage into regions which are presumably "external"—whatever that may mean—to the mathematics itself.

Two questions now present themselves?

First: Can the constructors of systems $S_r$ as to M-T ever rest satisfied with their *"foundations"* until they have provided adequately developed operative constructions in this *"external"* region? This question we shall leave for the realists of M-T to answer for themselves.

Second: Is it not probable that alongside the systems $S_r$ as to M-T there is room within mathematics for rival *"foundation"* systems, $S_r$ as to M-O? Here the name of Brouwer will at once come to mind, and it will be suggested that his "Intuitionism" is exactly such a system $S_r$ as to M-O. Superficially, and in Brouwer's own estimation, his system holds such a place. Practically, however, it develops in great part along different lines, and to it consideration will be given in a later chapter. If any such system, $S_r$ as to M-O, has been perfected I am not aware of it: and it is no loss that we do not have to spend time in dissecting one.

Much more profitable is it to observe the dominance of operational considerations in the work of two mathematicians, Poincaré and Kronecker. Both of them felt strongly that presentations M-T—to use the terminology of this book—could not make a mathematics without the full and vivid incorporation along with them of aspects M-O. In examining their writings we must take many of their views garbed in the psychological language which was current in their day and which they used or modified to their needs. We must allow for this psychological background—which is wholly insignificant, indeed, one way or the other—and transform their psychological expressions and formulations into such other manner of speech as will best convey their mathematical meanings. The citations given from their works must always be read in this spirit. It is not their psychology but their mathematics in which we are interested and from which we can gain benefit. It has been the fashion to sneer at Kronecker and accuse him of philosophizing,[1] and to express wonder that a man of his mathematical power could go so far astray. In the case of Poincaré the sneers have been directed more at his outmoded psychology: and under that excuse his incisive, and often unwelcome, analysis has been disregarded. Sneers will, however, not avail in this field: and until a consistent theory is secured, these two men continue to hold a lance directed straight at the heart of "*foundation*" theories of the realistic M-T type.

The influence of Kronecker, as well of Poincaré, is clearly seen in Brouwer's early work, however far he later departed from it. Appraisal, not merely of influences, but of the actual standpoint that any constructive mathematician occupies in these respects is far from simple: and the very judgments that mathematicians pass upon one another differ widely. The difficulty is that the tests are too often based upon accidents of superficial historical connection or of personal predilection, rather than on standards internal to the mathematical development itself: and this again gives emphasis to the remark that exploration as yet is far from going deeply enough into the essential issues involved. Poincaré, for example, apparently saw Dedekind and Kronecker as of one school, and he used the Dedekindian "Schnitt" as an illustration of the Kronecker approach.[2] Hilbert, on the contrary, writing twenty years later, sees these two men as opposed to one another.[3] Hilbert

[1]So the gossip of Netto cited by Pierpont, American M. S. Bull., 1928, p. 37, and the outcry of Weierstrass against Kronecker cited in the same place, p. 39. Weierstrass' objection to Kronecker's assertion that "arithmetic can point the path to analysis" taken in connection with the prevalent form of statement used by the present generation that Weierstrass' own great achievement was to arithmetize analysis (so Pierpont, idem, p. 35) is just one more illustration among the thousands of the futility of the judgments which mathematicians are able to pass upon the nature of their own work in terms of the conventional language they have available for such purposes. The differences of verbal meanings in the instance above can readily be identified, but the forms of expression are hopelessly inexact.

[2]Le science et l'hypothèse, p. 31.

[3]Hamb. Abh., vol. I, pp. 160-162: vol. VI, p. 80: Math. Ann., vol. 95, p. 167, p. 174.

sees himself in sharp contrast to the actual infinite of Dedekind and Frege,[4] since he substitutes in its place an ideal construction: but others see Hilbert rather as in line with their tendency, and as preserver of the "Cantorian paradise," while merely transforming its technique. Brouwer has always regarded himself as the founder of a "school," rather than as a participant in that consistent line of scientific progress within which "schools" should be abhorrent. Russell's system can be inspected either as a first approximation to Hilbert's, or as a rival to it, or as a much deeper and more *"fundamental"* approach: and as a matter of fact all of these varieties of appraisal are to be found in the current literature. The various formulations of mathematical induction exhibit this situation, since each writer has a different way of appraising the exact import of the other's formulation: and even the various distinctions as to "complete" induction are not consistently held.[5] In such a situation, and in this era of our ignorance, the characterizations of Poincaré and Kronecker which follow, may be regarded by some readers as radically wrong. Occasionally even an effort is made to show that Poincaré had become in his later years sympathetic to the realists.[6] These differences of appraisal rest in differences of implicit approach: and we should recognize that no comment in this field has validity beyond the range of its presuppositions: and that our great obligation is not to wage conflict over the appraisals, but to seek progress in clarifying the presuppositions.

Kronecker proposed to develop analysis wholly out of algebra and arithmetic.[7] First handling negative numbers and rational fractions through the use of the modulus, he then examined algebraics through the aid

---

[4]Math. Ann., vol. 95, p. 167, p. 190: Hamb. Abh., vol. I, p. 163.

[5]See a passage later in this chapter for one illustration, and compare Weyl's discussion of Hilbert, Hamb. Abh., vol. VI, p. 86.

[6]So Felix Bernstein, Deutsche Math.-Ver., vol. 28, p. 65.

[7]His construction is to be found in his essay Über den Zahlbegriff, Werke III, p. 251, reprinted from J. für Math., vol. 101, p. 337, 1887: "Ich glaube dass es dereinst gelingen wird, den gesammten Inhalt aller dieser mathematischen Disciplinen zu 'arithmetisiren', d. h., einzig und allein auf den im engsten Sinne genommenen Zahlbegriff zu gründen." (Werke III, p. 253). An earlier draft may be found in Philosophische Aufsätze, published in honor of Zeller. See also his paper Grundzüge einer arithmetischen Theorie der algebraischen Grössen, J. für Math., vol. 92, p. 1, 1882.

of the interval. "The so-called existence of real irrational roots," he wrote "rests wholly in the existence of intervals of the required construction. Reckoning with the separate roots of an algebraic equation rests upon the possibility of their isolation."[8] He saw the materials of mathematics spread out in language,[9] and in this language he found the ordinals present as a reservoir of designations before us in fixed serial arrangement which we could apply to any collection of distinguishable objects.[10] Number ("Anzahl") was constructed from this, and the cardinal was "Anzahl" of ordinals.[11] He held that the number-concept had been corrupted in the course of its application to geometry and mechanics,[12] and asserted that the "so-called natural sequence of numbers ("Zahlen") is nothing other than the sequence of the corresponding ordinals."[13] Following Gauss he exhibited the distinc-

---

[8]Werke, III, p. 272: "Die sogenannte Existenz der reellen irrationalen Wurzeln ist einzig und allein in der Existenz von Intervallen der angegebenen Beschaffenheit begründet: die Zulässigkeit der Rechnung mit den einzelnen Wurzeln einer algebraischen Gleichung beruht ganz und gar auf der Möglichkeit sie zu isoliren, also auf der Möglichkeit eine Zahl, wie die oben mit *s* bezeichnete, zu bestimmen." And further: "Ist eine solche Zahl *s* bestimmt, welche die Eigenschaft hat, dass die Intervalle von der Grösse 1/s hinreichend klein sind, um die verschiedenen Wurzeln derselben Gleichung zu isoliren, so wird das 'Grösser' und 'Kleiner' der Wurzeln einfach durch die Aufeinanderfolge der bezüglichen Isolirungs-Intervalle definirt."

[9]Idem, p. 274: "Um diese Formen einfach erscheinen zu lassen, bedurfte es vor Allem einer geeigneten Ausdrucks-und Darstellungsweise für die Zahlen selbst, und hieran hat der Menschengeist gewiss seit grauer Vorzeit anhaltend und mühsam gearbeitet."

[10]Idem, p. 253: "Ein Vorrath gewisser, nach einer festen Reihenfolge geordneter Bezeichnungen, welche wir einer Schaar verschiedener und zugleich für uns unterscheidbarer Objekte beilegen können."

[11]Idem, p. 255.

[12]Idem, p. 253.

[13]Idem, p. 255: "Die sogennannte natürliche Reihenfolge der Zahlen ist nichts anderes als die Reihenfolge der entsprechenden Ordnungszahlen."

tion between the arithmetical disciplines on the one side and geometry and mechanics on the other as one in which numbers were just the production of the mind—"bloss unseres Geistes Produkt,"[14] while geometry and mechanics combined admixtures of space and time as external realities never under full intellectual control.[15]

What Kronecker gives us is a partial construction and a distinct approach towards a theory of number operating in its own semantic right. Along with Gauss and Weierstrass he sees the number system operatively,[16] and we shall note in a moment how Poincaré in his statement of induction made a generalization of this approach, without, however, arriving at a generalization of the full linguistic background. To talk gravely about Kronecker's "mathematical nihilism"; to regard it as a threatening destruction of the greater part of established mathematics; to harp upon his chance remark about the natural numbers being "the work of God"; is to let extraneous views mostly of trivial importance dominate mathematical judgment. Kronecker's own life of achievement is sufficient evi-

---

[14]Idem, p. 253. The phrase, "bloss unseres Geistes Produkt," as it stands, should be taken as a primitive wording of a significant attitude. Its import lies in its interpretative implications for mathematics, rather than in some trivially dogmatic rendering of the words themselves. Kronecker also cited with approval the famous saying of Gauss: "Die Mathematik sei die Königin der Wissenschaften, und die Arithmetik die Königin der Mathematik."

[15]Idem, p. 253. Note also p. 254: "Der Vorrath von Bezeichnungen den wir in den Ordnungszahlen besitzen ist deshalb immer ausreichend, weil es nicht sowohl ein wirklicher als vielmehr ein ideeller Vorrath ist." The operative value and implication is here very plain under the psychological manner of expression.

[16]As for Weierstrass, of course, he also saw number systems in relational absolutism, and his work became legitimate source for two lines of development.

dence that there was nothing destructive in his approach to mathematics.

Poincaré's critical and interpretative investigations in this field are far-reaching and powerful. Like Kronecker he had a keen eye to the linguistic embodiment of mathematics[17] and he, too, saw the ordinals as underlying the cardinals.[18] In a significant passage he brought this view to bear sharply against the "relational" interpretations, remarking that in order to get a relation, one had to have the things to be related, and that this plurality among things involved the counting process, the ordinal system, as prior to the relational.[19] He saw geometry as a system of conventions, but not arbitrary conventions.[20] Discussing Hilbert's axioms for geometry, he pointed out that Hilbert was successful only on the presupposition of an already finished analysis which he could use.[21]

For induction Poincaré gave the sharpest statement that has yet been made, allowing for his psychological background, and reading it in terms of his surround-

---

[17]See for example his rules for dealing with the problems of the infinite, Dernières Pensées, p. 135, p. 138. The two following passages, both cited in free transcription by Pierpont (op. cit., p. 40, p. 44) will serve to bring Kronecker and Poincaré into comparison in this region. Kronecker: "Definitions must contain the means of reaching a decision in a finite number of steps and existence proofs must be conducted so that the quantity in question can be calculated with any required degree of accuracy." Poincaré: "Is it possible to reason on objects which cannot be defined by a finite number of words? Is it even possible to speak of them, knowing what one is speaking of, pronouncing only empty words? Or on the contrary should one not regard them as unthinkable? For my part I do not hesitate to respond that they are pure nonentities."

[18]Dernièrees Pensées, p. 116: Rev. de métaph. et de mor., 1906, p. 27.

[19]Science et méthode, p. 177: Rev. de métaph. et de mor., 1905, p. 830: Dernières Pensées, p. 116-122: Foundations of Science, p. 462-3.

[20]Le science et l'hypothèse, p. 66: Foundations of Science, p. 29.

[21]Dernières Pensées, p. 122.

ing discussion. "Si une propriété est vraie du nombre 1, et si l'on établit qu'elle est vraie de n+1, pourvu qu'elle le soit de n, elle sera vraie de tous les nombres entiers."[22] Induction for Poincaré most emphatically needed no proof; and this, in fully developed semantic organization would be equivalent to recognizing its M-T and M-O aspects as systemic.[23] Induction is at once necessary to mathematics and irreducible to logic. It is "le raisonnement mathématique par excellence." It does not prove truth, but coherence. Herein Poincaré's vision rests firmly in the historical and operational development of arithmetic and algebra, and, like Kronecker's, is sharply opposed to the distortions produced when the numbers are moulded to a contrasting mathematical form. It is striking indeed that in the very era in which the geometries have been given increased postulatory freedom, this ancient and fully comparable approach to numbers should have been for the greater part abandoned by seekers after "*foundations,*" whose course has been to degrade both systems realistically in order to combine them: whereas the indicated line of development would seem plainly to be the union of the two postulatory approaches in a more complete postulatory synthesis.

It may be worth while to assemble some of the attitudes taken towards induction by way of showing the great confusion in treatment which exists at the present time. Poincaré's induction is of a very different type from that of Peano or Russell, or from that

---

[22]Science et méthode, p. 159: Foundations of Science, p. 452. An earlier formulation running to positive whole numbers instead of "all the whole numbers" is to be found in Le science et l'hypothèse, p. 65; Foundations of Science, p. 64.

[23]See Chap. IV, Proposition I, with the accompanying text in Par. 6, and notes.

of Weyl in his "Gesetz Aleph," "das aus dem Nichts die erste Zahl erzeugt."[24] Poincaré himself has discussed the differences between his type of induction and others of his period in various essays.[25] It is true that he also described induction as the reasoning which permits one to pass from the finite to the infinite,[26] but in this he had his operational infinite in mind.[27] Psychologically, in language akin to some of his predecessors, he described it as "a property of the mind itself"[28] but this is a phrase of the kind we have repeatedly met, to which we may assign no direct meaning of its own, and which must be reduced by background analysis if one wishes to establish its import for the problem the man who uses it is immediately pursuing. One may readily find formulations of induction by different mathematicians in language which currently and loosely would appear to be "the same language" for all: and yet each statement will be widely variant from the others. One may compare the latest Hilbert formulation of what he calls "Der Inhalt des Prinzips" by which he means an expression in current language of what the principle is supposed to yield in symbolic language: "Wenn ein Prädikat von der Zahl 1 gilt, und wenn es, falls es von irgendeiner Zahl gilt, auch von der nächstfolgenden gilt, so gilt das Prädikat von jeder Zahl."[29] This might serve for a satisfactory translation of the Poincaré formulation cited in a preceding paragraph, and yet its meaning is radically different. The Russell formulation might also be considered, so far as language goes, as of the same type. "Any property which belongs to $x_0$, and belongs to $x_{n+1}$, providing it belongs to $x_n$, belongs to all the x's."[30] Here, however, the stress is on the "properties" as the basis of the knowledge system, while in Poincaré's formulation "propriété" is little more than a loose linguistic component which aids him in conveying his meaning. Wawre has characterized Poincaré's sense of induction as "narrow"[31] in contrast with the "larger" sense of the term, commonly referred to as "complete induction." It is "narrow" in the particular sense that it was formulated with respect to whole numbers, while

---

[24]Math. Zeitschr., vol. 10, p. 57.

[25]Rev. de métaph. et de mor., 1905, p. 835: 1906, p. 867: See also the entire debate with Russell in this Revue, 1905, 1906 and 1909.

[26]Le science et l'hypothèse, p. 22.

[27]See Dernières Pensées, p. 131: "Et c'est ce 'l'on pourra' qui est l'infini."

[28]Foundations of Science, p. 40:

[29]Hilbert und Ackermann, Grundzüge der theoretischen Logik, p. 83.

[30]Introduction to Mathematical Philosophy, p. 8.

[31]Rev. de métaph. et de mor., 1924, p. 447.

Hilbert's formulation, as we have given it, is for "Zahl" and Russell's is for "x's." But Wawre means more than this: he means that it is regarded as narrow just because its generalization is not in a system of "properties," despite its use of the term "propriété": in other words just because of that very characteristic which is here regarded as giving it its sharpest value.

Poincaré's approach was brought out characteristically in one of the latest publications of his life, his lectures at Göttingen.[32] Here, as before, he was in-inclined to put the paradoxes to test through a strict evaluation of linguistic forms. He offered a striking new form of proof for the Cantorian non-denumerability: but he at once turned back upon it and showed that the proof itself depended upon linguistic rules: and that conflicting arguments were similarly dependent upon the rules set up for them: so that the present paradoxes were no true issues: Both Richard and Cantor, for example, could be "right" if each chose his own procedure. As to "Aleph-Eins" he said politely: "ich bin nicht ganz überzeugt dass sie existiert": but all that he really admitted in this "existence," even as a possibility, was a definition, and that, even, one which could not surely be spoken of without danger of contradiction. "Ein aktual Unendliches gibt es jedenfalls nicht."

---

[32]Sechs Vorträge, Fünfter Vortrag, Göttingen, 1910.

## VIII

## THE SEMANTIC NUMBER SEQUENCES

Suppose now some one should say: "Despite all this apparatus of analysis for "Character," "Symbol," "Number," "Zahl" and "Menge," you have not yet told us what the natural numbers *are*."

Suppose, thereupon, he should flatly ask the question: "What *are* the natural numbers in a system of semantic consistency?"

Under semantic postulation: (a) no answer would be given until as much exactness was attained in the use of the term "are" as in the use of the term "natural number": (b) such exactness would be dependent upon analysis of all mathematically pertinent word-clusters involving both the terms "number" and "are": (c) the answer, when given, would have validity only within and for the purposes of the fully consistent semantic construction; and (d) despite this explicit limitation, the answer would possess better standing as knowledge than any answer whatever of unlimited pretense but vague unanalyzed implication.

Employing the procedure of Chapters IV and V we have at least the beginnings of a reply. Under the propositions therein set forth we exclude all of the confused existential implications of finite-infinite and of whole-part and quantity: retaining, of course, nevertheless, all of the consistent mathematical construction, for which such terms are conventionally employed as labels. Similarly we exclude all the confused implications of other common-reference descriptions, such as concrete-abstract, subjective-objective and particular-general. This is to say that in any definition beginning "Natural numbers *are* . . .," the import of the word "are" is held within the consistent system of mathematical construction. Again, it is to say, that if natural numbers are specified as M-T, then the "M-T" and the "are" must both be held within a system $S_s$.

The contrast of this procedure with that of realisms, which seek a firm answer at the *beginning* of the inquiry with respect to some "are," taken under a current convention of "existence," is manifest. Typical answers of this latter type are the following. Russell defines the natural numbers as "the posterity of zero" in a scheme of induction in terms of "properties that belong to" things.[1] For Weyl they are the "Erzeugung" of the "Gesetz Aleph," "die aus dem Nichts erzeugte," and from their "Wesen" all mathematics depends.[2] For Brouwer they are the "Folge $\zeta$," which is the basic intuitional reality in mathematics.[3] For Hilbert they are primarily the immediately given "Objekte"—the particular "Objekte" which he chooses to set down at the start of his list of materials of mathematical construction:[4] but they may also become observable as "individuelle Prädikatenfunktionen," under a very fortunate preordained harmony whereby "die Prädikatenfunktionen, welche die Zahlen bilden, sich vollständig mit Hilfe der logischen Symbole ausdrücken lassen."[5] For the "Mengenlehre" in general they are *"real"* components of a continuum of "Zahlen" in the creed of the "Auswahl."[6]

---

[1]Introduction to Mathematical Philosophy, p. 22, p. 8.

[2]Math. Zeitschr., vol. 10, p. 57.

[3]See Chap. IX.

[4]Hamb. Abh., vol. I, p. 163: "Die Gegenstände sind die Zeichen selbst" . . . "Am Anfang ist das Zeichen" . . . Das Zeichen 1 ist eine Zahl."

[5]Hilbert and Ackermann, Grundzüge der theoretischen Logik, p. 86.

[6]See Chap. V, Par. 20.

As mathematics is found today the natural number sequence is seen entering structurally into all its organizations. This is true under such an extension of theory as that of Dickson in his construction of algebraic integers, and it is true in the approach to transcendentals through fundamental series. Indeed, more broadly, it is evident that wherever two elements, propositions, statements or even words, are employed, the natural numbers play a part, if the analysis of procedure is fully carried out. If, under such a construction as that of Dedekind, the stress on the "*fundamental*" is shifted elsewhere, nevertheless the structural necessity of the use of the natural numbers is attested by the prompt appearance of the "Auswahl" without which, or without some substitute for which, no progress is made.

Characteristic of the natural number sequence is that it is well-ordered: and the definitions of well-ordered to which we are accustomed all involve and rest upon the identification of a "first" term. Under the tests of the analysis we are employing, the term "first" in such definition is realistic, not semantic. What is mathematically important in the well-ordered series is not the realistic "first" term or "unity," but the semantic "first" term, or base, which is the "1" of Word-Cluster III after it has been stripped completely of its coloration from regions of realistic application. The word "base" merely emphasizes the fact that the realisms have been left behind. Using it instead of "first," the definition of well-ordered remains as secure mathematically as it was with the term "first," and the range of procedure is not lessened: while a gain in precision is made. This basic 1 is the basic M-T of the natural number sequence, and is established within the sequence in its full equational M-O.

In the recent elaborated realistic constructions Null is substituted for "1" as basic M-T. The realists are driven to this by their "logic," which they take as in control of their mathematical procedure: and the appearance of Null as basic term may be taken as certain test of the dominance under logical control of particularistic realism in the construction. It is the realistic "1," the "One" or "Unity," which is the seat of the paradoxes, both of Null and of the Infinite. For the right to select a basis term as needed, reference may be made to Rule IV in Chapter III, and to Proposition VIII in Chapter V.

As description of the natural number sequence we may specify:

1. equational procedure in M-T and M-O,
2. stages of procedure as M-T,
3. procedure among stages as M-O,
4. a basic M-T, namely 1,
5. no finite M-T,
6. no infinite M-T,
7. no null M-T,
8. the conventional use at will, for any desired procedures, of the basic term as a "first" term,
9. the conventional use at will, under equal justification, for any desired procedures, of a "last" term balanced against the basic M-T as "first" term: nevertheless without derogation of continuing procedures M-O as at other times and for other purposes desired.

This natural number sequence enters into many forms of number organization. An organization very commonly used is that called the decimal system, this system being the currently convenient choice among systems of radix fractions, which are as numerous as the natural numbers themselves.[7] Each form of num-

[7]The phrasing ''as numerous as'' manifestly conflicts with the formulation of Alephs, but is the proper phrasing here nevertheless.

ber organization may be called a transcription. Each organization is safely consistent wthin its transcription, and the transcriptions are safely consistent among one another: *providing* they are held to semantic use, and are not mis-read under realistic distortion.

For the decimal form of transcription we may add the following additional specifications:

10. a basic M-T, taken as interior to the sequence and named 1,
11. no "first" term and no "last" term,
12. tabular transcription, in multiplication and division, by tens,
13. the decimal point as M-O separating multiplications from divisions with respect to the basic M-T,
14. the use of 0 as M-O for tabular displacement of figures by tens,
15. the dot over a figure to the right (thus $.\dot{0}$) for periodically continuing M-O,
16. dots to the right (thus, .0. . . . .) for continuing M-O under a specified operational procedure,
17. the power series for continuing M-O to the left.

In inspecting the decimal transcription it is customary to read the terms to the left under a special rule, namely that of the realistic natural number sequence, this procedure being characterized as denumerability: while the terms to the right, read under another specially enforced rule, in the magnitude series, are called non-denumerable, since it appears that between any two adjacent expressions in a column, say between 0.a,b,c,. . .n,1,$\dot{0}$ and 0.a,b,c,. . .n,2,$\dot{0}$, under naive cancellation of the periodic zeros, an infinity of intervening terms may be developed. Such a reading is practically useful for many purposes, and of course at all times permissible, if one holds clearly before one's self what it is that he is doing: if, that is, one makes explicit postulation, and confines his conclusions to the regions of his postulations, without application at any critical point of realistic dogma. Taken as a delivery about "*reality*," or as a report on "*foundations*," it is, however, akin to the illusions about line or configuration which are exhibited in almost any text-book on experimental psychology. If we read to the right in this special way, it is our duty to read to the left in a consistently corresponding way, whereupon we get non-denumerability for all whole numbers as well as for all decimal fractions: this time taken, however, with respect to the figures in the columns of transcription to the left, proceeding leftwards from the decimal point, instead of with respect to figures in the columns of transcription to the right, proceeding rightwards from the decimal point. It is, however, possible under a different rule to read in both directions so as to secure denumerability of similar nature, and this procedure is easily illustrated in the case of binary fractions: what is true for them being true under induction likewise for the decimals.[8]

We must add, therefore, two additional specifications which are alternative ways of postulatory completion, for special purposes of the M-T presentation of the sequence of natural numbers in their decimal transcription, namely:

18. the formula $.\dot{9} = 1.\dot{0}$ as specific application to decimals of specification No. 9, with the linguistic value of holding the entire transcription within bounds for special purposes.

---

[8]See Chap. XI.

19. the formula that where the separation of rational end points of nested intervals converges on zero, the M-T specification of zero may be read as a point of the continuum for special purposes of study.

The first formula is that of applied mathematics, as where the numerical operation is taken as running perhaps from the length of the sodium wave to the diameter of the stellar universe, or from an assumed orbital space enclosure of an electron under the Bohr picture to that of the universe: or as where the decimal development of pi beyond seven places is regarded as without significance for the work in hand. The second formula is that used in constructions bringing geometry and number systems together in "*real*" analysis.

I repeat, what is indeed sufficiently evident without it, that I am in no sense attempting firm mathematical specification, much less construction. What is before us is merely an attempt to bring out in ordinary crude imperfect language, the background, the environment, the colorations of implication, which affect mathematical number constructions. The materials before us are of the commonest every-day kind, naturals, decimals and zero. Common and current though they are, they mean many things to many men—and these, indeed, things that involve immense differences of ultimate development. Our problem is to clarify or purify the symbols and their implications, not to develop them in any sense: and I hold firmly to the remark in the "Introduction" that this work of clarification must be done primarily, not in symbols, but through the use of materials that run all the way down into language, perhaps past words-common, and into that "inchoate implication" persisting in all of us, which so often glorifies itself under the name of philosophy.

In the above lists of characteristics we have the beginnings from which an answer may be developed to the question: "What are the natural numbers?" for the precise purposes of mathematics. The natural number sequence is in effect that specification of M-T in a system $S_s$, which is basic for many of the widest purposes of mathematics. It is semantically basic in the development of series, and in geometrical and analytic uses, in the same sense and no other, that the number 1 is basic in the natural number sequence itself: in neither case is a realistic fixation seen in its favor.

In the constructions immediately surrounding the natural sequence, such as those of decimals, 0 appears primarily as M-O, and not as M-T. Under semantic consideration we are fortunately freed from the necessity of deciding whether 0 *is* or *is not* a number. Under Proposition VIII we are free to take 0 as M-T at such times, and in such ways and for such purposes, as we wish. We are free, indeed, at any future time, if by so doing we can secure full consistency, to take 0 as basic M-T. This is something that at the present time has not been done with full consistency, despite the fact that the *"foundation"* theories most prevalent today dogmatically take it as a number, and in especial as a *"real"* number, to make possible their realistic constructions of number and the continuum.

Let us consider this situation with respect to 0, in connection with the situation of the "exceptions" which we find appearing so frequently in mathematical formulations. I will assert that no formulation which in its basic construction involves the appearance of an exception, can be accepted as *"fundamental"* for general mathematical interpretative purposes. The exception is prima facie a failure of consistency. That mere statement is sufficient.

Consider the ordinary definitions, or presentations,

of number in mathematics. If we begin with elementary instruction in arithmetic, we are shown numbers such as those from 1 to n, then we are shown the negatives, the number-line, and 0: and on this basis we are told that 0 "is" a number. In almost the same breath, however, we are told that an exception exists in regard to division by 0, although the procedures of addition, subtraction, multiplication and division have all been essential in constructing the number-line. The appearance of this exception at once stamps our general construction and definition as one of imperfect consistency. This construction is manifestly before us as a convenient practical arrangement, but the slightest analysis shows that the content or value of the word "is" in the sentence "0 is a number" is not the same as that of the word "is" in the sentence "8 is a number." If, on the other hand, 0 is taken as M-O instead of realistically M-T, the need of an exception disappears.

If we go further and inspect the possibilities of the group theory with respect to number sequences, we find a similar situation. For a group with the rule of multiplication, 0 is not taken as an element: but for a group with the rule of addition 0 is taken as an element. And yet the additions, subtractions, multiplications and divisions are not four, nor even two, different operative systems, but they are all phases of one equational operation. This is not to deny the propriety of these different group organizations, given the materials from which they are constructed: but it is to deny the propriety of regarding these constructions as in any sense "*fundamental*," and it is to indicate the M-T and M-O characteristics as the seat of the difficulty.

The attention of the mathematician is distracted from the importance of freeing his most general constructions in consistency from the inclusion of any exception, by the multiplicity of exceptional situations that occur in the constructions he deals with and by the variety of their types. First of all there is a confusion in the common-reference description particular-general. Any particular case is in a sense an exception to the general rule, though in other senses it is exemplification of the rule. Then under the manifold possibilities of alternative axiomization, differences between mathematicians appear of the kind commonly called *"temperamental."* Some men strive to set up an organization that goes as far as possible in generalization, and so reduce the number of exceptions to a minimum: while others delight in sharply phrased constructions, attended by small constellations of exceptions. In such a working atmosphere, the exception as to 0, even when the problem before the mathematician is one of *"foundations"* does not ordinarily appear to him decisive with respect to consistency. He is accustomed to "consistency with exceptions," and he accepts it even here, even for *"foundation"* purposes.

The situation in this ultimate case is somewhat as follows. The mathematician inspects the world of mathematical phenomena before him, and in that world he notes that division by 0 is indeterminate. He says sometimes that division by 0 yields the answer "infinity": and at other times he says that it is a meaningless operation. His position either way is a realism in the sense in which we have used the term. In other words he says in substance: "That is the way the phenomena appear before us: that is the way they "are": 0 and 8 "are" both numbers: perhaps there are some further problems with respect to that word "are," but they are philosophical problems and they don't concern me." In all of this he is merely shirking his own problem, which is to analyze his own form or forms of "are," for the purposes of his own consistencies.

For an interesting illustration of the "exception" in the case of decimals, see Klein's discussion of the fact that every finite or infinite decimal fraction can be taken as representative of one definite "Zahl": while, on the contrary, one indeterminate case appears if we attempt to establish that every "Zahl" provides us with one single definite decimal. This, he tells us, is the only bit of vagueness ("die einzige Unbestimmtheit") upon which we will stumble ("stossen"): whereupon he proceeds to pass easily over it, and to declare that exactness is unlimited in the representation of "Zahl" by "Dezimalbruch" ("absolut genau") ("die Genauigkeit ist unbegrenzt").[9] The exactness is indeed adequate for all Klein's immediate purposes: but when inquiry runs beyond such purposes, and into *"foundation"* regions, the status in which Klein leaves the "exception" reminds us inevitably—as we are so often reminded in similar discussions—of the world-famed baby story and of the excuse of the peccable mother: "But it is such a *little* one." One may examine also the appearance of the exception (division by zero) in the postulates Huntington sets up in his Fundamental Propositions of Algebra.[10] He accepts the exception as, let us say, "fact," and without discussion. That he regards exceptions in general as annoying is shown by his remark on the general algebra of complex quantities, in comparison with sub-algebras.[11]

---

[9]Anwendung der Differential-und Integralrechnung auf Geometrie (eine Revision der Prinzipien). Reprinted as Vol. III of Elementarmathematik vom höheren Standpunkte aus: p. 4.

[10]In Monographs on Topics of Modern Mathematics, J. W. A. Young, editor, p. 188.

[11]Idem, p. 196.

Under the semantic approach there is no rigid external control. The theory does not have to conform to some assumed conventional reality. If there is inconsistency the duty is to carry the analysis back to consistency, or as far towards it, as, at any time and in any given state of knowledge, one may go. The appearance of an exception is merely an evidence of incomplete analysis and of the use of defective language of systematization. Just as the many exceptions which were necessary to early formulations of Euclidean geometry were removed when a wider generalization was made, in which plus and minus signs for rotations were used, so in any other case in mathematics, the wider formulation, the wider generalization, the wider language, may be sought. Above all in the "*foundation*" regions is this essential.

## IX

## BROUWER

The case of Brouwer requires attention, not for the intrinsic importance of either his philosophizing or his *"foundation"* theory, but in order to show what happens when a bridge of compromises is constructed between a realism in the region of M-T, and a separately generalized realism in the M-O region of mathematics. No attention need be given his creed of "intuition," for this disintegrates under any frank and careful analysis of the meanings of words:[1] and as for his dictum about the law of the excluded middle, perhaps all that is necessary to remark is that he set it up at any early stage as a tool to enable him to escape proofs he didn't like, and that ever since he has been striving to evade part of the consequences. It is desirable for us to avoid all these pretentious generalities of discussion, and to hold our consideration to an exact examination of his working technique at some critical point in his construction. For such consideration I will take his construction of "greater and less." In order to deal with it, it will be necessary first to develop his Mengengesetz, and this will take much space, even though we omit all but the directly pertinent aspects.

[1]This will be readily apparent to anyone who endeavors to read carefully and appraise the latest Brouwer essays, cited as (I) and (J). See also the observations as to the sociological background for the rules in Chap. III, just prior to the statement of Rule I.

Citations to Brouwer's most important books and papers in this field will be made by the index letters in the following list:

(A) Over de grondslagen der wiskunde, 1907.

(B) Die möglichen Mächtigkeiten: Atti, Fourth International Mathematical Congress, III, pp. 568-70, 1908.

(C) Intuitionisme en Formalisme, 1912: published in Wiskunde, Waarheid, Werkelijkheid, 1919.

(C-1) Translation of (C) by Arnold Dresden: American M. S. Bull., vol. 20, p. 81, 1913.

(D) Begründung der Mengenlehre unabhängig vom logischen Satz vom ausgeschlossenen Dritten: Verhandelingen der Koninklijke Akademie van Wetenschappen te Amsterdam, Eerste Sectie, vol. 12, nos. 5 and 7., 1918-19.

(E) Intuitionistische Mengenlehre; Deutsche Math-Ver., vol. 28, p. 203, 1919.

(F) Besitzt jede reelle Zahl eine Dezimalbruchentwicklung?: Math. Ann., vol. 83, p. 201, 1921.

(G) Uber die Bedeutung des Satzes vom ausgeschlossenen Dritten: J. für Math., vol. 154, p. 1, 1924.

(H) Zur Begründung der intuitionistischen Mathematik: Math. Ann., vol. 93, 95, 96, 97, 1925-6.

(I) Intuitionistische Betrachtungen über den Formalismus: Sitzungsberichte der Preussischen Akademie der Wissenschaften, Physikalisch-mathematische Klasse, pp. 48-52, 1928.

(J) Mathematik, Wissenschaft und Sprache: Monatshefte für Mathematik und Physik, vol. 36, p. 153, 1929.

In the following discussion not only are long citations from Brouwer's writings introduced without translation or paraphrase, but his German terms are freely employed in the midst of the English text. For this practice no apology is necessary: since what concerns us here is the precision or lack of precision with which Brouwer makes his own development, not some approximate report in English upon the situations he is discussing. Some of his technical terms may tolerate approximate translation, but others will not even permit that. His word Menge does not have the same meaning as the word Menge in the classical German Mengenlehre: and therefore technically it *is not* the same word. Anyone interested at all in his development will find it necessary to make the examination in the languages Brouwer himself uses. I may add further that no such study can be made profitably by analysis of a single one of his publications; nor, if confined to a single stage of his development. Full durational inspection of his transformations of terms and methods from 1907 to 1929 will be found necessary for their proper appraisal.

Using the interval for the study of numbers in his earlier essays, Brouwer stressed the operational view of mathematics as over against the realistic-relational,[2] and flatly rejected all transfinite cardinals except that corresponding to the Aleph-Null of Cantor.[3] As he proceeded, he found, however, that his theoretical construction was not adequate to incorporate the work mathematicians were actually doing day by day, and work which he himself wanted to undertake, in the investigation of the continuum. To handle this he required the analogue of Aleph-One as well as of Aleph-Null. In his own manner of expression, to Menge A, cardinal a, i. e., the Menge of the denumerably infinite, he added Menge C, cardinal c, the Menge of the continuum.[4] To bridge over from one to the other without using the prohibited law of the excluded middle in infinite regions, he has developed a highly complicated

---

[2]See (A).

[3](B), p. 571: "Es existiert also nur eine Mächtigkeit für mathematische unendliche Mengen, nämlich die abzählbare." (C), p. 21: "Is deze machtigheid aleph-nul de eenige oneindige machtigheid, waarvan de intuitionisten het bestaan erkennen": p. 22: "De voor den intuitionist zinlooze stelling, 'Aleph-een is grooter dan Aleph-nul.' "

[4]Brouwer still rejects any higher transfinite cardinal. His own statement of the stages of his transition in his views will be found in (E), see especially the note on p. 205 thereof. I do not mean to imply that Brouwer's "A" and "C" are the exact equivalents of the classical "Mengen" of corresponding designation. The various differences are well enough known. They are, however, introduced by Brouwer to answer the same needs and to cover the same ground. In Brouwer's own language in (E): "Die klassischen Kardinalzahlen *a* and *c* bleiben bestehen." The peculiar difficulties that Brouwer has with the "real" are from the present point of view a wholly unnecessary importation from conventional philosophy: and many of Brouwer's most highly elaborated disputations become pointless under semantic examination.

mechanism. Our interest is not in how many cog-wheels he uses and what their pattern, but in the material they are made of and the value of that material. If he uses two cardinals, a and c, one "greater than" the other, we want to know in what sense one is "greater than" the other, and whether this is the same sense in which 3>2: further we want to know this strictly in terms of Brouwer's own consistency, not in terms of some general idea of what he is driving at: and we want to know it in terms of what he means by, or implies by, or expects us to understand by, the various technical terms he uses in his development.

The Brouwer Mengengesetz was first formulated in terms of "Ziffernkomplexe" which yield "Zeichen" and, "Zeichenfolgen:" and later in terms of "Nummern" which yield "Zeichenreihen" and "Folgen von Zeichenreihen." The "Nummern"—Brouwer himself employs the quotation marks on his introduction of the word—are a special kind of "Zeichen," those namely of the "Folge ζ der 'Nummern,' 1, 2, 3, 4, 5........" which are "especially useful" in mathematics. A Menge is a Gesetz, or law, by which, when you have, or choose, a number, you get, under such and such conditions (which conditions are not the specially important feature for us just now), infinite series of "Zeichen." Every "Folge von Zeichenreihen" produced in this procedure of unlimited choosing is an "Element" of the "Menge." The "Gesetz" itself, the "gemeinsame Entstehungsart" of the "Elemente," is to be designated as the "Menge" itself.

In its latest form the Mengengesetz reads: "Eine *Menge* ist ein *Gesetz,* auf Grund dessen, wenn immer wieder eine willkürliche

Nummer gewählt wird, jede dieser Wahlen entweder eine bestimmte Zeichenreihe mit oder ohne Beendigung des Prozesses erzeugt, oder aber die Hemmung des Prozesses mitsamt der definitiven Vernichtung seines Resultates herbeiführt, wobei für jedes $n>1$ nach jeder unbeendigten und ungehemmten Folge von $n-1$ Wahlen, wenigstens eine Nummer angegeben werden kann, die, wenn sie als n-te Nummer gewählt wird, *nicht* die Hemmung des Prozesses herbeiführt. Jede in dieser Weise von einer unbegrenzten Wahlfolge erzeugte Folge von Zeichenreihen (welche also im allgemeinen nicht fertig darstellbar ist), heisst ein *Element der Menge.* Die gemeinsame Entstehungsart der Elemente einer Menge M werden wir kurz ebenfalls als *die Menge M* bezeichnen."[5]

This construction has been regarded as very obscure by specialists in the Mengenlehre. For a careful examination of it as a technical mathematical construction, the essays of Karl Menger, based on a year's residence at Amsterdam in immediate contact with Brouwer, should be read.[6]

Here is a construction highly significant as far as it goes. If we could stop here, and read the words with liberality of interpretation, we might say that we had before us exactly that type of construction, deriving from Kronecker and Poincaré, in which the aspects called M-T and M-O in the present paper, are on the way to being taken as systemic, and in which basic use is made of the connectivity W. The statement of it by Brouwer is, however, manifestly in need of full clarification with respect to the technical terms he uses, and especially with respect to "Ziffer," "Zeichen," "Nummer," "Zahl," "Gesetz," "Wahl" and "Erzeugung." Such clarification Brouwer does not give us. He uses these terms, and most dangerously the last three, just as though they meant something certain which everybody knew. He is satisfied to have

[5](D), p. 3: (E), p. 204: (H), vol. 93, p. 244.

[6]Bemerkungen zu Grundlagenfragen, Deutsche Math-Ver., vol. 37, pp. 213-226, 1928.

found a form of expression, a way of talking, through which he can read operatively the situations of Menge A, cardinal a.

As samples of concealed problems in the first four of the terms listed, which Brouwer does nothing to clarify, consider the following expressions: "Die Menge der Nummern, d. h., der Zeichenreihen von Zeta":[7] "Die Menge der positiven und negativen ganzen Zahlen (d. h., genau genommen, die Menge der diese Zahlen bezeichnenden Zeichenkomplexe)."[8] "Diejenigen Nummern welche höchstens fünf Ziffern enthalten."[9] One knows of course what phenomena he is referring to in each case, but that is not the point at issue: the point is that "Ziffern," "Zeichen," "Nummer" and "Zahl" should be words of exact meaning and not uncertain circumlocutions, if they are to be employed in the most highly generalized postulates and propositions of mathematics.

Nowhere is any attempt made to give definite organization to this group of terms. In a passage just preceding the introduction of the Mengengesetz in its latest form as above quoted, he does indeed tell us that "der Mathematik liegt eine unbegrenzte Folge von Zeichen bzw. endlichen Zeichenreihen zugrunde,"[10] and that this "Folge" is determined by a first "Zeichen" and by the "Gesetz" that, out of each "Zeichenreihe," develops the one next following: after which he remarks: "Insbesondere ist zu diesem Zweck die Folge $\zeta$ der 'Nummern,' 1, 2, 3, 4, 5......, brauchbar." He "grounds" mathematics, that is to say, in "Folgen von Zeichen" without telling us in what sense of grounding: and he makes the sequence of natural numbers in some sense typical without telling us in what sense: he makes "Gesetz" basic without distinguishing between the various operational and relational implications of that word: he sets up "Menge" by the aid of $\zeta$ and the kind of "Gesetz" $\zeta$ offers, then subordinates $\zeta$ to the position of a sample Menge (though all it can be a sample of is itself), and very soon, as we shall see, transforms it again as "Spezies." While the Brouwer "Menge" is not confined to $\zeta$, it should be very clearly confined to situations of which $\zeta$ and its "Gesetz" are typical, if Brouwer's language is to have any intelligible meaning: for the issue of this "typical," whatever it may

[7] (H), vol. 93, p. 245.

[8] Idem, p. 249.

[9] Idem, p. 247.

[10] Idem, p. 244.

be, is the heart of the whole problem. In (D) Brouwer's language was that $\zeta$ was a "Folge" of "Ziffernkomplexe," and that the "Element" was produced by the "Menge." In (H) in the quotations already given, $\zeta$ becomes a "Folge" of "Nummern," and the "Element" is produced by the unlimited "Wahlfolge." This whole exhibit is one of linguistic confusion from the very start.

I greatly regret to be compelled to discuss so harshly Brouwer's development, when I am in such general sympathy with what he originally aimed at, and with what he still has the purpose to advocate. For friendly interpretation and appreciative discussion of the better aspects of his work see essays of Weyl,[11] Wawre[12] and Dresden.[13] But if one turns from these kindly discussions to Brouwer's own latest contributions, the essays of 1928 and 1929[14] one finds in a setting of crude and imperfectly assimilated linguistic and sociological data, only a developing mysticism and a blind dogma. As towards Hilbert especially, Brouwer lets personal antagonism dominate; and he assures us that "der Intuitionismus auf der Grundlage seiner konstruktiven Mengendefinition und seiner Haupteigenschaft der finiten Mengen schon einige Lehrgebäude der eigentlichen Mathematik in unerschütterlicher Sicherheit neu errichtet hat."

To reach Menge C, cardinal c, Brouwer is forced to reinterpret his "Mengen" as "Spezies." "Spezies" is a technical verbal tool, the introduction of which Brouwer regards as his next most important achievement after the formulation of the "Mengengesetz" itself.[15] Whether or not "Spezies" is consistently constructed with respect to "Menge" is vital to the entire Brouwer theory. In it lies the peculiar B-Br connectivity.[16]

Here is Brouwer's presentation:[17]

---

[11]Math. Zeitschr., vol. 10, p. 56, p. 70: Symposion, Sonderdruck, Heft 3, p. 20: Hamb. Abh., vol. VI, p. 86: Philosophie der Mathematik und Naturwissenschaft, Sec. 9, Intuitive Mathematik.

[12]Rev. de métaph. et de mor., vols. 31 and 33, 1924, 1926.

[13]American M. S. Bull., vol. 30, p. 32.

[14](I) and (J).

[15]See (E), p. 205.

[16]See Chap. V, Par. 21.

[17]See (H), vol. 93, p. 245.

"Mengen" and "Elemente von Mengen" are named mathematische "Entitäten."

The "Spezies" is set forth as an "Eigenschaft," "begrifflich fertig definiert"[18] which only an "Entität" can possess.

"Spezies" are of various orders.

"Mengen" are special cases of "Spezies" of the first order.

In order to appraise this presentation observe first that the terms Brouwer uses are all words of conventional and inexact implication, and that he does nothing to clarify them.[19] Observe next that whereas the set of unclarified terms, "Wahl," "Erzeugung," "Gesetz," used in the "Mengengesetz," were of a quasi-operational-subjective order, this new set is of a quasi-absolutist-relational-objective order. If the use of one set of such terms is questionable, the use of two such sets is little more than verbal magic.[20]

---

[18]Contrast this phrase with the phrase "im allgemeinen nicht fertig darstellbar" in the Mengengesetz as cited above.

[19]The fact that we know what the mathematical situations are to which Brouwer is referring does not help out at all: what we are interested in is the consistency of his own development.

[20]By way of illustration we may hypothetize a biologist with a working attitude akin to Brouwer's. He would consider, for example, a *cow*, and living in an era of evolutionary thought with rich genetic materials before him, he would define the cow under Gesetz, that is, operatively in evolution. But feeling a need of exact differentiation of the *cow* as *animal*, he would proceed as follows: 1. The cow, "im allgemeinen nicht fertig definiert," is a biological Entität. 2. Cow-ness is a characteristic, fixed and sure, "begrifflich fertig definiert," a "Spezies" which only a biological "Entität" can possess. 3. The cow of "Gesetz" is a special case of the "Spezies" cow-ness. 4. Cow-ness is a "Spezies" of the first order. 5. There are "Spezies" of higher orders. 6. Animality is a "Spezies" of the second order. But right here we must stop. There is no telling what our hypothetical biologist would do next—probably whatever he felt like doing in accordance with his "intuition." This would, nevertheless, all be very fine if he could bring his two systems of expression into full linguistic consistency. The case is no different with Brouwer.

Characteristic of Brouwer as operational procedures are his emphasis upon construction rather than upon definition, his footing in Gesetz taken as rule of construction, his use of "Erzeugung" or the production of one series by another or by "Wahl," and his antipathy to carrying any systems into regions in which he cannot follow, or pretend to follow, the "Erzeugung." Characteristic of him on the relational side are his footing in "Eigenschaften" "begrifflich fertig definiert," his "Spezies," his double meanings for "Nummern," which at critical moments appear rather as definitions than as operations, and his actual advance far beyond the regions of "Erzeugung."

Brouwer's purpose is clear. He aims to provide a description which will cover the realistic-relational statements and procedures of mathematics in supplement to his previous description which covered the operative statements.[21] We may say, in the symbolism of our present analysis, that while in the "Mengengesetz" Brouwer attempted to give recognition to the M-O aspect of his materials, in the "Spezies" he aims to set up the M-T aspect. But his method of procedure is a mere verbalizing. It leaves him free for double-dealing with his materials in whatever way he wishes. In "Mengen" alone he could not have reached C, but under "Spezies"—that is, merely by adopting the word and using it—he finds that he can set up C along with A.

Brouwer does, it is true, make an effort on the operational side to show how C can be obtained as a "Menge" direct. One phrase he uses is that C is "die Menge der unbeschränkt fortgesetzten Folgen von

[21]Karl Menger describes "Spezies" as Brouwer's way of getting a "Bezeichnungsweise" for the "Totalität der Elemente einer Menge in seinem Sinne" Deutsche Math-Ver., vol. 37, p. 221.

Nummern.''[22] The play here is in part on the word ''Nummern,'' because if ''Nummern'' remained consistently ''Zeichen,'' this would not lead to C. It is also on the word ''unbeschränkt,'' for that which was an ''unbegrenzte Wahlfolge'' in the ''Mengengesetz'' now loses its formulation in ''Wahl,'' and becomes objectively ''unbeschränkt fortgesetzten *Folgen.*'' The quibbling with words is not mine; it is Brouwer's. The merest beginnings of an analysis of Brouwer's phrasemaking show that the ''unbeschränkt'' in the later passage is a flat negation of both the ''Wahl'' and ''Gesetz'' of the earlier, and without ''Wahl'' and ''Gesetz'' in the earlier sense the procedure is not that of Brouwerian ''Menge'' at all.

Again he describes C as the result obtained when it comes to pass that every choice of a ''Nummer'' always and only produces the ''Nummer'' itself.[23] This again is juggling with words. It gives iteration in place of ''Wahl,'' and so negates ''Wahl.'' One can visualize readily the situation Brouwer has in mind, but one cannot rationalize it in Brouwer's language.

We may summarize Brouwer's position thus far as follows:

a. Using the systematized connection of natural numbers, he seeks to define collections of such num-

---

[22]See (H), vol. 93, p. 251. In (D), p. 9, Brouwer had used the phrase, ''die Menge der unbeschränkt fortgesetzten Folgen von zu $\zeta$ gehörigen Ziffernkomplexen,'' but in line with his other shifts of phrasing, abandoned it for the words cited in the text.

[23]See (H), vol. 93, p. 244, footnote 2: ''Zur Erleichterung des Verständnisses sei auf den speziellen Fall hingewiesen, der eintritt, wenn sowohl von Beendigungen wie von Hemmungen des Prozesses Abstand genommen wird und wenn man ürberdies jede Wahl einer Nummer immer nur die Nummer selbst erzeugen lässt. Dieser Fall liefert die Menge C.''

bers in a way in which the connectivity between them will be included in the definition: and he proposes to spread this treatment over all M-T of the system W, as well as over the natural sequence.

b. He uses the terms "Ziffer," "Zeichen," "Nummer" and "Zahl" with various shifts of implication to such degree that the reader cannot succeed in holding him down to the exact meaning of any one of them with respect to the others.

c. He uses without clarification terms of dubious meaning such as "Wahl" and "Erzeugung" and even also "Gesetz," the implications of which in each special case are nevertheless vital to his procedure.

d. In order to pass from this "Mengen" construction to that of the continuum, he introduces another form of description using a different set of unclarified terms, "Eigenschaft," "Entität" and "Spezies."

e. He thus sets up Menge A by the first method and both Menge A and Menge C by the second method, and arbitrarily identifies the Menge A of the second method with that of the first.

f. By means of obscure phrasing in which "Gesetz" becomes "unbeschränkt," and "Wahl" becomes "always the same," he purports to support this procedure.[24]

g. In order to make this construction useful in his mathematics it is next incumbent upon him to show the cardinal c is greater than the cardinal a;[25] and this

[24]One may refer also to his earlier expression as to "the intuition of the bare two-oneness" and "the fusion of continuous and discrete" (C, 1), p. 85: "Deze intuitie der twee-eenigheid, deze oerintuitie der wiskunde" (C, p. 12). This is however little more than sentimentality.

[25]"Die Menge C ist grösser als die Menge A": (H), vol. 93, p. 253.

indeed in the exact sense of greater and less among natural numbers.

The exposition of such a proposition as this last under classical Mengenlehre has within its own system no difficulties. The issue of greater and less is an issue of one-to-one with respect to "Dinge," the "Dinge" being selected and defined to fit the conclusion to be secured by the proof. Aleph-Null and Aleph-One are put before us, their situation is that of greater and less, and the construction of greater and less used for them is extended over "finite" numbers. This is not a statement of historical emergence, but it is a statement of the constructive status today.

With Brouwer's combination of "Gesetz," "Erzeugung" and "Eigenschaft," of "Menge" and "Spezies," the case is however entirely different. With respect to him we must have not merely his proof, but the materials of it, clearly before us. These are as follows:[26]

1. Two "Elemente" are *"gleich"* or *"identisch,"* when for each n the nth "Wahl" "erzeugt" for both the same "Zeichenreihe." (Note that "Gleichheit" is introduced in terms of "Erzeugung: also that by coupling "gleich" and "identisch" distinctions of possibly great ultimate importance for the theory are fused.)

2. Two "Menge" are "gleich" or "identisch" when for each "Element" of the one "ein gleiches Element" of the other "angegeben werden kann." (Note that this also must be founded in "Erzeugung,"

[26]See (H), vol. 93, p. 245, p. 246, p. 247, p. 252.

but that the phrase "angegeben werden kann" seems carefully chosen for its non-committal value).

3. Two "Spezies" are "gleich" or "identisch" under phrasing similar to (2). (This remains "Erzeugung" in implicit characterization, despite the fact that "Spezies" are "Eigenschaft," "begrifflich fertig definiert.")

4. Two "Mengenelemente" are *"verschieden,"* when the impossibility of their "Gleichheit" "feststeht": which is to say, Brouwer adds, when one has "Sicherheit" that in the course of their "Erzeugung," their "Gleichheit" "nie . . . wird beweisen lassen." (This, again, is in terms of "Erzeugung." The phrasing of the first form of statement is adapted to conform to Brouwer's view of the excluded middle.)

One may recall that Brouwer's world includes, not only finite and infinite, but also possible hybrids. "Es existiert kein Grund zu behaupten, dass jede Menge oder Spezies entweder endlich oder unendlich sei. Dagegen steht fest, dass eine Spezies nicht gleichzeitig endlich und unendlich sein kann."[27] This passage alone suffices to reveal Brouwer's verbal realism, the abandonment of his original constructional attitude for a superimposed relational realism, and the extremities into which his opportunism has driven him.

5. Two "Spezies" are "verschieden" under phrasing similar to (4). (This is again in "Erzeugung," despite a subject which is "Eigenschaft.")

6. A "Spezies" is *"diskret"* when for any two "Elemente" it can be recognized (erkannt werden können) that they are "gleich" or "verschieden." (Discreteness, built up verbally in a chain of statements resting on "Erzeugung" is now ready to be

[27] (H), vol. 93, p. 248. Compare also (G), p. 3.

taken in fixed relational interpretation. The "erkannt" like the "angegeben" in (2) is carefully chosen for its non-committal value).

7. When between two "Spezies" M and N, an "eineindeutige Beziehung" can be established (hergestellt werden kann), we write $M \sim N$, and say that they have the same "Mächtigkeit" or "Kardinalzahl."

8. The "eineindeutige Beziehung" is a "Gesetz" whereby (a) to every "Element" of M an "Element" of N is ordered in such way that to "gleichen" and only to "gleichen Elementen" of M "gleiche Elemente" of N correspond: and (b) every "Element" of N is ordered to an "Element" of M. ("Gesetz" is here no longer "Erzeugung." It is instead an inspection of finished products, or, we may rather say, of products inspected as if finished up to any given moment of inspection: or, again, we may say, of the status taken instantaneously).

9. Two "Spezies" are *"äquivalent"* (and their "Kardinalzahlen" likewise) when two "Gesetze" are found, the first, $G_1$, that of (a) in (8) above: the second, $G_2$, establishing M with respect to N exactly as $G_1$ established N with respect to M. Equivalence,—i. e., the joint appearance of $G_1$ and $G_2$,—is called an Eigenschaft, which we also express through the formula, $m=n$.

10. *Greater* and *less* appear when we have before us a "Gesetz" $G_1$, but as for "Gesetz" $G_2$ "kein Gesetz existieren kann": or vice versa. We then write $>$ and $<$.

Here, now, is Brouwer's presentation of the situation of "greater and less" in mathematics, examined with respect both to its materials and their development. Before applying it to the cardinals a and c, let us summarize its characteristics.

While *"gleich," "identisch"* and *"verschieden,"* which enter into the presentation of "greater and less" are established in "Wahl" and "Erzeugung," the "greater and less" itself appears in "Eigenschaften."

While the former have to do with "Zeichenreihen," the latter have to do with "Zahl:" and there is no interpretation of the transition from "Zeichen" and "Zeichenreihen" through "Nummer" to "Zahl."[28]

The medium of expression transforms itself always with obscurity of implication through terms such as "erzeugen," "angeben," "feststehen," "Sicherheit," "erkennen," "herstellen" and "existieren."

The word "Gesetz" has entirely transformed its meaning in the development from the "Gesetz" of "Erzeugung" to that of "Eigenschaft."

The critical point of transition is the term *"diskret."* This term is born in "Erzeugung," of the earth earthy, but comes to gain something of a glorified soul in "Eigenschaft," "Eineindeutigkeit," "Äquivalenz" and "Zahl." To mediate this beatification we have nothing by way of machinery but the obscure implications of "erkennen." We rest in papal infallability, et praeterea nihil.

So therefore when we come to the proof that c is greater than a we have a formal, wholly relational statement, with nothing of "Wahl" or "Erzeugung"

---

[28]Compare the "d.h., genau genommen" cited and the other illustrations already cited.

left and only a "Bekanntwerden to organize distinctions and definitions. The proof is as follows:

*"Die Menge C ist grösser als die Menge A.* Ein Gesetz, das jedem Elemente g von C ein Element h von A zuordnet, muss nämlich das Element h vollständig bestimmt haben nach dem Bekanntwerden eines gewissen Anfangssegmentes *a* der Nummernfolge g. Dann aber wird jedem Elemente von C, das *a* als Anfangssegment besitzt, dasselbe Element h von A zugeordnet, so dass die Formel a $\geqq$ c sich als kontradiktorisch erweist, während man andererseits leicht ersieht, dass c $\geqq$ a ist. Hiermit ist die Behauptung bewiesen."[29]

Here we have a restatement of the classical proof, but so far as the "Gesetz" of "Erzeugung" and "Wahl" goes, we have a complete non sequitur. The situation is as follows:

If the discreteness of the "Mengengesetz" proper is maintained, namely that in which the "Menge" and the "Gesetz" of "Wahl" are merely two different ways of speaking of the same mathematical material—that established in "Zeichen," "Zeichenreihen" and "Nummern" by the aid of an emphasis M-T within a system of M-T and M-O united—we have a well known algebraic "greater and less" but we do not arrive at C at all.

If we set up the discreteness of "Eigenschaft," and of the Menge C, on their own basis, then we have their

---

[29]Brouwer helps out his organization of C with A by the use of the term "reduzierbar unendlich" (H), vol. 93, p. 248, which he defines as a case in which the "Teilspezies" is "abtrennbar." This indicates well enough what he has in mind, but is merely one more name given to a situation to avoid its analysis.

own type of "greater and less," but we have no manifest connection with the "Mengengesetz."

If we set up A in this second field along with C, and along with the discreteness of "Eigenschaft"—that is, if we make the proper definitions to begin with—we can spread our "greater and less" over the whole system according to our desire and need, and with authority to be held wholly within the limits of such desire and need.

If we then, however, attempt to interpret the two systems of discreteness in one by playing with words, the implications of which are unanalyzed, as Brouwer does, we have no proper theory, no consistency, and in the usual case, no probability of consistency in prospect.

Brouwer's development is rejected by many mathematicians as a mutilation, and as a destruction of much important past achievement: it is rejected by others as clumsy, exceedingly difficult to handle, and lacking in all the essentials of mathematical beauty. These objections would be of no more than passing force, if he could attain consistency. But of consistency he has none in the special region we have been considering. There is no need of spending time in examining the details of his x-zählbarkeit nor the varieties of his "Mächtigkeit": they are merely mechanical aids for bridging over the deep functional split which we have seen to be present in his work.

However, it should be added that what we have here called inconsistency, does not appear as inconsistency to Brouwer himself, and "is" no inconsistency "for him." Here is the service his "Intuition" renders:

and I believe we can say the only service it renders. He has a problem, one of two kinds of denumerability and of greater and less over their full field. Intuition attacks the problem. If intuition can force "Wahl" and "Gesetz" and "Eigenschaft" and "Spezies" and "Menge" into the necessary semblance of consistency, what more, Brouwer seems to ask us, could be wished?

# X

## RELATIONS AND OPERATIONS

We have gone our way throughout this essay in frank disregard of what we have called "common-reference descriptions";[1] and in disregard also of many current devices for "*foundation*" discussion, such as "concepts," "logic," "intuition" and "truth." One such device, namely "relations," has, at several stages, forced itself incidentally upon our attention.[2] To it we must now give more definite consideration.

The word relations is entangled in one direction with the word objects, and in another direction with the word operations. Moreover, with respect to operations it exhibits two types of entanglement; one concerning the operative aspects found "*within*" symbolic procedures themselves; the other with respect to the "mentally operational" procedures which, in all constructions realistic with respect to M-T, are taken for granted as "*underlying*" them or as operating "behind" them.[3]

Should we propose to offer a systematic treatment of relations in mathematics, it would be our primary

---

[1]See the list in Chap. III.

[2]See Chap. IV, Par. 7 and Par. 10. Recall also the manner in which relational presentations entered the development of Brouwer and became overlaid upon his operational procedures, causing his many shifts in the meaning of terms, and the specious doubling of his terminological values.

[3]See the development for Hilbert, Chap. V, Par. 25, and Chwistek's effort at further reduction of such materials, Chap. V, Par. 21. See also the opening paragraphs of Chap. VII.

obligation to deal with it in terms of the development of Russell, running from his early postulations for geometry through his great construction in the Principia Mathematica. This we shall not undertake, and for two reasons. In the first place, its outcome has been unresolved paradox, with respect to which Russell's great abilty, his long continued application, and the labors of his many disciples are guarantee that he has secured from it all that one may hope to attain. In the second place, even the beginnings of such a treatment would find us involved in intricate philosophical problems; and these, under our semantic manner of approach, would require us to analyze and display a great horde of word-clusters, representing different forms of the entanglements with objects and operations mentioned above: a task far beyond our range or requirements in the present work.

In place of this I shall content myself with a field report upon the word Relations as it appears in two regions of usage: first in Hermann Weyl's construction of the mathematical foundation problems: and second in the many systems of postulation for geometry which have been bequeathed to us by workers whose period of greatest activity comprised the end of the last century and the first decade of the present.

## I. Hermann Weyl

Weyl acquires a special interest for us, from our own point of view, because he undertakes his investigation, not primarily as a mathematician brooding within the field of his study, but more as a scientific observer, recording, classifying and constructing from without: and it is characteristic of him that, in his inspection, he sees directly before him, not only such and such mathematical constructions (including their specialized operations and relations), but also such and such a physical world, first as crude datum and then as theoretical physical statement, and, finally, such and such psychical existences, minds, powers and capacities. These last items we may label Weyl's "factual psychic," as a term which best indicates how they stand in his system: and without them his presentation would not hold together at all.[4] Citations will be in the main from his Philosophie der Mathematik und Naturwissenschaft.[5]

Weyl sees geometry as the historical predecessor

---

[4]This "factual psychic" in the form in which Weyl uses it is a phenomenon which is specially and concretely characteristic of the terms of the German language. I do not refer to any special psychological or philosophical theory or set of theories, but to the linguistic bed in which theories flourish. If, in other words, one takes these German terms, organizes them in word-clusters, and studies their connectivites, on the basis of the rules of Chapter III, one finds the special psychic discreteness which Weyl uses appearing in very pronounced form. In his latest publication in this field, that in the Rice Institute Pamphlets (p. 252), he frankly adopts the "reality" of the "you" and of the external world as the embodiment of "higher truth."

[5]Handbuch der Philosophie. Also separately published 1927. (Cited herein as "Phil. Math.")

Other books and papers in this field by Weyl are the following:

Das Kontinuum, 1918.

Der circulus vitiosus in der heutigen Begründung der Analysis; Deutsche Math.-Ver., vol. 28, p. 85, 1919.

Über die neue Grundlagenkrise der Mathematik; Math. Zeitschr., vol 10, p. 39, 1921.

Randbemerkungen zu Hauptproblemen der Mathematik; Math. Zeitschr., vol. 20, p. 131, 1924.

Die heutige Erkenntnislage in der Mathematik: Sonderlruck des Symposion, Heft 3, 1926.

Diskussionsbemerkungen zu dem zweiten Hilbertschen Vortrag über die Grundlagen der Mathematik: Hamb. Abh., vol. VI, p. 86, 1928.

Consistency in Mathematics: The Rice Institute Pamphlets, vol. XVI, p. 245, 1929.

and model of logic, so that "even the Aristotelian logic was in substance an abstraction from mathematics."[6] Assuming that this thesis can be established, then it would seem to be just one more reason for holding logic in the leash of mathematical consistency. Weyl, however, apprehending his logic, as resting in factual mentality and regarding mathematics rather as a special use of it, sees nothing inconsistent in asserting forthwith that logic rules. "Indeed," he says, "the ultimately firm establishment of mathematics itself appears to be impossible, until full reckoning with logic has been secured."[7] This logic, for Weyl, begins with definition, and proceeds to proof:[8] it begins with immediate (unmittelbar gegebenen) data and proceeds to ideal elements:[9] it establishes certain objects as "separate beings" (Sonderwesen)[10]—so the natural numbers—and its further procedure is "combinatory."[11] But his mathematics nevertheless goes far beyond the Aristotelian logic, despite this professed basic dependence upon it, and commands a two-fold creative procedure.

As scientific observer Weyl is very keenly alive to the two great characteristics of mathematics, the mutual organization of which makes so much trouble

---

[6]Phil. Math., p. 3.

[7]Idem, p. 3.

[8]Idem, p. 12.

[9]Idem, p. 6.

[10]Idem, p. 7. Here is the "X" of our alternative realistic and semantic postulations in Chapter II. Such an "X" Weyl understands as running *not* between "Erscheinung" and "Ding-an-sich" in terms of "*kennen,*" but to "Dinge" in terms of "*wissen*" (op. cit., p. 22): this distinction is, however, of no importance whatever for our form of analysis, lying wholly apart from it. See also op. cit., p. 49 on the application of the "System als Ganzes."

[11]Idem, p. 9.

for the "*foundation*" theories. On the one side he sees before him the operational and constructional features which Brouwer has desired to stress: and on the other side he sees the great relational certainties which predominate in Hilbert's attention. Neither may be ignored.[12] The natural numbers (despite their characteristic as "Sonderwesen"), and whatever developes from them, are primarily the operational: while the continuum and what is assimilated to it are relational. Here the two creative procedures are called in to help.

Induction among numbers is "the very soul of the mathematical art of proof," "an entirely new and peculiar element which Aristotelian logic did not yet know."[13] But Mengenbildung, the constructions of aggregates, also offers a case in which mathematics "controls a creative power of definition, by means of which new ideal objects appear": "a creative power of definition which itself is neither more nor less than the forward march from 'Eigenschaft' to 'Menge' "[14] —an assertion which it is very difficult indeed for us to put into sufficiently full-bodied English words; for it implies a certain glorification of the simple common

---

[12]Symposion, Heft 3, p. 32: Hamb. Abh., vol. VI, p. 88. Weyl himself makes frequent mention of the double nature of his interpretations. Thus in one passage (Phil. Math., p. 5) he writes: "Hierdurch ordnen wir die genetische Konstruktion dem ruhenden Sein der Relationen unter: später werden wir freilich gerade umgekehrt alle Relationen durch konstruktive Prozesse ersetzen."

[13]Phil. Math., p. 28: "die eigentliche Seele der mathematischen Beweiskunst": "ein ganz neues und eigenartiges Moment, das die Aristotelische Logik noch nicht kennt."

[14]Idem, p. 8: "verfügt über eine schöpferische, neue ideale Gegenstände erzeugende Definition." Idem, p. 11: "die schöpferische Definition ist nichts anderes als der Übergang von der Eigenschaft zur Menge."

attribute, quality, property or characteristic of everyday life and expression, and its ultimate fixation in infinity or infinities.

Not one word is offered in interpretation of these two "creative souls" with respect to each other: their two-in-oneness is a bare assumption, resting in that "factual psychic" which is the controlling power of the whole theory: and so we get, not with explicit emphasis and interpretation, but casually and as if manifest to everyone, the following: "The objective of the mathematical theory of the continuum is to be found in the possible "Mengen" (or the infinite series) of natural numbers";[15] where these possible "Mengen" or infinite series are calmly and simply taken as equivalent expressions. Right here is, however, the heart of the problem. We know that mathematics has relational and operational presentations which can be handled "practically"—that is, in the mathematician's daily work— in consistency: we know that interpretative structures round and about them fail to secure consistency for the two together: we know that consistency right here is our need: and what Weyl offers us is a psychological-logical seed-bed of "factual mentality" in which two "creative" mathematical plants are growing, and the assumption that the two are the same plant.

On the operational side Weyl takes strong position

---

[15]Idem, p. 33: "Objekt der Kontinuumlehre sind die möglichen Mengen (oder die unendlichen Folgen) natürlicher Zahlen." Compare also, (p. 33): "Ein dem Schnitt gleichwertiges Mittel zur Festlegung der reellen Zahlen ist die unendliche Folge," which is again a sound "practical" remark, but nevertheless in no way obviating the difficulties involved in the following sentence (p. 37): "Das Gesetz, bzw., die Eigenschaft legt die intendierte reelle Zahl exakt fest."

as to the "priority" of ordinals over cardinals:[16] and there is no point in the whole range of general discussion at which operational and relational approaches come into sharper or more frequent rivalry than this. And from the intuitionist standpoint it is mathematical induction, he holds, which preserves mathematics from becoming a monstrous tautology.[17]

But on the relational side, also, he makes the strongest affirmations. Mathematics is "the science of the infinite":[18] it is the "general theory of relations, hypothetic-deductive in nature."[19] "Definition itself is the root of the 'alls,' from which one makes further advances by aid of complete induction."[20] The interpretative hopes arising from the theory of limits, he says, were not fulfilled, and Cauchy's criterium itself demanded such a fixation of the number concept as was at length secured through the Dedekindian cut.[21] Mathematical induction, he holds, can be given its foundations in the transfinite employment of the concepts "all" and "some" in the "Mengenlehre."[22] His solution of the inconsistencies which arise under an

---

[16] Idem, p. 28: "Daher scheint es mir unbestreitbar das die Ordinalzahl das Primäre ist." Compare the views of Kronecker and Poincaré set forth in Chap. VII of the present book.

[17] Idem, p. 51: "was die Mathematik davor bewahrt eine ungeheure Tautologie zu sein."

[18] Idem, p. 53: "Die Mathematik ist die Wissenschaft vom Unendlichen."

[19] Idem, p. 23: "Die reine Mathematik ist nach moderner Auffassung allgemeine hypothetisch-deduktive Relationslehre."

[20] Idem, p. 42: "Die Definition selber ist also die Wurzel der Allgemeinheit, von welcher man weiter schreitet durch die vollständige Induktion."

[21] Idem, p. 37: "Der Beweis des Kriterium erfordert jene Festlegung des Zahlbegriffes, wie sie dann im Dedekindschen Schnittprinzip erreicht wurde."

[22] Idem, p. 39: "auf die transfinite Verwendung der Begriffe 'alle' und 'es gibt.'"

unlimited relational approach is, however, just another opportunism, involving the requirement of "umfangsdefinit" in connection with his "Urteilsschema."[23]

One might readily exhibit many apparent inconsistencies in the phrases that have been cited. Weyl is able to read them as coherent, and so can other investigators using his background: while at the same time still others find the gaps of meaning to be shrieking: that is just the trouble here and always with this form of psychological *"foundation."* Weyl's coherence lies in his "factual psychic," and that is the end of it; until that region of factual psychic is analyzed and absorbed linguistically into mathematical expression, so far as it proves to be at all pertinent. It is enough if I have brought out the nature of the development of the operational and the relational features in such a system, and the extraneous means which are necessary to give them the appearance of holding together. The extent to which his "philosophical" system is hampered under its bondage in conventional language is all the more significant when one recalls the radical vigor with which Weyl has employed the operational point of view in his important mathematical and physical investigations.

## II. Postulation for Geometry

In his endeavor to give geometry an improved—and hopefully even a perfect— organization by means of

---

[23]Idem, p. 40, p. 42. See Chap. V, Par. 16: and compare Weyl, Symposion, Heft 3, pp. 15-16: Math. Zeitschr., vol. 10, pp. 41-42, and Deutsche Math.-Ver., vol. 28, p. 85.

systems of consistent postulation, the geometer starts with certain initial presentations, which he very commonly calls "undefined,"[24] in contrast with other presentations which he secures under sharp "definition," or "naming," in the course of his development. Certain of these initial presentations are called by him "objects" or "things," illustrations being point, line-segment and plane. Others he calls "relations," illustrated by order and by equivalence. And in addition to these he, in every case, whether he admits it openly or not, makes use of still a third presentation or agent or material—whatever it may be—which we may call "operation,"[25] illustrated in the translations and rotations required for the treatment of congruence.

Now it is notorious that the geometers who construct these systems do not agree among themselves as to what is to be called thing, and what relation: and further that the great majority of them do everything in their power, whether with scruples or without, to drive the operational aspects, if not wholly out of their systems, at least out of sight. In some systems the point is the sole undefined thing or object. Often what

[24]The term "undefined" represents to the geometer the basic "*abstractness*" of his field of work, as controlled through the dependable procedures of logic, which again have locus in his "mind," while at the same time in some strange way being "the same" for all minds. In other words, the term has for him merely certain values of practical convenience. This would be unobjectionable, perhaps, for his purposes, were he consistent in his further use of the term "definition," taken as "formal": but we shall offer several illustrations of what is common to perhaps all systems of axioms—the furtive introduction, namely at later stages, of new basic materials under the guise of formal definition.

[25]Some discussion of the character of postulates which refer to "formative processes" through which objects or relations are invented or constructed may be found in Carmichael, The Logic of Discovery, pp. 119-20.

is undefined object to one system appears as defined or derived object to another. What is relation in one system may appear as thing in another, and vice versa.[26] It is by his dependence upon the common-reference description, "abstract"—although he has no sound construction for "abstractness" itself—that the geometer finds authority and justification for these freely varied manipulations of materials that are common to all.

Should we desire to classify these systems of postulation, or sets of axioms, as they have more often been called in geometry, and should we take as criterion the use of thing, of relation or of operation as basic, we should find a successful classification in such terms wholly impracticable. Nor should we have greater success if we tested the systems with respect to what things, what relations or what operations they took as basic. It is possible, however, to group them roughly with respect to the trend of interest or emphasis which is dominant in the individual geometer and in his construction. So appraised, we find that two early workers in this field, Pieri and Padoa, are commonly interpreted as building from the operative aspect of geometry, motion, with the point in use by them as the sole undefined object before their atten-

---

[26]The requirements will of course vary if we are considering projective geometry as distinct from the descriptive or analytic geometries. It should be emphasized here that the question as to what set of axioms for geometry is practically of the greatest value to geometers, whether in one or another branch of their work, is in no way before us; and the fact that an incoherence is pointed out in a system in the linguistic region which now occupies our attention, does not involve in any way criticism of the system with respect to such "practical" purposes.

tion.[27] Schweitzer may also be mentioned in this group because of his stress upon the presentation "generating relation."[28] On the side of relations, Russell,[29] as is well known stands foremost, the "relation" being a delivery of logic, and the "point," which is of course also necessary, being inspected as an "entity," or, what is much the same thing, as an "incident" in its field. Veblen should be listed here because of his stress on the single relation, order, which, with the point as likewise undefined, he greatly desired to make his sole reliance. On the side of things or objects, Hilbert is the leader in emphasis, and to his construction, which surpasses all others in reputation, we shall shortly return. Coolidge likewise illustrates this trend, when he professes to start with just two kinds of objects, one the point, and the other the distance-object.[30] If we examine other systems, such as those of Pasch, Peano, Schur, Vahlen and Veronese, we shall find great differences among them as to what presentations are objects and what relations, as to which of these are initial and which are derived: and we shall

---

[27]See comments by Coolidge, Huntington and Veblen in various of their writings later to be cited.

[28]A Theory of Geometrical Relations: American J., vol. 31, p. 365, 1909. Schweitzer assumes a formal equivalence between expressions for relation, class, and operation. Op. cit., p. 374.

[29]The Principles of Mathematics, Sec. 376.

[30]The Elements of Non-Euclidean Geometry, p. 13, 1909. The procedure of Coolidge in respect to the issues before us is unusually interesting. It is easy for him, by fiat, to turn distance (which more commonly is considered a relation) into an "object" and to classify it exactly as "object" along with one other such "object," the point, the two being all that are needed. He balks, however, apparently at treating congruence in the same way and at making it likewise an "object," but instead describes congruence as a "relation" between two distance-objects. (op. cit., p. 14, p. 24.) Continuity, he introduces as an "assumption." (p. 24.)

also find great differences between what they themselves propound as their initial materials, and what commentators upon their work regard as more properly to be taken as fundamental in their approaches.

All of this means that there has been in fact no competent study by any of these men of the interconnected mathematical values of these three presentations of embedding language,—objects, relations and operations,—which are not merely vital in their systems of axioms, but vital also in every detail of everyday geometrical procedure. Several of them have discussed the situation at length, as for example, Veronese, but always from some special psychological or philosophical point of approach.[31] Hilbert, as we have seen in earlier chapters, long after his scheme for geometry had gained world-wide fame, found it necessary to go much further, and to attempt the reduction of all mathematical materials in all branches of mathematics to the form of objects. I shall confine myself here to a brief examination of the systems of Hilbert, Veblen and Huntington, with respect to their embedding conventions of language: and solely to exhibit the confusions with respect to the three characteristic types of presentation or material of which they all make use.

Hilbert's system of axioms for the foundation of geometry was first published in 1899, and has passed through seven editions and been widely translated.

---

[31]None of these philosophical and psychological constructions or efforts at construction has as yet proved itself germane to the mathematical problem proper. One recent work in this field, marked by great acuteness of thought, is Jean Nicod's Foundations of Geometry and Induction, 1930.

He begins with the declaration:[32] "we think three different systems of things"—"wir denken drei verschiedene Systeme von Dingen." These are respectively, points, straights and planes. He proceeds at once to regard these things or systems of things as "present in relations." We "think them," he says, as in mutual relations—"gegenseitigen Beziehungen"—designated by such words as "are situated," "between," "parallel," "congruent" and "continuous." The relations are thus incidental to the things, and given with them.[33]

We have now merely to note what happens when congruence is given its axioms. He states that his axioms "define congruence," and along with congruence "define motion."[34] This, it is evident, is very far from "formal" definition. In his earlier editions he felt free to remark quite casually that, given this axiom,

---

[32]Grundlagen der Geometrie, 7th edition, p. 2, 1930. The phrasing is the same in all editions. How much is involved in the phrasing—how many different word-clusters may be secured by study of this one group of seven words—will be apparent, if we glance at the two earliest English reproductions. Townsend, in his translation of the book, makes this: "Let us consider three distinct systems of things." Halsted in his reproduction under the title, "Rational Geometry," puts it: "We think three different sorts of things." The former eliminates the characteristic Hilbertian mental operation set forth in "denken": the latter eliminates the "system" aspect which holds Hilbertian "relations" into the construction of "things." Both make the situation easy for "practical" use in geometry: but both evade the underlying problems.

[33]Hilbert's attitude here can be appraised by examining his explicit statement twenty-five years later for such situations as he saw them arising in his general "*foundation*" theory. See the last citation in Chap. V, note 30. It is to be observed that even in this latest statement the issue does not arise to full incorporation in his postulation, but is merely an elaborated expression of background verbal implication or dogma.

[34]Grundlagen der Geometrie, 2d ed., p. 7: 7th ed., p. 11: "Die Axiome dieser Gruppe definieren den Begriff der Kongruenz und damit auch der Bewegung."

then one line segment could be laid off, "abgetragen," upon another.[35] But in his last edition this statement is dropped, and what appears in its place can hardly be taken other than as complete reversal of his first rendering. The axiom, he now says, "requires the possibility of the laying off of lines"—"Dieses Axiom fordert die Möglichkeit der Streckenabtragung."[36] There is here paucity of conflicting words, but no paucity of conflict itself. In Hilbert's own language, and without the use of any imported manner of interpretation, congruence is a relation, it is a relation adhering to things-in-system: but it also involves something that is other than relation, something that is operational, extra-relational: and this moreover in such a way that we seem justified in the critical comment that without this "other than relation," then no "things" whatever would be present such as Hilbert has placed before us as initial data.

Turning now to Veblen, we find that in the earlier of his two leading essays in this field, he declared that he would proceed from one single relation, order, taking as additional material one single object, the point. He announced that he would define line, plane and motion on this basis:[37] and definition for him, it should be remembered, is strictly nominal, formal; it is mere naming, symbolizing, and must in no event add any-

[35] Idem, 2d ed., p. 7: 5th ed., p. 10: "Wir sagen auch kürzer: eine jede Strecke kann auf einer gegebenen Seite einer gegebenen Geraden von einem gegebenen Punkte in eindeutig bestimmter Weise abgetragen werden."

[36] Idem, 7th ed., p. 11.

[37] A System of Axioms for Geometry: American M. S. Trans., vol. 5, p. 344, 1904. Also he casually assumes the operations of counting as available .

thing in the way of content or new meaning. Criticism was prompt,[38] and modification was necessary. But in his later construction Veblen still mentions no basic materials upon his opening pages, save the one "undefined" relation, order, and the one undefined object, point.[39] It is not until he reaches the subject of congruence, that he mentions the need of an additional "undefined" relation, congruence.[40] Congruence, one cannot help feeling, is only grudgingly given this status by him but even then it remains useless to him until he proceeds—I quote his own words—"to extend its significance by means of a definition":—extension of significance by definition, and that in a system in which defintion is wholly nominal, formal, mere symbolizing, naming. Nor is even this sufficient, for he proceeds to fall back for conveyance of his meaning upon such operational phrases as "a kind of intellectual matching," "superposition" and "distance as measured by a tape-line."[41] It is sufficiently clear that he has only made a small part of the advance that was manifestly necessary for the revision of his earlier postulation.[42]

---

[38]See especially R. L. Moore, Sets of Metrical Hypotheses for Geometry Idem, vol. 9, p. 487, 1908. Moore's results were taken over by Veblen in his later work.

[39]The Foundations of Geometry: in Monographs on Topics of Modern Mathematics, J. W. A. Young, editor, 1911.

[40]Idem, p. 27.

[41]Idem, p. 27-9. In this essay the operative number system enters by "definition." Idem, p. 12.

[42]Veblen is not only hampered but rigidly restrained by the conventional logic which he takes over as matrix within which, by arbitrary dictum, all mathematical work must be carried on. What is merely tool of mathematics becomes thus its incubus. The notions of "class" and "belonging to," he asserts, are "primitive": without them, no logic: without logic, no mathematics. See Veblen and Young, Projective Geometry, I, pp. 1-2.

Finally, if we consider the construction of Huntington, we find great advances in the special region of consistency we are examining, but with many open gaps and unanalyzed problems still remaining. Huntington proposes to establish his postulation by the use of a single class, spheres, and a single relation, inclusion.[43] By the presentation "sphere" he assembles the object-aspect of geometry in one "class," (though why, when dealing with a single class, the terminology of class should be retained at all is not clear): and by the presentation "inclusion," he similarly assembles the relation-aspect of geometry (though, along with it, so much of the operational aspect, that, again, it is not apparent why the term, relation, should be retained).[44] Moreover, should we describe this relation of inclusion, as one of sphere-inclusion, as Sheffer has suggested,[45] we may report Huntington as on the verge of a systematic statement of the objective-relational-operational appearance of geometry in one system;—on the verge, but, unfortunately, that is all. When dealing with congruence, when rotations and translations must be taken into account, these latter are not recognized in the postulation, but,—following the tradition—merely given casual reference as "necessary":[46] and similarly the number-line is introduced in a manner well outside the possibilities of his postulation

[43]A Set of Postulates for Abstract Geometry expressed in terms of the simple relation of inclusion: Math. Ann., vol. 73, pp. 522-559, 1913.

[44]Class and relation are, of course, verbal survivals of the logical frame, out of which Huntington in this paper makes considerable advance, despite his formal insistence that he works wholly within it.

[45]The General Theory of Notational Relativity (privately issued) 1921.

[46]Math. Ann., vol. 73, p. 534.

proper.[47] He attempted to separate postulates of "existence" from other postulates which he calls "general laws," but the attempt merely served to reveal that some of the "general laws" were merely "existence postulates in disguise," as Huntington himself recognizes:[48] and this indicates a flaw in the distinction itself, a flaw that lies in the region of what we have studied under the names M-T and M-O in this essay. Again his characterization of three or four of his definitions as the "most important"[49] has a similar indicative value for a construction, in which all definition is supposed to be formal.

The study of these various aspects of Huntington's postulation will be found very profitable: but it should be carried on, not in terms of a "logical," examination of any particular one of his papers at a particular time and place—not in terms of any meanings taken in "instantaneity"—but, as we have found in other similar investigations, in terms of the durations and transitions of the experimentation and development of the writer from his first attacks to his last.[50] Only thus can the hidden implications and valuations be brought to light. Huntington's first sets of postulates,[51] those for absolute magnitudes, rested basically

---

[47]Idem, p. 535.

[48]Idem, p. 523: p. 524: p. 542.

[49]Idem, p. 524.

[50]The logical tests are dependable only when this underlying survey is firmly made: though they gain an appearance of dependability, where, and insofar as, the basis seems firm. Compare Poincaré's remark about Hilbert cited in the text following Rule I in Chap. III.

[51]American M. S. Trans., vol. 3, 1902. Other papers to which reference will be made appear, Idem, vols. 5 and 6: Annals of Math., vol. 8, 1906: and in Monographs on Topics of Modern Mathematics, J. W. A. Young, editor, 1911.

upon certain "rules of combination."[52] Inspecting these today we can see that they partake of both operational and relational character. He proceeded sometimes with relational, sometimes with operational, formulations: and in one paper, designed for a wider class of readers, he found it desirable to employ two sets of symbols for zero and unity, the one set objective in reference, the other operational. In the latest of these essays, prior to his construction for geometry, that on Fundamental Propositions of Algebra, he made use of two classes of things, two rules of operation, and one kind of relation: but his distinctions between these types do not bear full analysis for consistency. He held that his development for algebra involved no arithmetic whatever, "not even the operation of counting"—thus finding logical solace—but his postulates themselves, on the other hand, he characterized as a "set of laws of operation." The problems involved are the same as those which we have found in the other sets of postulates we have been considering; and his latest set, that for geometry, ranks in effect as a step in advance towards their full recognition and solution.

---

[52]For Huntington's distinction at one stage between "rules of combination" and "dyadic relations," see American M. S. Trans., vol. 5, p. 289.

## XI

## THE DENUMERABILITY OF DECIMALS

We shall proceed next to examine the issues of denumerability and non-denumerability as they appear in the system W of the Word-Cluster II*A. This, however, will require an appraisal of attitudes and proofs used in other types of mathematical construction. As heretofore, I shall avoid all attempt at technical mathematical development, and shall hold myself primarily to the linguistic setting of the problems.

Decimals and all radix fractions and, in general, the transcendental numbers are, since Cantor, regarded as non-denumerable. Many varieties of attitude are, however, found: and the status of the issue is far from being finally settled. For logico-mathematicians the non-denumerability of the radix fractions is an article of faith. Such theorists offer us explicit proofs: but their proofs are dependent upon a highly specialized presentation of their materials: and, beyond that, they involve, always tacitly, and often expressly, the assertion that we, as human beings, are compelled by the nature of our minds to proceed in their prescribed logical forms, and in those forms only. Other mathematicians are most apt to yield a conventional acceptance to the current "proofs," modified, however, by a certain sceptical curiosity. The more an individual mathematician's interest lies in algorithmic development, and the less he seeks formal fixations, the more pronounced his scepticism is apt to be. Surrounding the whole issue lies the historical severance of the three great lines of mathematical development, the urge towards their common organization, and the deficiencies in analysis which have thus far prevented the establishment of a firm and unassailable construction.

After I have discussed the varieties of attitude and judgment which enter into the current presentations of denumerability, I shall proceed to a form of proof that decimals, along with rationals and algebraics, may be so ordered as to be denumerable. It is a proof which I shall assert to be valid within its own construction. The real issue, however, does not lie between this proof on the one side and the Cantorian proofs of non-denumerability on the other: but between the systems of construction in which the proofs arise and in which alone, as proofs, they can claim validity. It is not an issue to be decided in some presumable world of existence and reality, under some presumable standards of eternal truth: but instead one of postulation, special or general, efficient or inefficient.

Attention must first be directed to what, exactly, it is that we propose to prove. The project is confined to the consistent, symbolic development of arithmetic and algebra: to the system W, that is to say, of the II*A.

We are not concerned with any problem of denumerability or of non-denumerability with respect to presentations of Word-Cluster III, "Number." These represent the pre-Cantorian situation and are so shot with vagueness as to be worthless for discussion.

Neither are we concerned with any realisms with

respect to M-T as applied to numbers. In other words we do not allow ourselves to be bound to the presentation "Zahl" of Word-Cluster V. For "Zahl" the question remains open, after our own argument is finished, as to how far, and for what purposes, and under what conditions, it is desirable to interpret decimals, either through "Schnitte" or through "Fundamentalreihen," as components of a continuum of "Zahlen."

We do not limit our discussion to any proposition which contains the formulation "the set of all decimals" in the technical meanings used therein for "set" and "all": since these technical terms have been adopted expressly to recast the decimals of the II*A into a specialized form for special purposes.

We do not propose to argue that a continuum of points in the sense of the system G of the II*B is denumerable. Here we have a linguistic organization, a semantic construction, arising from sources different from those of the II*A, and developed by different techniques.

These other issues which we reject from our present consideration have interest and importance, each in its own place. But it is not by a confusion of many issues and formulations that progress is to be made: rather by analysis and by the segregation of each formulation for specialized examination of its own.

Concerning ourselves solely with the decimal development of the II*A, the proof of denumerability is so direct and simple that for anyone recognizing the semantic nature of mathematical consistency as contrasted with the realisms of conventional language, it hardly needs statement. The difficulty which we must face is not one of proof but of communication: it is the difficulty of breaking down the long-established clottings of conventional meanings of words; the difficulty of expelling these conventional meanings from the interpretation of symbolic mathematical procedure; the difficulty of overcoming their dogmatic discoloration of whatever is said. It is the difficulty of the idioms, the varieties of language, in Poincaré's phrase, which men use, and which they will not learn, and which they will not consent to interpret, one into another.

For the discussion to have significance for mathematics, the following questions must be faced:

Are the decimals of the II*A clearly distinguishable from other renderings for the word "decimal," as established in other word-clusters, that is to say, in other ranges of linguistic implication?

Are they the decimals to which mathematicians should give foremost attention, or do they yield only an incidental or subordinated presentation?

In especial, for the *"foundation"* problems of mathematics, are they the decimals upon which reliance must be placed.

Our answer here is "yes" to the first and third questions; the answer to the second question remaining open to each mathematician, in accordance with his inclinations, aptitudes and field of work: providing, always, however, that his decision is formulated under a postulation which, if realistic, does not descend to the levels of dogmatic realism.

Let us begin by setting before ourselves the question "Are decimals denumerable?": and let us inspect this question, not realistically with respect to ourselves as master-"*minds,*" or with respect to decimal-"*existence*" as actual; but semantically, with respect to what the inquiry contains, with respect to what it is "within language." Before us we have three "words" in a "form of organization," and we have thus four aspects, phases or elements of the linguistic inquiry to examine. We now ask: "Upon which one of these four aspects can the greatest reliance be placed, when we proceed to seek an answer to the query which the full sentence propounds?" I will assert that the most reliable aspect or element is the word "denumerable." This word puts before us the natural numbers in their mathematically dependable separable presentations, in their operational sequence indefinitely or infinitely onward, and in their dependable inductive procedures. Herein it puts before us likewise their dependable procedure in "one-to-one."

By contrast, the word "decimals" is subject to various understandings or interpretations which we cannot assert to be as yet clearly analyzed or classified, the prevalent interpretation of the last generation having been a logistic recasting of its meanings. The word "are" is still more uncertain and various in its readings, the status for it being so bad that hardly any two men today agree exactly as to all the implications and shadings of meaning they are using in their attempts to communicate one with another. For the remaining aspect, the "form of organization," the case is no better; and indeed its varieties of implication are as numerous as those of the word "are" itself. Manifestly there is no sound purpose served in a discussion of the denumerability of decimals which does not seek as great precision for the other aspects of the inquiry as it does for the word "denumerability" itself.

Now, however, if we phrase our proposition as we have at the beginning of this chapter, namely, that "decimals of the system W of the II*A are denumerable," we introduce precision both for the word "decimal" and for the word "are": and in particular we make the word "are" a presentation of and within the symbolic development of consistency in number-theory.

The decimals of the II*A are presentations of Word-Cluster I, "Character"; this word-cluster being taken semantically and without manipulation or degradation by realistic interpretation. They are, further, presentations of Word-Cluster II, "Symbol," this again under semantic postulation, and so that the connectivity W organizes their M-T and M-O aspects fully, with no residue left for manipulation by *"realisms,"* whether those of a *"subjective"* or of an *"objective"* type. They are therefore neither *"relations"* nor *"things"* in arbitrarily imposed renderings of such terms as relation and thing. We have in them the connectivity Dk of "Character" and the connectivity D of "Symbol." We have in them under this construction whatever there is of mathematically consistent meaning in such vague conventional expressions as *"discrete," "separate," "independent," "individual," "identical"* and *"organized in system,"* without any reliance upon the substantiality or consistency of those conventional expressions themselves.

If, side by side with this connectivity W, we inspect the connectivity G of the II*B, and if we bring it to mind in its earliest form of presentation, the Euclidean point, we recall that here also we have "Character" and "Symbol," but that the Dk development in G is not the Dk development in W. Semantically these two can be combined in consistency, the requirement, as we have seen in Chapter IV, and especially in Proposition V, being the abandonment of the realistic finite-infinite common-reference description as it survives in the aspects and presentations M-T.

As between the systems W and G, denumerability "belongs" to the former. It does not in the same sense "belong" to the latter, however well it may be practically used to some extent in connection with it. This is simply a statement of the linguistic and semantic situations which mathematics places before us. Decimals and all radix fractions arise in the system W under its consistent development.

Under semantic organization of the systems W and G, and by practical working determinations as to the distinctions M-T and M-O within them, we are free to combine them in various ways. We may decree for some purposes, if we wish, that *pi* shall have a value to five decimal places. We may, if we wish, set up a number system, using assumed siderial distances, or assumed orbits of electrons, as a guide to fixations. We may also, if we wish, organize radix development and all transcendental numbers to the points of the continuum. All three are practically useful procedures. In the last of these three cases we "take" the radix fractions "as if" non-denumerable. That goes without saying, once the points of the system G have been selected as a guide to the organization. To all this as practical working technique, or as deliberate semantic specification, no objection can be offered, as has repeatedly been said.

However, when we consider the currently offered "proofs" that radix fractions are non-denumerable, we find that underlying them are fixations of M-T, taken, not with recognition of their semantic values, but as realistically basic. Since these proofs run back to Georg Cantor, and are characteristic for all that development of mathematics known as Cantorian, we shall consider them in the main with respect to his treatment.

Cantor's great achievement was, I take it, that he, more than any one else—though he had many fellow-contributors to this end—provided a form of organization and a terminology in which the number-series and the points could be studied in a common system, and that he made the first important special studies in this field. Inspecting his materials under the general form of "*things,*" taken as applicable to his numbers and to his points, to his finites and to his infinites alike, he observed that the infinite of the continuum of points, taken as a "thing" is a very different "thing" from the infinite aggregate of natural numbers. With this, of course we have no quarrel. Express the difference in terms of "Mächtigkeiten," of transfinite cardinals, or of Alephs, and you have two strikingly different situations: that is clear. But it is also as ancient as the Greeks. To establish the two Alephs in a common system, what Cantor had to do was to take the decimals, or any radix fractions, of numerical calculation, and identify them, as an aggregate, with the continuum of points. The fundamental series taken as *"things"* had to reach the points of the continuum, these again taken as "things," and to be not only "dicht," but "insichdicht."

Using, now, our framework of Word-Cluster I, "Character" and Word-Cluster II, "Symbol," and the distinctions of W and G, but embodying the presentations realistically as *"things,"* observe what this requires of us by way of credulity. We must *believe* that in a family of realistically "discrete" numbers there may come into being by some miraculous intervention members that have the characteristics of realistically "continuous" points. This is not merely the equivalent of a "sport" in biology. It is such a sport as if a human being full-brained sprang overnight from a family of Lepidoptera, or as if a sowing of teeth should yield an army of men. To call it a miracle is not to say for a moment that mathematics could not perhaps accomplish it—it is only to warn against credulous belief in what it is perhaps all too convenient for us to believe.

In the course of his long and thorough study of his problem Cantor, on the one hand, gave clarity of meaning to the procedure of denumerability, and extended greatly its ranges into the field of numbers: on the other side, he believed that he could prove that denumerability did not extend to the entire decimal development. His proofs of denumerability for rationals and algebraics[1] are so well known that they need

[1]J. fur Math., vol. 77, p. 258, 1874. Idem, vol. 84, p. 250, 1878.

no description here. It is necessary, however, to show their status as proofs in connection with the wider development. Both of them disregard the order of magnitudes, and secure denumerability by a specialized ordering. Such ordering is a device—we may even say a trick, a clever mathematical trick—which accomplishes well its purpose. It inspects each rational or algebraic number as a separate "thing": then it manipulates these "things" in temporary disregard of their inductive mathematical character. Cantor's inspection of his numbers as such separated "things" was of a practically realistic nature: nevertheless there is nothing in his immediate use of it, that is to say in his immediate proofs of denumerability, which is not legitimate when the inspection of the numbers is that of M-T in semantic construction.

It is easy, however, to convert his inspection, and along with it his mathematical results, into judgments of a realistically rigid type.[2] If one looks upon the separated numbers, each as a sort of "actual existence" of some kind, and if one assumes that he understands such "existence" sufficiently well to be dogmatic about it, he will now proceed to say of the rationals, and of the algebraics in general, that "they," as such existences, "are," existentially denumerable. Into such an assertion there enters, however, much

[2]This passage is not meant to have any bearing on Cantor's own philosophical views, but is simply a comment on differences of attitude as seen from the present point of view. Cantor himself stressed the conceptual attitude towards number, and placed himself sharply in opposition to the linguistic approach of Helmholtz and Kronecker. Such forms of the issue have, however, little remaining importance. For Cantor's views in these respects see Jourdain's remarks in his translation of certain of Cantor's papers under the title, The Theory of Transfinite Numbers, pp. 80-81.

extra-mathematical implication. Mathematically the safe and dependable statement is that these numbers are denumerable when and as ordered for that purpose, but not when taken in their order of magnitudes. In this form of statement one rejects entirely the conventionally existential "are" as not pertinent to mathematical expression, and lets the "are" of each of the two parts of the statement become fully systemic within its direct range of application.

In the same paper in which Cantor published his proof of the denumerability of algebraics in terms of the height or rank of equations, he included other matter which was to become of the highest importance in his further development. He gave a new proof of Liouville's theorem as to non-algebraics: he gave a proof that the Liouville numbers were not denumerable: and he made a generalization of the proposition of non-denumerability.[3] That is to say, instead of leaving the question open as to whether denumerability could be extended onwards, through the discovery of new special devices, into the field of numbers, he proclaimed that there were limitations to its range, and that there existed "numbers" which it could not reach. This was the first of his two proofs of non-denumerability. It was presented in the language of the theory of limits, and was, in effect, that numbers exist which are limiting points that do not belong to the aggregate of dense numbers.

This construction has been of the highest use in mathematics, and will remain so. Nevertheless it has no direct bearing on the question, directly put, as to

[3]J. fur Math., vol. 77, 1874.

whether radix fractions are denumerable or non-denumerable. It furnishes an excellent method to treat them as non-denumerable, but that is all. Its argument may be presented either in the form of a construction of the system G of the II*B, or it may be presented in the specialized language of limits. In the former case, its applicability to decimals rests solely on the identification by explicit convention of transcendental numbers with points of the continuum: an identification which is useful and, legitimate, but wholly of a "practical" nature in the sense that it renounces further analysis, and proceeds under the guidance of immediate needs. In the latter case, the specialized language of limits is one which has permitted great clarification of mathematical work, but which does not proceed definitely into "foundation" constructions, and towards the type of assertion such constructions require.[4]

We shall turn now to Cantor's later proof of the non-denumerability of decimals, that, namely, of the "Diagonalverfahren." We need not take this proof as though it were one which ranked among the most assured of mathematics. As a matter of fact, it is not. While it is widely accepted, it has also often been brought into question. Its ready acceptance depends

[4]In interpretations of the first of these two Cantorian constructions it is common to make use of a distinction between the "ideal" and the "material." This again is a form of language that is rapidly becoming of historical interest only. Thus Huntington says: "If we wish to find an example of a non-denumerably infinite class we must seek it among the classes whose elements are ideal, not material entities." The Continuum, 2d ed., p. 32. Hobson remarks that in fundamental theory a conceptual distinction must be made between rational numbers and the real numbers to which they correspond. The Theory of Functions of a Real Variable, 2d ed., vol. I, p. 30.

upon the inspection of "numbers" as separate "existences" under non-mathematical points of view of the types we have previously discussed. The very fact that it is indirect proof means that it can be regarded as valid only if, and so long as, the underlying analysis through which its materials are presented is held to be complete and safe. We examine it, nevertheless, because it is the only proof for the non-denumerability of radix fractions which builds directly within the constructions of arithmetic and algebra themselves, and the only one, therefore, that concerns the system W of the Word-Cluster II*A, taken in isolation. Cantor himself described it as "a much simpler proof," and as one "independent from considerations of irrational number."[5] We may perhaps infer that for almost twenty years he had felt the need of a more direct establishment of his construction in terms of algebraic symbols, or their direct representatives, alone.

For the general logical status of the Cantorian proofs reference may be made to Hilbert and Ackermann, Grundzüge der theoretischen Logik.[6] Chwistek's attitude upon the logical status of the Alephs, and the attitude of Lukasiewicz with respect to the proofs for the "Diagonalverfahren" are noted in Chapter XIV of the present book. An examination of the text books and special treatises in this field shows that the presentations of the "Diagonalverfahren" run the whole gamut from postulation to dogma; from a loose matter-of-fact acceptance to carefully guarded technical development; and from casual mention to the assertion that this procedure is one of the most powerful techniques the Mengenlehre possesses.[7]

---

[5]Deutsche Math.-Ver., vol. 1, p. 75, 1892.

[6]Especially pp. 104-6.

[7]For careful statements one may consult Hobson, op. cit., vol. I, pp. 81-82, and Huntington, op. cit., p. 33. Other convenient references are Pierpont, The Theory of Functions of Real Variables, vol. II, p. 288: Townsend, Functions of Real Variables, p. 40; and Dienes, The Taylor Series, p. 9. An unusually full discussion is given by Fraenkel,

For more general purposes two recent surveys of the history, background and approaches to the problem may profitably be examined. These are Tobias Dantzig's book, "Number, The Language of Science,"[8] and an essay by Harold T. Davis, "A Survey of the Problem of Mathematical Truth."[9]

Dantzig writes so vividly about the Cantorian Alephs that his report appears almost to be one of direct observation upon unquestioned situations within mathematics. Truly enough he sets forth the various definitions, hypotheses, practical arrangements and subterfuges upon which the constructions rest, but he subordinates them for the purposes of his treatment. Giving these latter their full recognition at every stage in the development, the question at once arise whether this appearance of factuality is not rather an illusion of convention.

Davis, on the contrary, offers his exposition directly in terms of the proofs and their validities, and exhibits a situation of manifestly greater intricacy and uncertainty. Both writers, however, are unfortunately compelled to depend throughout upon linguistic tools of the weakest order, such as "inherent faculties of the mind," "intuition," "concept sui generis," "intuition of time," "reality" and "truth": and in both of them description and critical examination are alike hampered thereby.

To secure his proof of decimal non-denumerability under the "Diagonalverfahren," Cantor sets his ma-

---

Einleitung in die Mengenlehre, pp. 43-50. Fraenkel regards the "Diagonalverfahren" as a fundamental form of proof, needed for a wide range of investigations, (an "überaus weittragende Satz"), which students should thoroughly master and comprehend in all its reaches. His explanation is readable and convincing, so long as one passes cursorily over such words and phrases as "entspricht," "darstellbar," "lauter Ziffern," "nicht die geringste Differenz," and "dass man die Ziffer 0 dabei ausschliesst oder wenigstens ihre nicht allzu weitgehende Rechte zuerkennt." One must also be prepared to ask no questions as to how decimal expressions, for themselves, are either "finite" or "infinite," and what such finiteness or infinity has to do with other mathematical uses of the terms. The difficulty with Fraenkel's development from the present point of view is that it lacks analysis of the linguistic structure in which it is presented.

[8]See especially his Chapter XI with respect to the issues of denumerability. Dantzig does not present the Cantorian diagonal procedure, but merely refers to it as a satisfactory "proof," p. 220.

[9]This essay forms the introduction to Charlotte Lowe Bryan's translation of Helmholtz' essay, Counting and Measuring. See especially pp. xiv-xix.

terials, namely, the decimal table or any table of radix fractions, before us in a form in which each number is a "thing" by itself. In his proofs of the denumerability of algebraics in general and of rationals in particular, he had also used this presentation as "thing." A great difference will, however, appear. In the denumerability proofs, his number "things" are of a type fully acceptable to the semantic development of M-T. In the non-denumerability proofs they are not. In the former case it was clear he was dealing with particular transcriptions; a circumstance evident enough from the fact that for rationals two different proofs were secured, each in its own transcription. In the latter case, that of non-denumerability, a particular form of transcription is used combined with a particular method of evaluating its symbols. His argument we may take as "logically" valid within that particular form and evaluation. For it to attain universal mathematical validity, however, it is necessary to identify this form with decimal "existence" itself. We are in effect required to acknowledge this particular form as the one, definite, "existential" form in which the decimals *must* be taken for purposes of inquiry. This form is as follows:

$$\begin{array}{l} p_{11}, p_{12}, p_{13}, \ldots\ldots\ldots \\ p_{21}, p_{22}, p_{23}, \ldots\ldots\ldots \\ p_{31}, p_{32}, p_{33}, \ldots\ldots\ldots \\ \ldots\ldots\ldots\ldots\ldots\ldots \\ \ldots\ldots\ldots\ldots\ldots\ldots \end{array}$$

the p's being the digits 0,1,2.....9, and with the proviso that each decimal is uniquely represented.

The introduction of such a proviso as this should alone be sufficient evidence that the construction in view, however interesting and useful it may prove, has no right to prominence within the *"foundations"* of mathematics. Indeed a firm grasp of the sources and ramifications of the proviso would at once do away with all need for the elaborated discussions of this chapter. The citations from Klein introduced in connection with the remarks upon the significance of the "exception" in mathematics towards the close of Chap. VIII, make this situation clear, however smoothly Klein passes over the chasm which, for the practical purposes of his immediate development, is not of dominant importance. Other pertinent remarks of Klein are those (op. cit. 1, p. 36) in which he sets forth historically that it was from the observation ("Betrachtung") of the decimals themselves, after their system of notation had been introduced, that the idea of the irrational number arose; and that thus it was in a sense the procedures of calculation themselves and their marked utility that dictated the use of the new concepts.

It is evident that the figures of any one decimal series are denumerable: that is, that any line read to the right is denumerable. It is evident also that the set of the figures of the first, second or nth element of all decimals is denumerable: that is, that any column read downwards is denumerable. The non-denumerability occurs in the Cantorian demonstration by the heaping of these two denumerabilities of figures upon each other. It is the "Mächtigkeit" which, in the presentation above, can be *"located"* in the lower right hand corner of the table.

When a logico-mathematician proclaims the argument from his sanctified logical throne to the unsophisticated world below, it runs somewhat as follows:

"If my opponent asserts that the set of decimals is denumerable, then let him make me a table like the one above which he says 'contains' or 'enables me to enumerate' all of them: whereupon I will show him a decimal he has not provided for. It is very easy for me. All I have to do is to offer him that decimal series which I will proceed to construct by rejecting each of the figures which lies in a diagonal drawn from the upper left hand corner downwards, and substituting for each so rejected figure some other. In my new decimal I offer him a first figure which is not $p_{11}$, a second which is not $p_{22}$, a third which is not $p_{33}$, and so on. If he then believes that by adding my offering to his collection he will overwhelm me, I will let him add it; and at once by the same procedure I used before I will construct still another decimal which he does not have: and so on ad inf. He is beaten: he cannot catch up with me: he cannot denumerate the decimals."

This manner of argument, though omitting, as here given, certain technical provisos that are necessary for its complete statement, brings out plainly those characteristics to which our attention must be directed. While an easy victory is secured for the disputant, it is the kind of victory that is gained by first hypnotizing the victim and then operating upon him.

The Cantorian of course wins if you let him arrange the decimals in the kind of a table he chooses, and if you let him juggle back and forth between the operative and the fixed realistic meanings of his figures. But no one, for that matter, could prove the rationals denumerable, if he were forced to deal with them in some arbitrary form offered him: nor could the algebraics be proved denumerable on that basis. In both those cases the denumerability is established by careful choice of a rule of arrangement or procedure. That same privilege may not be denied the man who argues for the denumerability of the decimals, save by wholly illicit realistic fiat. All that is necessary, then, for us to do in order to prove the denumerability of the decimals is to set up such a rule.

For the purpose of the inquiry as to whether decimals are or are not denumerable in their own free development in arithmetic and algebra, we shall assume liberty of choice in ordering them, exactly as Cantor assumed it for the ordering of algebraics and rationals. We shall insist upon this as a right, and we shall assert that this right carries with it the further rights which we specifically assert: (1) to inspect the decimals directly as they arise in the system W of the II*A: (2) to observe them throughout in the full symbolic development in which they proceed: (3) to reject the arbitrary requirement that they be taken as uniquely represented: (4) to reject any dictum which begs the question by identifying them in advance with the points of the continuum of the system G of the II*B: (5) to refuse any and every demand that we fixate them in any specialized logical language.[10]

The ordering to be adopted in place of that imposed by the "Diagonalverfahren" is one which will at once be recognized as of frequent use in the more recent literature of the "Mengenlehre." Its procedures have been elaborately developed. What concerns us here is the basic reading of its symbols, and their valuation in the system to which they belong.

Since what is true for decimals is true, in the issues before us, for any radix fractions, we may simplify our account by illustrating the proposed manner of ordering for the special case of binaries: and thereafter we make use of the more familiar manner of expression in terms of decimals.

---

[10]For the difficulties that logic is now facing, as it is forced to more careful analysis of its own procedures, see Chap. XIV.

The manner of ordering which we choose to employ is as follows:

| 1 | 2 | 3 ............ k .................. |
|---|---|---|
| | | 0 ⋰⋱ |
| | 0 | |
| | | 1 ⋰⋱ |
| 0 | | |
| | | 0 ⋰⋱ |
| | 1 | |
| | | 1 ⋰⋱ |
| | | 0 ⋰⋱ |
| | 0 | |
| | | 1 ⋰⋱ |
| 1 | | |
| | | 0 ⋰⋱ |
| | 1 | |
| | | 1 ⋰⋱ |

In this ordering "all" binary expressions from $.\dot{0}$ to $.\dot{1}$ have place. I put the word "all" in quotation marks merely to preclude logical renderings of that word which are specially designed to color the symbolic development and to decide the issue for us implicitly in advance. The "all" which we have before us is whatever "all" may be developed in the system W of the II*A, and the caution as to its use is to be understood only with respect to the issues of generalized consistency. For our preliminary inspection and organization, we have "all" of these expressions before us in the same sense that we have "all" the natural numbers before us when we write 1, 2, 3, 4, 5, 6, 7, .......... (leaving any possible differentiation of "alls" free to develop itself within the symbolic system itself): and we have "each" of them before us in the same sense, whatever that is, in which we have *pi* before us when we write 3.14159........ in decimal development.

We may inspect an expression of the form:

$$n_1\, n_2 \ldots\ldots\ldots\ldots n_k,$$

k being any integer, and the n's having the range indicated by the radix chosen, let us say that of decimals: and we may call this expression a "segment to k."

Using this "segment to k" we may now enumerate decimal expressions of the three following forms:

$$(1) \quad 0.n_1\, n_2 \ldots\ldots n_k\dot{0}$$

$$(2) \quad 0.n_1\, n_2 \ldots\ldots n_k\dot{1}$$

$$(3) \quad 0.\overline{n_1\, n_2 \ldots\ldots n_k} \;:$$

namely all those in which a "segment to k" is followed by a periodic 0, all those in which it is followed by a periodic 1, and all those in which it is itself periodic.

Along with these we may enumerate likewise all expressions in which a "segment to k" is followed by a periodic portion which itself has the form of such a segment, thus:

$$(4) \quad 0.n_1\, n_2 \ldots\ldots n_k\, \overline{n_{11}\, n_{21} \ldots\ldots n_{k1}}.$$

More generally, for an arbitrary k, the numbers represented by the expressions:

(5) $0.n_1\, n_2 \ldots\ldots n_k\, \overline{m_1\, m_2 \ldots\ldots m_\kappa}$ , $\kappa = 1, 2, \ldots\ldots k$

(6) $0.n_1\, n_2 \ldots\ldots n_\lambda\, \overline{m_1\, m_2 \ldots\ldots m_k}$ , $\lambda = 0, 1, \ldots\ldots k-1$

form a finite group. Letting k = 1, 2, 3,......, we have a method of enumeration in which any specified repeating decimal has its place. We thus have a method of enumeration of the rationals which is different from the conventional one. Instead of enumerating rationals in the form of number-pairs, or by the device of algebraic rank—in other words, in forms of transcription differing from that of the radix transcription— we have their enumeration directly in their radix form itself. Instead of being compelled to set up equivalences between the rationals and repeating decimals, and to qualify the decimal development by a special proviso, we are able to permit the full decimal development to proceed unhampered by any special rule or requirement.

We have, however, in this ordering much more than a mere enumeration of repeating decimals, even though it is these and these only that we pick up and set to one side, as already enumerated, at each stage of our procedure. We do not pick up the algebraics under a special, decimally irrelevant, device as in the Cantorian procedure, but we let them proceed along with transcendentals. It is the requisite ordering itself, one must remember, and nothing else, that is necessary and sufficient to secure denumerability. We have directly before us, present within our mathematical grasp, and in process of enumeration, at any k, the full transcendental decimal development up to that k. We have this structure up to any k, and—if the tautology may be permitted as a manner of emphasis in this informal discourse—we have it up to any k whatsoever lying beyond, and no matter how far beyond, the k we have already attained or inspect as attainable.

We have now freed ourselves from the confused implications of the older distinction between denumerable and non-denumerable: or, perhaps more cautiously, we should say that we have freed ourselves from some of its evident confusions: since, in this field of analysis, it will be a rash man indeed (the logician alone excepted) who will venture to feel confident that he is clear of all confusion whatsoever, until he has some generations of settled practice to look back upon for support.

We may generalize the expression "segment to k" which we have used in specific instances in the symbolic formulations above, and we may say that for all decimals, transcendental or other, we now have them before us in their development as "segments to k."

It is true there are always the possibilities beyond k. Beyond k is a region we never reach. But the same is true of Cantorian denumerability. Using the series of natural numbers as itself denumerable—or, if one prefers, as itself denumerability—there are always natural numbers beyond k for which we have the rule of denumerability, but not the finished act of enumeration. The same is true, and in the same sense, for binaries, for decimals and for all radix fractions. The rule is established for their enumeration as fast as they are reached. We do not, it is true, have what in an analogy we regard as a "straight" line of numbers running, so to speak, towards infinity: we have instead, under such a rather childishly pictorial aid to understanding, something we would call an infinitely branching line: but a similar condition exists for rationals. There is a distinction here, one of many we may make, but it is no radical distinction: it is no "*foundation*" for anything whatever.

We are in a position, then, to say that we have the decimals before us as denumerably dense, and as free from that special coloration which made them appear as "dense-in-themselves."

We may, if we wish, at any stage truncate the entire decimal development, and bring it into correspondence with rationals: or, by contrast, we may, if we wish, assume its extension beyond "any k," and give such an assumed extension an assumed or "practical" meaning in organization with points of the continuum. What we are not justified in saying, however, is that in this latter "practical" procedure we have at length achieved a basic and fundamental presentation of mathematical reality. We are not permitted to say that rationals and some other numbers *are* "existentially" denumerable, while decimals in their full development *are* "existentially" not so denumerable. Indeed, such an "assumed extension" is not really a procedure of a type different from that of the "truncating" mentioned above: rather is it itself just another form of truncating. If one will consider the dicta that are necessary to bring radix fractions and points into correspondence (omitting the difficulties of the "Auswahl," and observing only the direct provisos) in the light of such discussions as that by

Klein previously referred to, he will reach the really shocking conclusion that the decimals, if let alone, will run "beyond" the points of the continuum, whatever that may mean, and that it takes arbitrary intervention to stop them there. The "beyond" of course means nothing, since the distinctions here are those which in popular expression would be called "qualitative" rather than "quantitative": they are distinctions which, for their analysis, require semantic investigation running far deeper than the linguistic level of such terms as "quality" and "quantity."

There is, it is true, another aspect of this question upon which we have not herein touched. It is before us as a "feeling" or "sensing" that whenever we attain to a natural or a rational, we secure it "instantaneously," complete and whole in its "existence," whereas we never attain to transcendentals in that way. The algebraics in general, however, are not "attained" in this sense, yet they are admittedly denumerable: and certainly anybody with a set before him consisting of *pi* and *e*, and of them only, would regard it as denumerable. This manner of "sensing" or "feeling," therefore, does not consistently hold. It has roots in the confusion of "transcription" with "fact," in the acceptance of certain transcriptions and the rejection or subordination of others, without adequate analysis of what it is that is being done. The issue involved may be labelled that of the "instantaneity of mathematical existence": but whoever seeks to establish himself expressly upon a definite position in the region of this issue will have a heavy task of clarification awaiting him. It is unnecessary to elaborate upon it here, since the whole development of this book has been concerned with it: not, indeed, as an attempt to secure formal logical distinctions with respect to it, but rather in the hope of extending analysis in the wide field of evolutional linguistic, semantic and scientific procedures within which such distinctions arise.

The logico-mathematician, we may feel assured, will not accept this presentation as valid. The primary reason that he will not accept it is that it is not what he wants. He starts with a realistic fixation for natural numbers on the one side, and with a realistic fixation for the continuum on the other. However much he may deny the "realism" of his fixations—and the word "realism" is a mere detail in the matter—the fixations are what he most assuredly exhibits. He knows that for practical working purposes the two fixations can readily be brought together. But this does not satisfy him: he seeks "foundations": and his foundations *must* be such that the fixations are rigidly maintained. To accomplish this he recasts his symbolic materials in logical form. The construction offered above, which is a development of the symbols without such logical recasting, evidently does not yield what he requires. Therefore he will reject it.

His position is substantially as follows—indeed I have had it advanced to me in just this form: "Your construction does not *mean* anything. *Meanings* must be supplied for the symbols of mathematics: and these meanings *must* accord with what every intelligent person means. You do not use such meanings. If you will not let me apply such meanings to your construction, then that construction is meaningless. If you will let me supply such meanings to it, then your construction is absurd."

There is, of course, no answer. What the realist offers is not an argument, but a retort. There is no use retorting to a retort. The assumption he employs is that often referred to as "the permanent mental nature of man." He will no doubt acknowledge an evolutionary process of the past in which mind and meanings and language have reached the status they hold today. But he recognizes nothing like it for the future. He rests in what he regards as a secure and indubitable status for his mind and its meanings. And if he insists on resting, we must let him rest.

Suppose now by way of experiment we take the form of arrangement for binaries given above, and let it proceed in both directions from the decimal point, not only towards the infinite series, but in the other direction as well, towards the infinite extension of the natural sequence. We secure the following exhibit of the binary number sequence:

$$\left.\begin{array}{r}\left.\begin{array}{r}\therefore 0\\ \therefore 1\end{array}\right\}0\\ \left.\begin{array}{r}\therefore 0\\ \therefore 1\end{array}\right\}1\end{array}\right\}\cdot\left\{\begin{array}{l}0\left\{\begin{array}{l}0\therefore\\ 1\therefore\end{array}\right.\\ 1\left\{\begin{array}{l}0\therefore\\ 1\therefore\end{array}\right.\end{array}\right.$$

If we are told that the full procedure to the right is non-denumerable, how can we in the same breath be told that the full procedure to the left is denumerable? One has merely to ask the question: the answer comes by itself. If the procedures to the right are not only dense but also dense-in-themselves, so also those to the left.[11]

I suggest this mainly to call attention to the importance of holding firmly to whatever linguistic-mathematical tools one uses, and to the danger of interpreting one part of a mathematical transcription in one way, and another part in another way, as may

[11]See Chap. VIII.

be convenient, under the realistic assumption of some external mathematical *"thing"* that binds the two together in the particular way one happens to want them to be bound for his immediate particular purposes. It is a striking illustration of the need of thorough and consistent analysis as between word-clusters I, "Character" and II, "Symbol."

This illustration is not to be thought of as a possible useful addition to mathematical knowledge. Rather it is to be regarded as of the nature of a trick problem in a text-book. If the reader can put intelligent meaning into the statements just made, then he may feel assured that the preceding line of argument has reached him. If he cannot put intelligent meaning into these statements, he may find it desirable—if he has sufficient interest in the subject—to refresh his memory as to the general characteristics of the construction used.

He should give special attention to the assertion, in the early pages of this chapter, that if we inspect semantically the sentence "Are decimals denumerable?" we shall find that the word "denumerable" conveys safely dependable meaning: while, in contrast, the words "decimals" and "are" do not convey such dependable meaning, and will not convey it without much carefully guarded analysis.

Now if the reader insists that natural numbers "exist," and that "denumerability" is derived or secured from them by right of their "naturalness," then of course he will regard it as an absurdity to argue that the positive integers can be ordered in any other than their denumerable form.

But he may proceed otherwise. He may shake himself loose from his existential assertions, and consider denumeration simply and freely as mathematical procedure. He will then be able to inspect various mathematical transcriptions in their standing as "Characters," and various developments of mathematical characters as semantic systems.

His next step will be to take the characters and system, or systems, of the illustration, just as they are before him, and to deal with them selectively. To these he applies the procedures of enumeration, and he will be enabled to apply them fairly and freely, without arbitrary restrictions from any source; and, above all, without performing unconscious legerdemain with his materials. If he establishes a structure of logical fixations to secure non-denumerability to the right, he will do it likewise to the left, where also he will get non-denumerabilty. If instead of a structure of logical fixations, he employs semantic development, and if he gets denumerability to the left, he will get it also to the right. One may fold the page containing the illustration perpendicularly through its central decimal point. Character for character, the left side will match the right. System for system, the development to the right will match that to the left.

Evident, indeed, is it that we are here taking very great liberties with conventionally popular mathematical ideas. The point is that we not only do it, but we know that we do it. The ordinary conventional realism takes its liberties, as it wishes, and prescribes that nothing more may be said about it. But we have no authority as yet in the world for assuming that the liberties taken by convention are of higher standing, by divine right, or by right of nature, than the liberties taken by postulation. Everything in modern science goes to show the opposite; namely, that the procedures of postulation have firmer footing and more assured values than those of dogma.

Further light may be thrown on the general situation in which the distinctions of denumerability and non-denumerability arise by an inspection of that very interesting problem known in the abstract "Mengenlehre" as "das Kontinuumproblem," the problem, namely, as to whether an Aleph "exists" intermediate between Aleph-Null of the denumerables and Aleph-One of the continuum: or, in other words, whether Aleph-One is properly to be called by that name or instead should have some other serial number, such as perhaps 4, or 11, or 44. The specialists in this field recognize this as a very important problem in their discipline, and have spent much pains and labor upon it, thus far wholly without result: but I doubt whether I have ever remarked any one of them who has brought out its full significance to *"foundation"* studies.

To characterize this problem we start with the two types of situations that exist in mathematics, those of "*discrete*" number and those of "*continuous*" points. We may call these two types of situations "a" and "c," using designations often given the transfinite cardinals which represent them. These names are, so to speak, "*qualitative*": and in advancing to a presumable "*quantitative*" treatment the names Aleph-Null and Aleph-One are substituted. Now the special framework of construction used in this development is "logical," whether logically "relational" or logically "objective": and the minute this framework is applied, indications appear of a further situation to be called "f": but if one has "f," then one has also a further situation, perhaps to be called "ff," and others beyond that until the grand situation, "aAa," aggregate of all aggregates, is reached. Most specialists in the "Mengenlehre" accept "f," but, as is well known, welcome any subterfuge which will enable them to avoid going beyond "f," while others discard "f" and confine themselves to "a" and "c." We have therefore a framework in use which indicates an infinite denumerable sequence of Alephs, running at its extreme to exactly the same paradox of thing and operation, only more magnificently phrased, that exists with respect to the realistically taken infinite of the natural numbers: but which, nevertheless, includes only two welcome members, namely Aleph-Null and Aleph-One, and which includes these, so that it is wholly uncertain whether the "Null" and the "One" are appropriately applied as subscripts. It is as if the natural number sequence were confined to one dependable number and one other number; the latter not yet definitely organized with respect to the first; and beyond that nothing but horrendous spooks.

One can hardly help remarking, no matter from what point of approach, that, however interesting and valuable the special developments concerning "a" and "c" may be, the framework of their presentation leaves much to be desired. Under semantic postulation we remark simply that Cantor had two situations before him, and that he made a neat combination of them under realistic readings of their components. If he had had still other situations before him, as, for example, one lying "*between*" "a" and "c," he would have introduced it at the start. If such an intermediate situation can be found, it can at any time be fitted in. But not until it is "found" will it be "proved" to exist: and the "finding" is beyond the range of the logical "proving" entirely.

We may leave the discussion here. Denumerability and non-denumerability are well-known mathematical situations, themselves variants in naming, that is all. Building them, as factual infinites, into a sequence of infinites, merely results in paralleling the sequence of natural numbers, and duplicating its realistic paradoxes on a grander scale. Taking the decimal series as organized to points in the continuum is a useful practical mathematical device. But dogmatically asserting that "the decimals are non-denumerable" is something very different indeed. And to make such an assertion without analyzing the variant meanings for "decimal" and for "are," and especially to make it as a "*fundamental*" assertion of mathematics, only serves to put one in a position in which the extent of his ultimate recantation will have as its measure the extent of his initial dogmatic assurance.

I take advantage of the opportunity to insert here a reference to a useful series of essays which comes to hand while the text is in type. It appears in Blätter für Deutsche Philosophie, Vol. IV, 1930/1931, under the collective heading, "Philosophische Grundlegung der Mathematik." These essays cover, from several different points of view, the immediate matter of our examination: and, beyond that, contain discussion which might repeatedly have been cited in Chapters IV and V, had it been available. For our present problem the paper by Karl Menger, "Der Intuitionismus" is of the most importance. It discusses more systematically than his earlier papers heretofore cited, the development of the "analytische Menge" and its relations to denumerability: following the line of progress from Borel, Lebesgue and Baire through Suslin, Sierpinski and Lusin, and giving indications of his own studies towards securing a systematic meaning for "Konstruktivität" in mathematics. With respect to Brouwer, Menger marks the lack of analyzed meaning for his typical phrase "begrifflich fertig definiert" to which much attention has been given in Chap. IX. Other essays of significance included in this series are Fraenkel's on the infinite in recent mathematics, Bernays' on the Hilbertian theory of proof, and Carnap's on mathematics as a branch of logic. An earlier section of the volume contains a series of essays on language and meaning which touch many of the recent scientific issues.

# XII

## NULL AS A "ZAHL"

The status of "zero" as a "number" has been described in Chapter V, Paragraph 13, and discussed, with reference to the issue of mathematical "exceptions," in Chapter VIII. I wish now to show what happens when "proof" is offered that zero is a number, and for illustration I shall take Caratheodory's group of sentences in which he aims to show that "Null" is a "Zahl."[1]

First, however, I will repeat the same set of remarks it has been desirable to make in previous analyses of similar type. If one says "Zero is a number," one should have precision for all the materials of statement, namely "zero," "is" and "number." Such precision has never been obtained in Word-Cluster III, "Number," for any one of these materials—witness the "exception" in the case of division by zero. It is, as we have shown, attainable in Word-Cluster II, under the procedures of Propositions I, V, and VIII. For the procedures under realistic postulation in the family of connectivities we have called B, the materials are taken, in the general case, as "zero," "is a," and "number"; and the "proof" always fails. In the case we shall examine, "zero" is taken under purported

[1]Vorlesungen über reelle Funktionen, 2d. ed., 1927. The citations are all from Caratheodory's "Einleitung," paragraphs 1-5, pp. 1-3.

precision as "Null"; and "number" similarly as "Zahl."

It is to be understood that no objection is entered to the statement that zero is a number for the pedagogical purposes of arithmetic, nor for any of the specialized purposes of algebra: nor is any objection made to the practical use of null as a "Zahl" in real analysis for any of the purposes which Caratheodory has in mind. Objection is made to Caratheodory's form of proof, both because of its failure as proof, and because of its needlessness in his work: and the discussion is included here, because it concerns the linguistic bed in which mathematical symbolization rests, which reaches back into the region of the *"foundation"* problems. When one proposes to argue beyond the range of certain limited purposes of practical development, then nothing short of full consistency with respect to the word "is," as well as with respect to the other terms used, will justify him. The word "is" itself becomes precise only when its range is limited within a field of fully consistent postulation.

In elementary arithmetic it is the prevailing custom to treat zero as a number, though of course always on the basis of guesswork as to what the word number means.[2] Practically the treatment is valuable. In Analysis zero, or null, becomes a real number, and is given axiom or proof to establish it, though here still the term "real number" in any implication it carries beyond that of classification with respect to complex numbers, awaits further clarification. In the *"foundation"* structures built in the regions in which real analysis is developed, Null is dogmatically a number if anything whatever is a number. However, even in elementary arithmetic, so long as an exception to the rules of division remains in the case of zero, the common statement is manifestly no more than a makeshift; while in the axiomization of real analysis the failure of consistency is more glaring still, as we shall proceed to show.

To avoid all possible misunderstanding let us distinguish the four following situations:

1. "Zero is a number": i. e., it can be advantageously so treated in arithmetic.

[2]The historic struggle over zero, like that over minus and over imaginaries, is merely before us as an illustration of changing conventions of language and *"belief"*: the detail's of the arguments in which these struggles have been couched are of no direct significance.

2. "Null is a Menge": i. e., the abstract "Mengenlehre" developes it in this form.

3. "Null is a Zahl": i. e., for practical convenience in real analysis a construction of Null as a "Zahl" may be successfully used.

4. "Null is a 'Zahl' in full consistency for all mathematical purposes": i. e., we have in its presentation in this way a mathematical *"foundation"* stone.

With the first three situations we are not concerned. We are concerned, however, with finding out whether the limited consistency secured for the third case, is capable of generalization for the purposes of the fourth, or whether defects in its presentation, indifferent for the purposes of the third case, become vital and destructive in the fourth case. I shall first present Caratheodory's "proof" that Null is a "Zahl"; second show its inconsistency; and third exhibit the background of confusion within which he is able to evade recognition of his own inconsistency of statement in its application to constructions wider than the one he is himself erecting.

Caratheodory's German text is cited directly and without attempt at translation because we are concerned with the particular words and phrases he uses in their particular linguistic setting: moreover, the German sentences will be as readily readable as any English transcription to all persons familiar with the issues involved or deeply interested in them. It will be observed that Caratheodory uses the two terms "Zeichen" and "Zahl," and that the former indicates the linguistic presentation without any effort at analysis as between "Character" and "Symbol": (for which he might have used "Ziffer" and "Zeichen"): while the latter indicates a presumable realistic reference for Zeichen: the whole procedure being under a more or less explicit understanding, without explicit postulation, of the type x-to-X, the "x" for Zeichen," and the "X" for "Zahl."

The "proof" rests on the Axiom of Subtraction (III) which reads: "Sind $a$ und $b$ irgend welche Zahlen, so gibt es stets mindestens eine Zahl $c$, so dass $a = b + c$ ist." The text of the proof itself, then, runs as follows:

"Wir führen jetzt die Null ein: es gibt nach III eine Zahl $\zeta$, so dass für ein gegebenes $a$ die Gleichung $a = \zeta + a$ besteht. Diese Zahl $\zeta$ ist von $a$ *unabhängig*. Denn aus $b = \zeta' + b$ folgt zunächst

$$b + a = (\zeta' + b) + a$$

und hieraus nach den Axiomen der Addition

$$a + b = (\zeta' + a) + b.$$

Es ist daher $a = \zeta' + a$ und somit wegen der Eindeutigkeit der Subtraktion $\zeta = \zeta'$. Die so definierte Zahl nennen wir Null und schreiben $\zeta = 0$."

This is a "proof" in the sense that it exhibits us a special case of $\zeta$'s in equation with "Zahlen" in which $\zeta = \zeta' = \zeta''\ldots$, and in which the $\zeta$'s are "unabhängig" from the $a$'s, $b$'s and $c$'s. This "unabhängig" being established, the special case is named Null. Evidently "unabhängig" is a word which requires much consideration: but we will pass that, since we know what Caratheodory has in mind, and we know that he is depending on our knowledge that he knows. That which both he and his readers have in mind is a "practical" situation in their work, and the "unabhängig" simply indicates this situation as it stands —a "something or other" of inquiry, no more and no less. The proof is plausible when read as a manner of talking about this situation: but we have next to see what it amounts to under careful analysis with respect to general mathematical uses.

Such an analysis centers around the terms "Zeichen" and "Zahl." Following our established method of procedure we shall examine these terms, not under any external theoretical or philosophical control, but solely for the consistency of their usage by Caratheodory himself within his own development. In the language of the proof the *a*'s and *b*'s are presented as, and are themselves in some sense, "Zahlen." However in his preceding "Axiome der Anordnung" (cited in full later in this Chapter), in which *a*'s and *b*'s are first introduced to us, they enter not as "Zahlen" but as "Zeichen" which represent (darstellen or bedeuten) Zahlen. Furthermore the symbol = (gleich) is introduced as holding between "Zeichen," under the definition shortly hereafter to be cited. We have therefore two cases to inspect, one in which the *a*'s and *b*'s are to be taken as "Zahlen" and one in which they are to be taken as "Zeichen."

Taking the first case, that in which the *a*'s and *b*'s are before us as "Zahlen," (and disregarding all difficulties about equation between "Zahlen" direct without the aid of "Zeichen"), an argument can be constructed only on the basis of a strict postulation of x-to-X[3] between linguistic component (let us say Character) and Zahl. That is to say, we have *a*'s and *b*'s before us in one sense of "are" as "Characters" while in another sense of "are" they are before us as "Zahlen": if we are to have any coherence, then, the x-to-X binding them together must be rigid. In this case, however, if *a* is a Zahl, and *b* is a Zahl, then also

[3]See Chap. II.

$\zeta$ enters as a Zahl, and if $\zeta$, then $\zeta'$. Under a rigid x-to-X, which means merely under genuine desire for consistency in an x-to-X postulation, the different $\zeta$'s cannot be got rid of: they cannot be reduced to one. (It is true, of course, that some possible principle might be introduced by which some a's, b's etc. in equation were determined to be Zahlen, and others, say the $\zeta$'s, were not—if there were any consistency to be attained thereby—but nothing is done of this nature). Caratheodory's procedure, viewed as carried on, then, in this first case, is wholly arbitrary, and his reasoning is specious: it is evident that he is not confining himself to "Zahlen," and to "Characters" in x-to-X with "Zahlen," but that he is using his "Zeichen" as tools for his presentation in some specialized sense which requires further investigation.

A caution is necessary against reading Caratheodory's term "Zeichen" with any of the specific meaning of "Symbol" as used for Word-Cluster II*B in the development of this book. Nor may it be read in the sense of Hilbert's term "Zeichen," as that term is described in Chapter V, Paragraph 25. It must be taken solely with such meaning or meanings as it presents in Caratheodory's own text, as determinable, so far as that is practicable, through the analysis of the text itself, and not otherwise.

How is it now with respect to the second case, that in which the $a$'s and $b$'s of the "proof," though called "Zahlen," enter consistently as "Zeichen." Here no x-to-X is required between each "Character" and its particular "Zahl," but consistency lies with the system of equation of "Zeichen" themselves. In Caratheodory's language, "Die Gleichung $a = b$ soll dabei bedeuten, dass die beiden Zeichen $a$ und $b$

*dieselbe* Zahl darstellen." In this case, if the reading of Zeichen for the $a$'s and $b$'s and for the definition of Gleichung is used in the conclusion $\zeta = \zeta'$, it most certainly must also be used in the premises starting with $a = \zeta + a$. Putting this application into Caratheodory's own form of phrasing we should get from him by substitution into the just quoted definition, something as follows: "Die Gleichung $a = \zeta + a$ soll bedeuten, dass die beiden Zeichen $a$ und $\zeta + a$ dieselbe Zahl darstellen."[4] Here, it is true, if the symbol $+$ always consistently held "Zahlen" apart, there would be help, but no such principle is introduced. Not only $a$ and $\zeta + a$, but also $\zeta' + a$, should represent (darstellen) the same "Zahl." In other words, in this second possible reading of Caratheodory's proof, namely that of "Zeichen," we have no "Zahl" $\zeta$ whatever before us, but instead a variation in "Zeichen." What his "proof" therefore gives us is the information that the $\zeta$'s are "Zeichen," not that they are "Zahlen," and his concluding sentence should therefore read: "Das so definierte *Zeichen* nennen wir Null und schreiben $\zeta = 0$."

Thus our outcome is that Caratheodory's "proof"

---

[4]There is no external standard of control to determine whether single "Characters" or "Character-complexes" form "one" "Symbol": nor, indeed, to determine what is a "single Character" or a "Character-complex." This is a problem for each system of Symbols to decide for itself. See Chap. IV, Pars. 1 and 2: and Chap. V, Par. 21. There are, of course, several different situations in mathematics for which Caratheodory, as his development proceeds, uses the same Character, 0. With respect to the symbol for gleich, $=$, Caratheodory uses it in his first fifty pages to cover some nine distinct situations. For this again, there is no objection whatever for the practical purposes of real analysis. There is, however, the greatest objection to permitting real analysis to present itself dogmatically in wider interpretations without the full clarification of this, and of many analogous situations within it.

can neither be read consistently in terms of "Zahlen," nor consistently in terms of "Zeichen." He has arranged his materials to suit his purposes, but so far as generalization can be made with regard to Null as a "Zahl," it is merely to the effect that one is free to take Null as a Zahl for certain special developments, if he finds it useful to do it.

We may present this analysis in a different form as follows:

Let us consider on the one side "Zahlen," and on the other side "Zeichen which represent Zahlen."

(1) Using Zeichen we write "greater than," "less than" and "equals."

(2) We assert that where each Zeichen represents a separate Zahl, we have, by the aid of (1), an ordering of Zahlen before us.

(3) We assert that in equation, where two different Zeichen appear on different sides of the sign of equation, they represent *"the same* Zahl."

(4) We assert addition as uniquely determined for Zahlen.

(5) We assert subtraction, likewise for Zahlen, but only so that "at least one" Zahl will result: then by application of (4) we "prove" that such a resulting Zahl is uniquely determined.

(6) We now inspect a case of common procedure in which we equate a Zeichen with "the same Zeichen plus a special Zeichen, Null."

(7) If we hold to (3), both sides of the Zeichen will represent the same Zahl, and that will be all there is to it.

(8) If we hold to (4) and (5), the Zahl determined by the "Zeichen plus Null" will not be the same Zahl as that determined by the Zeichen alone.

(9) However the special Zeichen or Zahl, known as Null, is necessary to us, and we cannot get along with either (7) or (8) in rigorous application.

(10) Since our framework of development is already rigidly established, our recourse must be a little liberality of treatment: and since there is much looseness in the description of the materials out of which this apparently rigid framework is made, that is easy for us.

(11) All we have to do is to introduce Null under the colorless name, Zeta, and treat it as a Zahl under (4) at the start, give it

treatment as a Zeichen under (3) where necessary during our argument, and declare it a Zahl in our conclusion.

(12) The end justifies the means.

Since the sole difficulty in this issue lies in the communication of meanings, which is greatly hampered by the confusion of realistic implications which slip along with words, unbeknown to us, as we speak and hear them, it may be worth while to go over the analysis again in a still different form.

Let us, then, consider:

A. A system of Zeichen, including a, b, c,......; $\zeta$, $\zeta'$, $\zeta''$, ......; $+$, $-$, $>$, $<$, and $=$.

B. A system of Zahlen, including Za, Zb, Zc......; Z$\zeta$, Z$\zeta'$, Z$\zeta''$,......; (Z+), (Z—), (Z>), (Z<) and (Z=).

C. A symbol, or indicator, $\rightarrow$, to sharpen the expression of the "darstellen" and "bedeuten" of Caratheodory's text. It is to be taken in the sense of the phrase "points at," as used in the Foreword of this book, and of the x-to-X of the Realistic Postulate in Chapter II.

We first set down the initial expression used by Caratheodory in presenting his proof for the existence of Null as a Zahl, namely:

"die Gleichung $a = \zeta + a$."

(a) We take the case in which a $\rightarrow$ Za: and in which we hold strictly to Caratheodory's statement about "Gleichung," cited earlier in the text (and again later in connecton with the "Axiom der Anordnung," and represented in (3) above).

Here if a $\rightarrow$ Za, then, under the symbol $=$, we further have $\zeta + a \rightarrow$ Za. With this we make no progress towards our desired proof, and indeed cut off its possibility in advance.

(b) We next take the alternative case in which a $\rightarrow$ Za: and in which $\zeta \rightarrow$ Z$\zeta$.

Here the symbol $=$ is given no interpretation by Caratheodory, and in its place the symbol (Z=) has significance. We must now inspect the right hand member of his original expression, namely "$\zeta + a$" in the form, Z$\zeta$ (Z+) Za. Then by the terms of his "Axiom der Addition," as carried forward by him into his "Axiom der Subtraktion" (which latter has been cited in the text, the joint situation being represented in (4) and (5) above) we must secure from this expression an "eindeutig bestimmte Zahl c." That is, we must secure Zc. Substituting this in the original expression, and under the full use of the required connectivity, we obtain Za (Z=) Zc. But this violates the connectivity of the system B of Zahlen: and is meaningless.

To show the background in which Caratheodory's manner of argumentation appears plausible, it will be necessary to construct explicitly the postulation B-Car[5] which is implicitly at work beneath and around his axiomization. In his opening paragraph he offers various linguistic materials which he employs as if unimpeachable for his purpose. These include:

1. "Theorien"
2. The fact that one "Theorie" rests ("beruht") on another
3. "Zahlen"
4. "Eigenschaften der Zahlen"
5. The fact that among these "Eigenschaften" "man...einige hervorheben kann"
6. The fact that from such selected "Eigenschaften" "die übrigen......folgen"
7. The application of the name "Axiome" to such "ausgezeichneten Eigenschaften"

In his second paragraph he adds to these materials

8. "Zeichen"
9. "Darstellen" and "bedeuten," apparently used interchangeably
10. "Dieselbe" (used by him in italics)
11. "Relationen"

I have no interest whatsoever in Caratheodory's psychology or philosophy: so far as I am concerned it is just as valid as anybody else's, for whatsoever it may be valid for. I am solely interested in the degree of consistency with which he uses the terminology arising therefrom within his own mathematical de-

[5]See Chap. V, Par. 21.

velopment and for the purposes of that development. Examined provisionally for that purpose we find the above items falling into three general groups:

(a) Mathematics as a system of knowledge embodied in communications between men: i. e., as social fact or phenomenon. Here we find the "Theorien" before us in the manner commonly described as "objectively." Here also would seem to belong the "Zeichen" as components of communication and of theory.

(b) That which the mathematics "is about": what it concerns, taken as "external" to it. Here the "Zahlen" belong.

(c) The operating mathematician, taken subjectively, mentally or "internally," in contrast to (b). Here the procedures and connections "Hervorhebung," "Auszeichnung," "Nennung," "Darstellen" and "Bedeuten" are typical.

While these three groups are undoubtedly to be distinguished as separate classes or types of phenomena, unfortunately we cannot allocate with certainty each term that Caratheodory uses to one or the other. The "Beruhung" of one theory on another, and the "Axiome" doubtless belong in (a): so possibly also the "folgen." But "Beruhung" and "Folgen" when investigated on their own account are commonly studied as (c): while "Axiome" are "Eigenschaften"; though the "Eigenschaften," being "of" Zahlen, are (b). The "Relationen" should also be (b), but like the "Eigenschaften" are badly entangled with both (a) and (c). As for "dieselbe," it is hopeless to attempt its classification, though without the use of it Caratheodory's mathematics could not proceed at all.[6]

Certain of these expressions Caratheodory could omit or replace with others, and we do not know just what he would leave standing for us if he should give direct study to this part of his development with respect to its internal consistency. We may, however, be certain that "Zeichen," "Zahlen" and "dieselbe" would remain, and further that these terms must be sharp and clear, if the development itself is to be sharp and clear.

I cite now Caratheodory's "Axiome der Anordnung (I)," together with two accompanying sentences of great significance:

"I 1. Die Zahlen können angeordnet werden, d. h., wenn $a$ und $b$ zwei Zahlen bedeuten, so muss von den drei Möglichkeiten

$$a = b, \quad a > b, \quad b > a$$

stets eine und nur eine erfüllt sein.

"I 2. Es gibt mindestens zwei Zahlen, die nicht einander gleich sind.

"I 3. Aus der Voraussetzung $a > b$ und $b > c$ folgt stets $a > c$."

"Die Gleichung $a = b$ soll dabei bedeuten, dass die beiden Zeichen $a$ und $b$ *dieselbe* Zahl darstellen."

"Allgemein kann man, wenn $a = b$ ist, in allen Relationen zwischen Zahlen das Zeichen $a$ durch das Zeichen $b$ ersetzen."

Here is complete confusion. "Zahlen" exist as (b) and have equation between them apparently as such

---

[6]Compare the remarks on "dasselbe," Chap. IV, Par. 2.

(b) (I 2). Equation runs, however, between "Zeichen," and both sides of the equation "mean" or "represent" the same "Zahl." There is an x-to-X between "Zeichen" and "Zahl"—sometimes. The elusive nature of the procedure appears further in the "Axiome der Addition (II 1)" which tell us that if there "are" two "Zahlen" *a* and *b*, then there is an "eindeutig bestimmte Zahl *c*" which we call the Sum. The "Zahlen" are (b), the Sum is (a) and the procedure is (c). It is the region of (c) which is relied on to hold it all together.

The implicit postulation B-Car, when made as explicit as we can, would appear something as follows:

B-Car. A Mathematical existences are before us in three realms: mathematical-world-existence, mathematical-mind-existence, and mathematical-linguistic-knowledge-existence.

B-Car. B "Zahlen" are mathematical-world-existence, separate or "discrete" in that realm.

B-Car. C "Zeichen" are mathematical-linguistic-knowledge-existence, and may (or may not) represent ("darstellen," "bedeuten") "Zahlen" in exact x-to-X.

B-Car. D "Gleichheit" is mathematical-linguistic-knowledge-existence, but it is to be treated as representing mathematical-world-existence by arbitrary conventional use of the alternative possibilities of B-Car. C

B-Car. E Mathematical-mind-existence is our ultimate reliance for ultimately eliminating inconsistencies, and making it unnecessary for us to concern ourselves with them now.

Under some such approach as this Caratheodory is prepared to read his presentation of Null as a "Zahl," as having the value of a "proof" based upon axioms. That it is the arrangement which he needs for his own constructive purposes is evident: and that such an arrangement is permissible and advantageous for specific purposes is also evident. For "*foundation*" purposes, or for anything beyond his immediate objective, it has no significance whatever.

# PART III

## Knowledge and Logic

## XIII

## SEMANTIC ANALYSIS

Our research into the linguistic structure of mathematics was completed in the last chapter. In the remaining chapters I desire to exhibit more broadly the characteristics and range of the technique which has been employed. This I shall do, first, by incorporating an essay which in a different terminology and from a different form of approach develops this more general technique under the name of "semantic analysis": and, second, by describing and analyzing some of the many endeavors that have been made in the past generation to reorganize or reestablish the Aristotelian logic.

Procedure thus far has been under a specialized scheme of postulation adopted because of its fitness for the problem immediately in hand. We placed over against one another two types of postulation, semantic and realistic, and we did this designedly in a definitely linguistic setting. We might, indeed, have called the second type of postulation Aristotelian, but that would have involved us from the start in much unnecessary disputation of a kind to distract attention from the problems immediately before us. On the other hand, we might have discarded postulatory formulation altogether, and, instead, have demanded of ourselves and of the reader that every time we used a term of critical import in our study, we should investigate its full range of meanings, and pause until we had attained full consistency in its use: in which case we would have been involved in such numerous and extensive explorations, separately conducted for each of our most significant terms, that little progress would have been possible. The scheme of postulation which we have employed stands, therefore, as, in effect, a special instrument chosen and employed for the most compact and expeditious classification and analysis of the materials of our study. That it has proved to be a practicable and efficient instrument is because, in the case before us, our materials, namely those of mathematics, are presented to us so directly in linguistic embodiment or form.

Nevertheless, even in establishing this specialized scheme of postulation, we have been compelled to make occasional reference[1] to ranges of "fact," of "experience" and of "knowledge," which, under current conventions, and in particular under "realistic postulation," are sharply separated, "existentially," from "language." With respect to these we have merely said that they also are before our attention in linguistic presentation, and that their "connectivities" whatever they are, are before us under linguistic form: and with that we have passed them over. In this curt treatment, however, it is certain that there will be an offense and a stumbling block to any reader who permits his established constructions in these ranges of "fact" and "experience" and "knowledge" to dominate his thought and distract his attention from the

[1]So, pp. 21, 24, 33, 41, 63, 65, 73, 77.

immediate objectives of inquiry: while, even for readers who force themselves in mathematical integrity to hold firmly to the postulation and pursue its consequences, curiosity may be aroused as to how such a procedure may reasonably be asked of them.

The present chapter presents, then, in a separate development, and indeed in a preliminary and experimental form, a wider analysis and postulation with respect to which the postulations of Parts I and II of this book, are a specialization. The relation between it and the preceding chapters must be taken somewhat as follows. The procedure which I here call "semantic analysis" is constructed as a technique of interpretation designed to control some of the difficulties in linguistic presentation and factual rendering forced upon us by recent scientific progress. It grew out of a study of the common characteristics of these difficulties as exhibited in various scientific fields: but it was specially nourished by study of the mathematical and sociological difficulties. Once set up, its value was merely that of an experimental organization of the locus of difficulty. The next step was not to speculate further about it, nor to attempt elaborations or seek increased plausibility for it, but to apply it. The application, then, was made in the mathematical-logical field, under the special postulations of this book. If this application has success or value, it follows that it in turn gives indications of widened utility to the general construction of semantic analysis in connection with which it was established.

The sections that follow are given substantially as they were completed some three years ago. In several important respects their forms of expression differ from those of the body of the book. In especial is this true of the use of the term "limits," a term that has almost entirely disappeared from the preceding investigation. These differences should be the source of no misunderstanding, since it is plain throughout that I am offering no finished system, but a mere experiment in interpretation: indeed the use of different manners of approach under such conditions may have positive advantages in increased understanding. Much the same may be said of the passages in the present essay which touch upon ground already covered more fully in preceding chapters.

Footnotes in brackets are additions made for the purposes of the present publication. The organization of the essay is exhibited in the following list of section headings:

1. Introduction
2. Subject, Object, Actuality
3. Mathematics and Sociology
4. The Conventional Background of the Problem
5. Preliminary Assemblage of Materials
6. Postulatory Approach
7. Postulates of Semantic Analysis
8. Connectivities of F, E, K, and L.
9. Symbols for the Present Paper
10. Verbal Technique for the Present Paper
11. Structure of the Field FEKL
12. A Differentiation of Scientific Approaches
13. The Foundations of Mathematics
14. The Background of Sociology
15. The Basis of Operational Physics
16. The Technique of Psychology
17. The Paradox of One-to-One Correspondences
18. Conclusion.

1. *Introduction.*

Comparing science and metaphysics, it is conventional to look upon them as if they dealt with separate subject-matters or occupied separate fields within knowledge. Distinctions of this type are closely involved in constructions of the "subjective" and the "objective," and in attitudes towards, or interests in, "reality" or "actuality." Even where no sharp definition is attempted, such constructions and attitudes are present, subtly and dangerously, as concealed implications of the theoretical language most commonly employed.

In contrast with formulations of this kind, one may draw a distinction between procedures of the type scientific on the one hand, and procedures of the type metaphysical on the other: and one may thus view the opposition as one of method rather than of subject-matter. I shall take this view, and shall regard the distinction as lying between the older and less reliable method of metaphysics and the newer and more reliable method of science. Ever since Comte made us aware of this general situation within research and knowledge, we have witnessed the steady encroachments of the scientific upon regions previously allotted to the metaphysical, a development which confirms the position here taken within empirical ranges, whether it justifies generalizations, as yet, or not.

It is my task to examine certain problems in scientific border territory, where statements in terms of subjects and objects and of actualities are the rule: and it is my hope in this examination to extend somewhat the reaches of the scientific method in this border territory. The attempt would be handicapped, should the procedure be appraised as metaphysical merely because it extends into certain fields or regions commonly regarded as the private domain of metaphysics. To avoid any such prejudicial attitude, and to attain a better chance for exact expression, I call attention at the start to this existing situation, and ask that any judgment passed upon the present essay be concerned with it solely as postulation and technique for increasing scientific knowledge, regardless of what subject-matters it touches. References to the philosophical and metaphysical will be, from time to time, unavoidable: but they will enter solely for the purpose of giving our work orientation with respect to prevalent conventions which concern it not at all. In order that there may be no misunderstanding even with respect to these most general references let the following characterizations apply to the terms scientific and metaphysical wherever they are used.

Let *scientific* be understood to require the presence of an organized nexus of descriptions, techniques and explanations, forming a body of such considerable extent that it asserts the right, and in general is permitted, to reorganize itself in its own way, and freely to establish such postulates for its work as by its own tests its work requires. Let *metaphysical,* in contrast, indicate those approaches to, or expressions of, knowledge, which either assume or propound primary positions by the tests of which all other knowledge is to be interpreted. Thus science will be that body of expression in which the most wide-reaching interpretation is to be anticipated only as the result of the most wide-reaching labors: whereas metaphysics will comprise all those short-cuts to the ultimate through which the heady intellect of man expects to anticipate or evade the labors of the future. In illustration, ethers that are solely mathematical formulas are scientific: ethers that are introduced as temperamental necessities to control the formulas are metaphysical. By corollary, the entire substance of scientific expression may transform itself in a generation, while nevertheless the working values of the system remain undiminished, however they become modified in range or in finer discrimination: whereas a metaphysical presentation faces always and only the alternatives, rule or ruin.

2. *Subject, Object, Actuality.*

We learn of subject, object and actuality at our mother's knee. Mother's knee is a wonderful place at the right age, but not necessarily dictatress of all knowledge. The attitudes and conventions about ourselves and the world, and the "knowledge" that we there acquire, while never satisfactory, have been at least tolerable to or tolerated by modern sciences in their earlier phases. Much progress in the gathering and assorting of information has been practicable by their use, and they were certainly vastly preferable to the animisms, magics and theological dictatorships of earlier generations. But this stage has now been passed, and the most radical difficulties have forced themselves upon scientific attention. If these difficulties affected merely the newer sciences or pretenders to scientific standing, the psychologies and sociologies, we might perhaps draw our robes around us and pass down the other side of the street. But they are vastly more serious than this. They affect mathematics and physics. They are present in the issues of wave and corpuscle, of field and electron, of momentum and position. They are present directly and vitally in all of the construction for the solution of the paradoxes of mathematics.

I shall be compelled to refer to subject, object and actuality from time to time, though they are terms to which, in ordinary use, metaphysical fixities of meaning, explicit or implicit, adhere, whereby they pretend to rule procedures. My attitude towards them is one in which I shall deprive them of all fixity of meaning—or, if I do not, then to that very extent will the failure of my effort be measured—and in which I shall use them fluidly, as crude and confused conventions which are the merest indications of a certain field of problems into which investigation must be made: and this on the understanding that if the investigation approaches scientific standards and in its results meets and cooperates with other scientific work, it will be worth while, no matter what the final fate of these terms may be: and that otherwise it will be worthless.

The problem is one of a form of analysis, involving, as all analysis does, words and things, or whatever it is that we mean by words and things when we separate these two terms. I call it here Semantic Analysis because it is an analysis of words and things, taken, not as a system of meanings in a subjective interpretation of the objective with a view to special tests of truth or actuality, but instead as a system of meanings of whatever kind, and under whatever interpretation, which we find displayed before us for investigation by the use of language. The term semantic dates in its more modern uses from Michel Bréal's Essai de Sémantique, 1897, as the result of which fused situations of psychology, philology and logic have been thrown up for examination.[2]

3. *Mathematics and Sociology.*[3]

Some theoretical sociologies use fixed individual subjects—men, minds, personalities—each in some sense counting one—as the basis of their interpretations: but they find that these unit subjects, wherever they appear, tend to distort or negate all of their descriptive social reports. Other theoretical sociologies emphasize an actuality in the social, and land in a metaphysical difficulty with the individual.

Mathematics, on the basis of units—discrete numbers, the counting of ones, induction, equation, substitution—grew to be the most authoritative and the most dependably useful of all the sciences: but by the very processes of its own development, because of a marked sociality which it has discovered among numbers, it has been led into an inextricable tangle of subjects and objects, relations, and operations, which, in the attempts to analyze them, have raised many doubts as to mathematical values and validities in general. These problems were inherent in the calculus of Newton and Leibnitz, and have evolved from infinitesimals through the Dedekindian cut, the logics of Frege and Peano, the Cantorian actual infinites, and the Russell-Whitehead class fixations, to the antagonisms of the Hilbert Axiomatik and the Brouwer Intuitionism.

---

[2]My earlier efforts to develop analysis in this background are indicated by the introductory inscription, "This book is an attempt to fashion a tool" in a volume, "The Process of Government," University of Chicago Press, 1908.

[3][See for elaborated discussion the articles, Sociology and Mathematics, The Sociological Review, July and October, 1931.]

In this development, the metaphysical problems of the one, the many, and sociality, of the whole and the part, have come to be closely akin for mathematics and for sociology: for the most exact branch of science and for the most inexact. In both cases scientific development demands scientific solution, i. e., solution "from within" the field of the investigation itself: in both cases success thus far fails: in both cases the existing attacks are metaphysical because fixities "from without" are permitted to have authoritative control, while the free development of postulation "from within," for the needs of the accumulating body of information in each science respectively, is inhibited. What Society is to the sociologist, that, from this point of view, the Cantorian "Menge" or the Russell "class" is to the mathematician: with this contrast, however, that while mathematics, starting from discrete number, finds its metaphysical difficulty in the "Menge," sociology, if and in so far as it starts with positively presented social descriptions—and if it does not so start, whatever it may call itself and whatever it may be, it is hardly entitled to the status of a separate science at all—finds its difficulty in the unitary individual. The troubles of both have to do with externally posited actualities, or reals: the mathematician puzzles over the actuality of the "Menge," if the discrete numbers are taken as naturals, as actuals, as reals: while the sociologist is confused over the actual values of his individual as soon as he has faced actual social presentations.

Given this situation it seems highly probable that any form of analysis which will result in helping one of these sciences in its borderland difficulties, will likewise help the other: nay, more, that any form of analysis which seems for the moment to help the one, but does not help the other, will in the end prove unacceptable for either.

4. *The Conventional Background of the Problem.*

Before attempting constructive treatment let us inspect more closely the conventional background of approach to both sciences, this being also the conventional approach, in one form or another, to most other ranges of investigation, whether physical, vital or psychological. And let us keep in mind that this background is not some permanent, absolute and inevitable status, but merely the adventitious background of the last few centuries.

This naively-given extra-scientific background presents in general a tripartite complex:[4] (a) real human beings with presumed definitely real mentalities: (b) an actual, or in some sense real and actual, world of matter and events: (c) a general, vaguely-characterized realm of knowledge (science) related to or relating with (a) and (b), and embodied or formulated in language or language structures of varying degrees of exactness: the kernel of this background problem being to interpret two or all of these with respect to each other, and in especial to interpret each science, taken as within (c) with respect to some fact aspect of (b). The direct attack on problems of interpretation of (a), (b) and (c) with respect to one another, after

[4] [Compare the attempt at provisional construction of a postulational background for Caratheodory's exposition, towards the close of Chap. XII.]

they have been taken as primarily separate, is what in general is called philosophy or metaphysics: and clearly so long as the (a) and the (b), with or without the vaguer (c), remain in such primary qualitative isolation from each other, its method must be of that type which we have called metaphysical.

The professionals of each particular science try to assume some special common meeting ground for these problems in their science, hoping that they can so strip the issue down that it will offer a minimum of interference with their work. The chemists, as the case has stood in their specialized intermediate field, have perhaps been in the happiest position of all, though they are rapidly losing this favored standing as they make advances in physical chemistry. The physicists have in the last decade become desperately involved in certain problems which they find, according to one personal attitude or another, greatly to interfere with their free progress in interpretation and with their mutual understanding. The biologists speculate at length, and for the most part unprofitably, as to organ and organism, part and whole, structure and function, vitalism and mechanism, being and behavior. The psychologists are split into almost as many camps as there are individual investigators. The sociologists, as we have seen, have not even the beginnings of intelligible footing: while the mathematicians, so long proud and aloof, now find that, by their own internal development, they have been forced into the most acute problem of all.

Nevertheless in its technical development, taken, that is, in isolation in (c), mathematics is still as reliable as ever; while the natural sciences have respectively their own degrees of exactness. But as over against them the reports from psychology, or from any other sources, on the regions (a) and the continuation of these into the regions (b) are extremely vague and uncertain in the sense that exact formulations are lacking to which the great body of investigators give joint adherence for their common purposes. In this situation we now face the astounding fact that the systematic scientist in the reliable fields, though he gives the "mental" sciences next to no credence in their own right, nevertheless takes them, often even in their crudest forms, as the basis for his general orientation of (c) with respect to (a) and (b) when the need of such orientation seems pressing to him. He takes the naively presented mentality of man and the naively presented actual external world as though they were definite and reliable points of orientation. He may tell us that this is the best that he can do, and he may perhaps cite Poincaré by way of authority, because of the background psychology Poincaré set up in his four general treatises on the values and procedure of science. But Poincaré wrote a quarter of a century ago, and while this great scientist showed his power in the very fact that he could so ably adapt the psychology of the time to his own ends at that time, much progress and many transformations of meaning have come since then: so that with respect to his psychology Poincaré is no authority to appeal to now. Bridgman in his recent "Logic of Modern Physics" somewhat similarly orients himself with respect to an asserted "permanent mental nature of man": but the outstanding feature of Bridgman's work is this, that while he formally sets up that "mental nature" as a precautionary background, he nevertheless does not fully submit himself to it, but tears it apart and forcibly reconstructs it to meet the impelling needs of his own investigation wherever and in whatever way the requirement appears. Each of these men in his own way has thus taken definite steps towards remoulding the (a) and to some extent also the (b) out of the (c).

Not nearly enough, however, has been done. If such background set-ups were "dimensional," in some sense corresponding to the ancient use of that term in geometry, or to its newer use in physics, there would be nothing against them in scientific principle. They might be successful or they might be unsuccessful, but they would at least be legitimately scientific efforts.

Such, however, is not the case as they stand. It is as separated realms that the compartments are offered to us, not as dimensions in a field of study. And in that naive sense I shall have nothing further to do with them, except as I try to place them in their naïveté. I shall try, instead, to inspect the field of knowledge directly from the point of view of its components, using mathematics as the simplest key. And I shall proceed in the attitude that what mathematics and the relatively exact sciences report on men and the world is much more significant than the ancient reports of cavemen, modified in modern times to meet the needs of merchants and warriors and politicans, embodied in language forms developed in long evolution for the purposes of practical every-day life, organized in Aristotelian logic, and erected here and there into this or that philosophy or theology, psychology or sociology.

5. *Preliminary Assemblage of Materials.*

Out of the preceding discussions let us pick out in a preliminary way the ranges of the materials which must be handled. We have, to start with, our Sciences, of which mathematics will serve as a type. Mathematics, as a science, is a branch, or alternatively perhaps, an aspect or method or intensification, of Knowledge. Mathematics, and along with it all Science and Knowledge, is also an affair of Language, spoken and written, of books, of muscular activity with paper and pencil and with instruments, of neurological processes, of meanings, of experiment and Experience, and of organization of Facts. Among all of these terms can we find any of such established and accurate values that we can hold fast to them, and find in them, as they are before us in our isolated definitions of them, the basis for systematized interpretation of the type scientific?

I doubt it. In illustration Hilbert erects a great Linguistic-Logical-Axiomatic, a structure of the form (c) above, and inserts it between the (a) and the (b) as a candidate for recognition as Scientific truth. Brouwer counters that such Language is a dead husk, and that all meanings and values must be sought directly in the Intuition, which has the form (a). But for us, as first-hand observers of materials before us, it remains evident that into Language must be read the values of Intuition, and into Intuition the values of Language, to give either of them any status as scientific materials. And the same is true for the other terms, such as Experience and Knowledge, above. Into each the values of the others must be read, wherever observation is untrammeled: and this no matter how strenuously the effort is made by any dogmatist to isolate one or the other of them, and to use it metaphysically for his foundations.

Meanwhile our requirement is that we attack this problem without any such external emphasis or prejudgment of the type metaphysical. We shall attempt it as follows.

Pick out a few terms,—or, better, let us say, a few words—all of admittedly elastic and inexact meanings, but all of general use in broad implications, so taken that, as nearly as we can tell, all the significant implications of the many phases of the problem can be assembled under them. Take them without definition, as mere indices of the main aspects of the investigation to be made.

Make this attempt by the use of the words, Knowledge, Language, Experience and Fact. The word, Knowledge, then, will represent the great stretches of science and information without necessary reduction into the contents of individual or otherwise described minds. The word, Language, will represent the formalized embodiment of this knowledge in certain activities—behaviors, or products of behavior—without any express position-taking as to inner or outer, individual or social. The words, Knowledge and Language, will together be indicative of the ranges (c). The word, Experience, will represent all the specialized references of a psychological, mental, or "mentally" logical nature, though without any postulated isolation of them from Knowledge and Language. The word, Fact, will represent all the specialized references to the "content" or delivery of science, that is, to existent or actual or assumed world-structure. The words, Experience and Fact, taken together, then add to our field all of the ranges of (a) and (b) without at any point definitional isolation from (c).

These four words, taken in their broadest, not in their narrowest, usages, then appear as clues to study. If their characterizations have been vague, that fact merely expresses their actual status in the knowledge of today. They stand as themselves subject to substitution or rearrangement in any way and at any time that the progress of investigation may require. They are permitted to introduce no authoritative direction as to procedure. They become, not the proudest, but the meanest, of our tools.

6. *Postulatory Approach.*

I. Any postulation is permissible.

II. The acceptance or rejection of any system of postulation shall be determined solely upon the basis of its adequacy for our most general technical needs.

7. *Postulates of Semantic Analysis.*[5]

III. Fact, Experience, Knowledge and Language form one field of investigation, FEKL.

---

[5][Investigators in this general field may be interested in appraising the above group of "postulates" in terms of Keyser's doctrinal functions as he has elaborated them in his recent comprehensive discussion (Yale Law Journal, March 1932). The "symbol," for Keyser, must symbolize "something" that is "object of thought or of sense" (p. 714). Postulates are "impliers" (p. 722). Postulates are "proposi-

IV. In the field FEKL, neither the F, nor the E, nor the K, nor the L, nor any specification of either, may be presented save in connectivity, immediate, mediate, or by implication, with the others.

V. The F, the E, the K and the L have differential values, each with respect to the others: and detached statements in terms of any one of them have the values of limiting expressions with respect to the others.

Critical words used in the framing of these postulates shall be understood under the following specifications.[6]

*Field* shall be taken to cover systemic connectivity of the general type exhibited in the development of the scientific method, without judgment for or against the use of specific atomistic constructions within it.

*Connectivity* shall be taken to cover every variety of connection, contact, or valuation, whether of the types scientifically, philosophically, or naively, described as

---

tional functions'' (p. 725). All propositions having the form ''P implies T'' are ''hypothetical'' (p. 726). Propositional functions, by contrast, are ''categorical'' (p. 727). Doctrinal functions of the hypothetical type are bodies of propositions where the postulates (P's) are indissolubly bound with their ''logical implicates, or theorems'' (T's) (p. 728). Doctrinal functions of the categorical type are bodies of propositional functions where the postulates (P's) are doubly bound with their ''logical implicates, or theorems'' (T's), first because of the interrelation of their variables, and second by the fact that ''though there is present no assertion of implication, yet some of the component functions do in fact imply all the rest'' (p. 728). Propositions in a doctrine have ''content,'' but propositions or propositional functions making up a doctrinal function have none'' (p. 729).]

[6][I here substitute the term ''specification'' for the term ''definition'' used when this essay was written. Definition, apart from its many casual usages, carries, in a context such as the present, the implications of logical procedure. It is an operation of L-Prop. as that is described in Section 9, following, on symbolization. For the preliminary purposes of the broader semantic procedure the word ''specification'' may be provisionally employed.]

space, time, matter or energy, or as logic or meaning, in the field FEKL.

*Atomistic* shall be taken under the limitations of the term "within."

*Within* shall be taken to mean, subject at all times to transformations in accordance with the requirements of the full developing system.

*Differential* and *Limit* shall be taken in provisional general agreement with the corresponding terms of mathematical analysis, and shall receive their fuller values from within the field in the course of its analysis.

Postulates I and II have the effect of generalizing the scientific position which Poincaré developed in his four methodological books published in the first decade of this century. Postulates III, IV and V have specifically the effect of extending Poincaré's scientific position beyond the natural sciences into all remaining fields of investigation, including those regions which Poincaré regarded as external to his range and which he handled in the form of a background psychology. The specifications which accompany the postulates have the purpose of depriving the postulates of capacity to harm us which might arise from their formulation in the available current language in which of necessity they are couched.

Workers in special logical fields in which postulates and definitions aim at maximum rigidity will doubtless deny that under their standards we have here any proper postulates or specifications at all. By the standards of the present paper, however, those very postulates and definitions which have rigid appearance in the logical fields, arise in a background of vague linguistic implication. They are affected, without formally recognizing it, by those very vaguenesses which our postulates have attempted frankly to exhibit. Moreover our postulates are provisionally established as clues to investigation. They are applicants for improvement through investigation.[7] As such they are proper postulates, and the accompanying specifications are proper specifications, even though their form is not that of axiom and definition in the old logic.

8. *Connectivities of F, E, K and L.*

*Language.* We have no phenomena of knowledge or experience or fact that are not in some way framed on, or involved in, words choate or inchoate. We make our references and distinctions as to ourselves and to all that we regard as beyond or outside ourselves, in language. Deity appears under verbal indications, even though the only term we may be able to give it is "the unknown." The Absolute is presented in terms, through chains of terms. The most mystical experience builds out of and into words. Fact is measured by clarity of expression.

---

[7]Postulates IV and V would indeed be reduced to the position of specifications of the term field in Postulate III, if the interpretation herein to be set forth should be established. That would, however, require a much more exact value for the term *field* than I am justified in giving it when using current languages and current dictionaries as a medium of communication. Instead therefore, of taking the *strong* course, giving full positive meaning to the term field in Postulate III, and proceeding to systematic development of the characteristics of the field, I take the *weak* course for purposes of presentation, and set up the three postulates, III, IV and V, separately, not asking the reader to adopt my personal view that the three are ripe for consolidation, but asking him merely to inspect the three as separate postulates, in order to observe what follows in the way of possible development of meanings.

Language is therefore before us as an aspect or phase of all knowledge, experience and fact.

It is evident that the implications of the word Language, thus used, run far beyond those of grammar or philology or conventional psychology. It may readily be said that some other word should be found to indicate this wide linguistic aspect of knowledge and experience and fact, while the word language should be confined to some more limited definition. Just such a word, namely "semantic," will be introduced later. For the present we will proceed by observing that in this very wide meaning of language, the linguistic aspect, influence, modulation, agency, is everywhere.

It is of course always permissible to any investigator, at any time, and for any particular purpose of research, to set up and adopt a restricted definition. Many such definitions for language are currently employed in the sciences, and they differ greatly among themselves, not only in their terms, but in the background implications they use and convey.[8] If one considers the old question as to whether there can be "thought" without "words," one will observe at once that the answer depends entirely upon the definition (including its implication) that is set up for words, for language. With a narrow definition the answer is in

[8]The common attitude towards language is instrumental: that language, namely, is a physical, or quasi-physical tool or behavior of men, having the characteristics of the factor (b) in section 4, but used by the factors (a) to secure objectivity or body for the presentations of the factors (c). When this instrumental attitude is given formal definition, and when the attempt is made to establish consistent expression for it in connection with the factors (a) and (c), it disintegrates entirely. It is useful enough for this or that special purpose, but for our wider purposes of investigation it is little better than incoherent dogma.

the affirmative. As the definition widens it tends to become, and may finally become, fully negative. Such an issue cannot arise under our present postulation: it is here to be classed among the meaningless questions, or, at the very least, among questions for the answers to which we have as yet no dependable approach or technique.

Recognizing, now, that we have before us a large group of such restricted or specialized definitions for language, we may distinguish three general ranges to which they are applied, three methods in which they may be employed. If any of them are set up wittingly, deliberately, for particular purposes of investigation, they are to be appraised as legitimate experimental procedures within their specified ranges of use. If any of them are set up dogmatically, absolutely, realistically, and proclaimed to be the necessary basis for the understanding and interpretation of all knowledge, then their method of employment is bad: it is presumptuous, metaphysical, and not here worthy of attention. If any of them are set up as postulations for scientific research, and as alternatives to the postulation employed in the present paper, then they are welcome and free to work themselves out and stand or fall by test of comparative results. What we have here to note is that any and every such definitional limitation of the word language is itself developed within language.

Our conclusion, and our postulation therefore, is that the field FEKL is involved throughout in the connectivities of language in this widened sense of that word.

*Experience.* We have no phenomena of fact, of language, or of knowledge, that do not have presentation and embodiment in experience. Experience is presented in language: it is a fact of rock-bottom value, if there be such fact anywhere: it is itself a part of the content of knowledge: and yet it itself so comprehensively touches all of these that it is not merely "part" to their "wholes," but it is itself a "whole," for which all of them are aspects or phases.[9]

Experience, so taken, is, like the term language, broadly taken. It is not limited to the experience of some trivially defined or crudely postulated individual "mind" at some crudely postulated instant of time: but it is the full range of all that we imply by the term. The narrowly stated "experience" is—again as was the case with language—either of a limited definition for a special purpose, or an assumption of a metaphysical type: both outside of our present range.

We report then for experience, as we did for language, a thorough-going connectivity with all the other formulations of the field FEKL. This is no more an assertion of mysticism or subjectivism, than the similar assertion as to language was one of logicism or objectivism. It is instead a notation of connectivity to be investigated.

*Fact.* Taking this term broadly, with the reference values of Actuality (or, perhaps better said, of Factuality) and deprived of metaphysical predetermination or assurance, we note that whatever presentations there may be of language, or of knowledge,

---

[9]For "whole" and "part" see Sections 11 and 12 following.

or of experience, are included here as and in Fact. Not-fact is fact in a special differentiation of language, or of experience, or of knowledge: a broader factual report on a narrower factual statement. Whether such Factuality purports to take up language and experience and knowledge into itself, or sets them off as over against itself: whether, i. e., it is taken broadly or narrowly, it still is true that it itself is set up within language by experience and knowledge, or, if you wish, within language and knowledge, by experience, or within any one or set of these terms, by the others, as you choose to take them: and that it itself has ranges of meaning which include them all. Again we have the intricate never-vanishing connectivity in the field FEKL.

*Knowledge.* I know not how knowledge can be defined or presented or in any way indicated except as knowledge of, by, for, or in, language, experience, or fact. All of its values involve these other terms. This is true whether taken as a system of meanings, of or in words or minds: or as a system of objects and relations of or in experience. One may combine these arrangements of terms in any way one will, and still exhibit the general situation of connectivity in FEKL: allowing particular adversaries to raise what particular objections they will, on the basis of their own rigidities of meaning, and leaving it to them to prove their rigidities and force them upon us if they can.

*FEKL.* Whatever we have of this world down to the last dregs of sensational presentation is garbed in Language. Nevertheless Language can never be taken save as a phase of Experience. But Experience frames itself as Experience of Fact, or as itself Fact. And the fulness of Experiencing of the world in terms of Fact is Knowledge. So that Fact, Experience, Knowledge and Language, whether taken one by one in isolation, or in whatever substitute phrase, are unworkable and for most part meaningless except in terms of the full field FEKL.[10]

9. *Symbols for the Present Paper.*

Let the general content of language be taken in four groups arranged with respect to progressive accuracy of employment, as follows: a) inchoate expression and implication: b) words-common: c) terms: d) symbols. Words-common may be taken as regions of language of general practical indicative value, marked by definite vocal or writing coordinations. Terms may be taken as a region of language—"within," or "above," or "beyond" words-common, according as one pictures it—marked by increasingly dependable descriptive

[10]The reader may feel that he would have selected different factors in place of the four chosen, and perhaps that he would not require all four to enable him fully to recover the field. His attitude will depend in the first instance on the characteristics of his personal system of terminology. Some investigators will be inclined to reduce the terms to three by consolidating the system of meanings in Language with Knowledge and then throwing philology into the region of Fact. Others, probably more numerous, will be inclined to consolidate Experience and Knowledge into one term: a procedure which, however, becomes increasingly difficult, the more fully one recognizes the validity of direct social descriptions. I myself set up the requirement at the end of Section 10 that the terms used be restricted to the smallest practical number. Further, I have no dogmatic justification myself for the use either of exactly four terms or of this particular set of four. In earlier experiments I used three. When I enlarged the number to four my inclination was long strong to balance them differently than I balance them here. My only justification for the choice of the terms, the establishment of the number used, and the arrangement given them, is the practical one that by this procedure I have secured more significant results than in any other way.

specification with respect to events and behaviors, their objects, adjustments, procedures: their region will be in general that of reasoning, argument, logic. Symbols may be taken as lying in the region of such rising exactness that they can be dependably used for purposes of the most exact interpretation, as for example, in mathematics, in which the symbol of equation is over large territories dominant. Inchoate expression and implication will have the values both of germinal trends towards words-common, not yet of accomplished parturition, and of the degradation of words-common in utterances of rhetorical and emotional delivery, such as political oratory, advertising slogans and rallying cries.

For our present purpose we can hardly say that we have true symbols available, since the requirement of exactness can be met only through coordinated use by many specialized workers. We may, however, set up a few quasi-symbols, by which we may avoid much of the vagueness of the terms and words-common, on which we would otherwise be compelled to rely in this paper.

Let the letters F, E, K, and L represent most generally and indefinitely the regions, respectively, of Fact, Experience, Knowledge and Language, as set forth in the preceding section of this paper.

Let the letters FF, EE, KK and LL represent assertions of dominance or finality on the part of each of these regions, taken separately, for the theoretical explanation of the field FEKL. Such assertions of control appear most commonly in the form of what are called philosophies: thus: FF represents pronouncements upon the universe as materialistic or mechanic: EE represents mysticisms or intuitionisms, set-ups of the soul and of the isolated ego: KK represents philosophies of the Absolute: and LL represents logistic realisms:[11] in each case more or less exactly, as the case may be, inasmuch as the philosophic variations and vagaries are countless. With such FF, EE, KK and LL we have, it is hardly necessary to say, no concern in this paper, save to note their arrogance and to take protective orientation with reference to them.

Let the letters F′, E′, K′ and L′ represent these different regions taken in naive isolation by tetrachotomy, trichotomy or dichotomy, as the case may be. For example let any "permanent mental nature of man" taken as in independent description, be E′: or any "actual" objective world, taken similarly in isolation, be F′. Taken in one combination or another along with an intermediate set-up in K′ or L′ or in some hesitating mixture of both, they represent the every-day background of approach described in section 4 above.

Let the letters F″, E″, K″ and L″ represent these regions taken in accordance with the semantic postulates of this paper, that is, with differential connectivity in some value of connectivity, each with respect to the other, which is itself the problem of investigation.

---

[11]The logistic realisms are the product of the last generation, but they have already attained standing comparable with that of the older types of world-interpretations: and their very presence and prominence is no doubt the source of that requirement which has been so strong in the course of this investigation for the introduction of an L aspect along with the F, the K and the E aspects in the postulation.

Let L-Prop represent language used in the general region of terms.

Let L-Symb represent language used in the general region of symbols.

Let the expressions F′rel.E′, F′rel.K′, F′rel.L′, and similar forms of relational presentation, represent interpretation of actuality with reference to experience, knowledge and language, on the basis of components F′, E′, K′ and L′ in the region of terms: the particular expressions given above therefore representing alternative formulations of the foundation problems of science and fact.

Let $\text{Lim}_{fek}\text{L}''$ be a type of expression representing the assumed-to-be-attainable, or best-possible-under-any-given-outlook values of L″ with respect to the other aspects of the field FEKL: similar expressions $\text{Lim}_{ekl}\text{F}''$, $\text{Lim}_{fkl}\text{E}''$ and $\text{Lim}_{fel}\text{K}''$ being assumed to be available as needed.

The expressions in the form F′rel.L′ therefore offer presentations in the general region of L-Prop; whereas the expressions in the form $\text{Lim}_{fek}\text{L}''$ give semantic values for the presentations in the general region L-Symb.[12]

10. *Verbal Technique for the Present Paper.*

Cut off as we are from the neat and well-groomed values of words as conventionally given us, the investigations which we make in this field where words and

[12][This linguistic adaptation of the mathematical use of limits rests in an interpretation of all limits as themselves linguistic procedures. It has been remarked in a footnote to Chap. IV that expression in terms of limits gradually disappeared from the development of Part II of this book as the work progressed.]

facts and knowledge are in a state, not merely of fusion, but of confusion, must be with the aid of a very humble instrument, the semantic drag-net. We cast our net out among the words and study our haul for their connections and implications. This is merely to continue further what we have already done in the selection of the expressions F, E, K and L for systematic use. For aid to this end we set up certain practical rules for our guidance, which may perhaps, until we acquire better, serve to keep us out of harm.

Let there be no attribution of fixed predominance to the term, Word, in the family of words, over the terms, Clause, Sentence, Paragraph or Chapter, or over the terms, Syllable, Letter, or Verbal Impulse.

Selecting any word, term, or symbol whatever, according to need, for a *clue,* let such other words as are brought into connection with it for study be chosen under semantic compulsion: namely by the test of those usages, meanings and implications which are most inextricably bound up with it, and from which isolation can least easily be secured.

Let such words be taken, not as though possessing extra-linguistic reference, clarity or validity, but as representatives or indices of *word-clusters,* among which word-clusters our clue-words have been located.

Let such words or word-clusters be restricted to the smallest practical number at any particular stage of the investigation.[13]

## 11. *Structure of the field FEKL.*

With the aid of our drag-net, and letting it range all

[13]The logician may recall, if he will, Occam's razor.

the way from the naïve attitudes of the practical man to the developed subtleties of the philosopher, we make selection of word-clusters and clue-words.

A primitive pair of terms manifestly to be taken into account is that which makes distinction of mind and matter. More subtly developed, but with locus in the same word-clusters is the distinction of subjective and objective. Since the material always, and the objective primarily, involve space, and since, in contrast, the mental and the subjective are by one device or another inspected as devoid of mensurable, dimensional, spatial characteristics, we find in "non-spatial" and "spatial" a third pair of terms yielding the same general linguistic-factual locus. Quality and quantity again belong in this group.

A second set of word-clusters is readily found containing oppositions which cannot possibly be left out of the reckoning. These sometimes take the form of the problem of the particular and the general: again they appear in the problem of the individual and the social. Merely to mention them is to exhibit age-long confusion, dogmatism of interpretation, and despair in analysis. Other oppositions associated with them are those of part and whole.[14]

Both of these sets of naïve oppositions, I repeat, together with all of their developed subtleties, are here taken, not as dependable, nor even as capable of direct elaboration, in their present forms, into any dependability—since twenty-five hundred years of

---

[14] [I have removed the detailed discussion of "part and whole" from the text. This word-couple is to be understood in analytic renderings as in Chaps. IV and V.]

philosophical history has produced nothing of general scientific acceptance in the way of systematic solutions—but instead solely as preliminary aids to investigation.

Let us now select the words subjective and objective as clue-words to the first set of word-clusters, and the words particular and general as clue-words to the second set. We may then make use of these for examination of the field FEKL in an effort to determine its structure, reminding ourselves that the F, the E, the K and the L, are themselves clue-words for word-clusters which we find before us in intricate and never as yet fully analyzed connectivities.

Let us first take the field FEKL under the presentations F′, E′, K′ and L′, that is, in distinctions by tetrachotomy, and set them down in the arrangement of Fig. 1. Here we at once find them crossed by distinctions of purported dichotomy. To the right of the perpendicular line, where Fact and Language are placed, we have generally speaking indications of the material, the spatial, the objective, and the quantitative. To the left, in Experience and Knowledge, we have, generally speaking, indications of the immaterial, the non-spatial, the subjective and the qualitative. Above the horizontal line we have roughly indications of the individual and the particular. Below it we have roughly the general and the social.

It is plain enough that none of these correspondences and contrasts are clear and precise, however dogmatically this system or that may proclaim some of them as fundamental. It is easy from some particular little peep-hole to give them, or some of them, the ap-

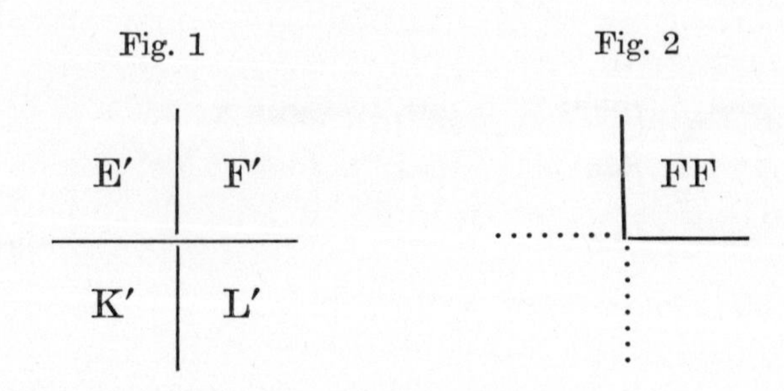
Fig. 1
E′
F′
K′
L′
Fig. 2
FF

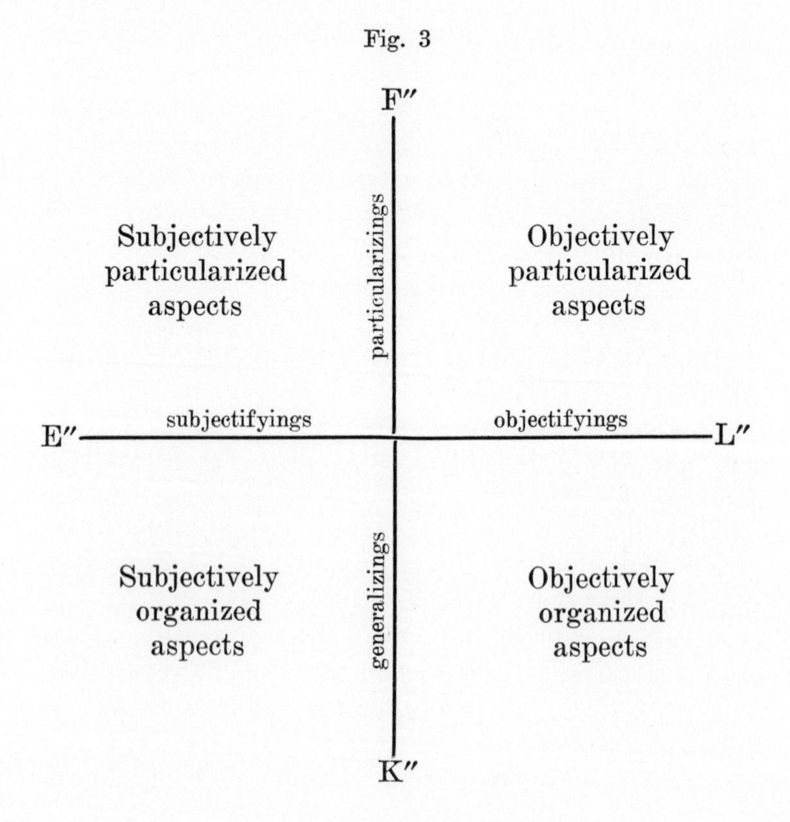
Fig. 3
F″
particularizings
Subjectively particularized aspects
Objectively particularized aspects
E″
subjectifyings
objectifyings
L″
generalizings
Subjectively organized aspects
Objectively organized aspects
K″

pearance of such rigidity: but the terms in which they are couched, as we are compelled to take them for first-hand study, are none of them sharp enough under general acceptance to yield precision for our purposes. Language, insofar as one can detach it as philology, is located on the objective side of whatever contrasts there are. Taken as semasiology language may transform into knowledge with values on the subjective side. Taken in individual words which are inspected as Fact, it may appear in the first quadrant, or as an exhibition of Experience, in the second. Knowledge has general values in contrast with the particular values of Experience; and Fact, in turn, has particular values as over against Knowledge, and objective values as over against experience. But each of these terms, as was indicated with Language, may take transformations of value. Nevertheless, despite all these possible transformations, one cannot fail to observe that something of importance is indicated in the arrangement of Fig. 1, something that demands investigation, however far it may be from having worthwhile form as it stands.

Considering next the field FEKL in the forms FF, EE, KK and LL, and experimenting with figures to correspond, we would get four separate figures of the general type of Fig. 2. Here if we select a dogmatism of FF, a mechanic philosophy, for purposes of illustration, the FF purports to cover the entire field, yet nevertheless not without the dotted tail lines, to be read with the values of "not quite." And so similarly with the EE, the KK and the LL.

Neither Fig. 1 nor Fig. 2 has any direct value for

us in this paper, since the FF forms are far too pretentious for our use, and the F′ forms, those of the practical dichotomies, are the very ones that set up the problems which, in the system in which they are set up, seem forever to prove insoluble.

By a transformation of Fig. 1, however, we may reach a presentation of the situation, which we shall find to have positively helpful values at our present stage, however primitive the construction may still be. It will make use of coordinates, such as are found in mathematics, though without the slightest pretense to any validity from what is merely an external analogy.

In Fig. 3 we inspect the field FEKL under the forms F″, E″, K″, and L″. For the x-axis we take transitions from Experience into Language and from Language into Experience. For the y-axis we take similar transitions from Fact into Knowledge and from Knowledge into Fact. Towards E″ we note subjectifying trends, and towards L″ objectifying trends. Towards F″ we note particularizing trends and towards K″ generalizing trends. We note these characteristics without any stress upon, and without any definition of, the terms transition and trend: and we make the arrangement, not because we have any reason for thinking it either comprehensive or sound, but because we are free to experiment in any way we want to, and because this particular experiment keeps showing superiorities over any other alternative that has happened to present itself.

Along the x-axis of Fig. 3, taken continuously, we may lay off regions corresponding to our grouping of words into inchoate expression, words-common, terms and symbols. This grouping of words is not a formal classification, but an exhibition of progressive aptness of discrimination within language. The implications that it carries are not confined to the positive side of the x-axis but stretch all the way from E″ to L″, and have the values of the entire E″——L″ transition. Along the y-axis we may similarly lay off every form of attitude towards reality from mechanic actuality to subjective absolutisms.

In our first quadrant we can now find the objectively particularized aspects of our entire field. In the second quadrant we can find the subjectively particularized aspects. In the third, the subjectively generalized (organized or socialized) aspects,[15] and in the fourth the objectively generalized aspects. We no longer have "facts" in one region, "minds" in another, "ideals" and "absolutes," Platonic or other in a third, and that terrible "logistics" of modern creation in a fourth. But we have the materials and meanings of all of these rigidly separated producers of paradox and confusion, represented in differential construction, in which we may see at least the hope of better understanding.

[15]One is completely at a loss for an established word that can be definitely used in this quadrant. We have the many meanings of organization, organism, organismic, social, socialization: we have various implications of "wholeness" in many ranges: we have the language of "knowledge" in its senses of comprehension and inclusion: but we have no word that even begins to convey the full set of meanings required without excessive over-emphasis of some minor range of application. In the next section, in describing analysis in this region I have called it "social," but that name is a mere stop-gap. In a lesser degree this same remark applies to descriptions for the other quadrants. I have made no attempt to make expression in the text conform precisely with either the wording in Fig. 3, or with that in the grouping of scientific approaches and analyses which follows.

This will all be very crude, for Fig. 3 is no doubt still deficient in many ways. We have no certainty that the F″, the E″, the K″ and the L″ offer the exact guides to interpretation which we shall finally require: we have not even the certainty that the number of lines of control we shall finally need is four, instead of some larger or smaller number. We are offering the merest sketch in a plane of what is undoubtedly a very complex many-dimensioned field of study. But we know very little of these situations today, and here, as everywhere, elaboration without the requisite labor is dangerous—speculative elaboration, that is to say, without the required protracted scientific assemblage and analysis of materials, and tests of constructions. We have given the term "symbol," for example, orientation towards L″, and we have described the symbol as in some sense a distillation of, or from, terms: but whether we shall use such words as "within" or "beyond" in characterizing the position of the "symbol" with respect to that of the "term," or what the best organization of it is, we cannot yet tell, however we may choose to deal with it for our preliminary purposes.

Nevertheless there is much that is accomplished by the mere exhibition of such unresolved complexities. It should at once be clear that psychology has no possibility of dealing authoritatively with problems of inner and outer until it can at the same time handle soundly problems of individual and social: and similarly that sociology can make no important progress with problems of individual and social until it can comprehensively handle them in connection with problems of inner and outer. It should, further, at once be manifest that interpretations for any science in terms of such dichotomies as subjective and objective, or of individual and social, and in general all interpretations which do not face clearly the issue as to whether they are using dichotomies or some different form of organization in these respects, are manifestly imperfect in their analysis and orientation.

12. *A Differentiation of Scientific Approaches.*

There is hardly any problem in which I take less interest on its own account than that of a classification of the sciences. To me the field of all knowledge is,—by hypothesis, at least, for twentieth century investigation—one single field. The remarks I shall make in this section are therefore to be taken as a by-product from what has gone before. In the latter part of the last century, following Comte and then Spencer, this problem of classification had a great interest. The real value for the scientific world of that day was to be found, however, not in the particular schemes of classification set up, but in the very possibility of bringing all of the sciences together in one general system. Out of the constructions of that period has come a wide-spread conventional inspection of a spatial and temporal physical world as before us and under our investigation in such a way as to yield Physics as a foundation science, with Chemistry and Physiology following in order, with a Psychology by the aid of a technique of "quasi-localization"[16] following next, and with a Sociology at the top, each successive science narrowing within the range of the others. Or, in terms of concrete descriptions rather than of techniques, we were supposed to inspect in succession the natural sciences, then those of life, then those of mind and then those of society. Mathematics has not been readily submissive to this organization and it has had various treatments, often appearing at the head of the list. Its assignment of position has, however, in the main, been governed by special considerations peculiar to the various writers as to the status of mind and matter, subjective and objective. Even the issue as to whether mathematics is to be classified as itself a science has long been moot.

Now in my own primary investigations which form the basis for the construction of semantic analysis, and which arose primarily from the need of finding a technique for handling the descriptions *individual* and *social* in a firm dependable way, I have observed that the required studies fell into four main groups. There has had to be sociological discussion, psychological discussion, physical discussion and mathematical-linguistic discussion. And these four groups of investigations have very definite localization in the four quadrants of Fig. 3. I am therefore inclined to suggest for further examination an arrangement of scientific approaches established upon the basis of semantic analysis; and this all the more because the old scheme of classification has collapsed, first in the

---

[16]See the discussion of a special case of quasi-localization, Revue internationale de sociologie, 37, p. 251. By "quasi-localization" I mean that allegedly scientific procedure which presents presumedly "inner," "psychic," "non-spatial" "facts," as if somehow "localized" in an "outer," "physical," "spatial" world, the dimensions of which they do not themselves possess.

Einsteinian macrocosm, and more recently in the DeBroglie microcosm, even though one convinces himself that the "quasi-localization" of "psychic" phenomena under the old scheme is still credible, or that parts and wholes may still be inspected as radically separated in living organisms.

We may offset to one another two great sciences, or systems of portrayal, description or specification, those, namely of Physics and Socialization: understanding by "socialization" here not a limited specialization with respect to human society, but the investigation of the full nexus of organization forms wherever they are found, and of whatever type. We may then consider in connection with them two great sciences of technique, Mathematics and Psychology. The physical approach has primarily for its aim the specification of fact; and while its "fact" was for many centuries regarded as "material," that way of presenting it has now broken down, and apparently forever: leaving physics, nevertheless, concerned as sharply as ever before with "fact," whatever its fact may turn out to be, whether corpuscle or wave, or possible alternative or substitute. The approach of Socialization presents itself primarily as the search for organization and coherence: and if this takes shape somewhat surprisingly as specification of Knowledge, with knowledge itself the organization aspect of the entire field of research,[17] the surprise will be confined to outsiders to

[17] It will be observed that the K in Fig 3 now begins to fill up with richer meanings than it had in the first descriptive presentation of the field FEKL. This appears in more detail when we come to inspect the place of biology among the sciences.

its difficulties: while those who have had to wrestle personally with problems of precise statement within its range will find themselves readily at home in considering it in that way. Mathematics is not only itself a form of language, but it has in recent years been compelled to involve itself most intricately in all the various phases of linguistic interpretation, prominent among which is logic, so frequently discussed with conflicting views as to whether mathematics is a form of logic or logic a form of mathematics. For us here the issue as between mathematics and logic is a passing quarrel, due to imperfectly formulated statements: while the great situation, the identification of mathematics and language in one general scientific and methodological region, gives itself emphatic exhibition. Mathematics and Linguistic interpretation may be considered together under the one name, Semantic Analysis. Psychology in its turn has technical work to do in holding Facts and Knowledge, Physics and Sociology, together on the "subjective" side, similar to the work which Semantics, Mathematics and Logic, has to do in holding them together on the "objective" side. The grouping then stands forth, with the understanding that Semantic Analysis includes mathematics, logic and all other forms of linguistic-factual interpretation, as follows:

| | |
|---|---|
| PSYCHOLOGICAL ANALYSIS (F″E″) | PHYSICAL ANALYSIS (F″L″) |
| SOCIAL ANALYSIS (K″E″) | SEMANTIC ANALYSIS (K″L″) |

The appended letters refer to the differentiation of regions in Fig. 3.

Suppose now that some one presents Biology for consideration with respect to this scheme of differentiation of scientific approach, and makes the assertion that its characteristics are not herein properly allowed for. A little consideration, I think, will show that exactly the case of Biology is in point to prove the value of the arrangement. Biological studies are covered by the physical-factual approach, under the dominance of its present-day clue-word, the electron, to their farthest extreme. Far, however, as this aspect, this method, of study may be carried, it remains but an aspect. Biological studies are also covered by the social-knowledge-organization-organism approach, and this likewise extends to the farthest sub-cellular extreme: and yet however far it be carried it remains but one aspect, alongside the other aspect. Biology presents directly and immediately the great concrete case of whole and part, organ and organism. A vitalism is merely an attempt to insert an interpretative element to take care of the manifest interconnection of the "physically" stated "facts," *after* these latter have been inspected as separate, and *when* the defectiveness of such separations is strongly felt. The semantic interpretation, in contrast, is carried on by differential valuations within a single field.

I refer back to the attitude expressed at the beginning of this paper that the distinction between metaphysical and scientific is one of method, a distinction between poor method and good method, between broken method and whole method. It is apparent now that the distinctions here suggested within the sciences themselves are also those of method, not this time between poor methods and good methods, but between interlocking methods of approach. So also the intermediate grouping distinguishing portrayal sciences from technique sciences is likewise one of method, and, indeed, probably one of provisional method, not one that is apt to hold its place, as knowledge develops.

13. *The Foundations of Mathematics.*

"Foundations of mathematics" is a phrase conventionally used to describe intricate discussions of the inter-valuation of geometry, number theory and analysis, and of the interpretation of all of these together in terms of "minds" and "facts." These discussions are carried on for the most part in the language form L-Prop, and by techniques F′rel.L′, and they offer the most striking present-day illustration of the principle of Simmel that in human knowledge the foundations are commonly less secure than the structures built upon them, and that the more "fundamental" the problems the more prevalent this insecurity.[18] The treatment of the foundation problems of mathematics under semantic analysis, recognizes the language L-Symb. as peculiarly that of mathematics, and applies it in the technique $\text{Lim}_f\text{L}''$ for the discussion of the wider problems. The first necessity here is a semantic theory of number, and such a theory is indeed an essential component in the wider generalization of the semantic analysis itself. In such a theory the initial identification of the linguistic number *One* with *one fact*

[18] G. Simmel, Soziologie, p. 13.

is abandoned. With the deprivation of the initial *One* of its implied reality, the problems of the "reality" of zero and of infinites, whether single or in hierarchies, disappear: for all these symbols are placed on the same operational basis. The operational treatment applies to the world taken as Fact, not in its units or elements, but in its operational entirety. These inquiries go too far afield to permit discussion here. A later section (§ 17) of this paper, while set up for the whole field, is, however, of special direct application in this region.

14. *The Background of Sociology.*

When the student of society is no longer required to give a realistic value to society as over against the individual, or a realistic value to the individual as over against society, or possibly unintelligible realistic values to both, his background difficulties have disappeared. Individual presentations, that is reports in individualized terms, appear as limiting expressions to reports in social terms. Reports in social terms may also be made to appear as limiting expressions to reports in individual terms. It is the first of these twin approaches which yields the greatest values today: the second is so hampered by tribal actualizations of personality that the clarified form is not easily apprehended or communicated, and will not be till long passage has been made through the alternative expression. At the same time subjective-objective contrasts, once they are taken as neither individual per se nor social per se, are also gone. A tool can be an external object, and a man's activity, and a society's development, all at one time and in one technical terminology: since the dichotomic splits in their rigid separations have disappeared.

As hints towards the approach in this field I will insert two rules taken from the provisional framework set up for this method of interpretation in a paper previously cited:[19]

I. All Language-Knowledge-Fact about men in society must be in terms which are not dominated by distinctions of durational and instantaneous, of spatial and non-spatial, or of social and individual: but which use such distinctions, if and when any of them appear, only as functional discriminations within the knowledge.

II. Whatever is taken as having environment, and whatever is taken as environment to it, must in all studies of life, of mind and of society, be equally participant in space, in time and in the social.

15. *The Basis of Operational Physics.*

The physics of Newton was a study of mass in a background of absolute, or Newtonian, space and time. With the development of the CGS units, it was until recent years assumed that these units as verbal expressions had direct and immediate correspondence to unit facts. The experiments of the last decade in the region of electrons and rays and the attempts at sub-atomic construction have destroyed this correspondence, not merely in its previous form, but in principle. The development on the theoretical side, starting with DeBroglie and continuing through

[19]Revue internationale de sociologie, 37, pp. 266-7.

Heisenberg, Schroedinger and others, shows this clearly: and Heisenberg's principle of uncertainty that the error in specifying position and the error in specifying momentum are in inverse ratio so that if certainty is attained as to the one the probability of error for the other will be infinite, is but a notation in a special field of a status which semantic analysis establishes for all knowledge. It was Einstein, who, marking a peak in the curve of development through Minkowski and Lorentz, led the way in this particular, by breaking down the old fixed concepts of space and time: and the inquiry of Bridgman into the operational construction of all physical concepts, has gone far towards generalizing the position. By operational physics we may therefore understand all physical investigation in which external i. e., extra-scientific, control has been abandoned, and in which the actuality values of any term in its mathematical or linguistic formulations are controlled solely by the inner developments of the science itself. From an unpublished paper on the postulates of operational physics I cite the following attitudes characteristic of it:

a. The subject-matter of physics is secured by the stress on Fact within the field FEKL, and the particular "subjects" or "objects" emphasized are secured by selections of particular formulations for attributions of substantive factuality-value.

b. The determination of such stress must be established wholly within the range of physical experience, experimentation and formulation.

c. Any such stress is legitimate as hypothesis, and

the choice among hypotheses rests with their utility within physics.

d. Fact, for Physics, shall be the factual value (reference, interpretation or implication) of physical language in the background of physical experience and knowledge.

e. Science, for Physics, shall be the self-contained linguistic-mathematical formulation of physical experience and physical fact.

f. Physical science and physical fact shall be alike durational and spatial, operational and transitional.

g. Factual and formulational correspondence shall be analytic.

h. No dichotomic (logical) separation between regions of fact and regions of knowledge shall appear in physics, either direct or by implication.

i. No one-to-one correspondence between word and fact shall appear in physics.

j. Existential implications shall have instantaneous values as limits to formulation, and shall in no other sense be treated as existential.

k. Facts, whenever for any purpose taken as durationally atomistic, shall be considered as within a field which is analytically systemic.[20]

16. *The Technique of Psychology.*

We throw out of account all constructions of nonspatial psychological existence. We throw out of ac-

---

[20][From the Preface to The Principles of Quantum Mechanics, by P. A. M. Dirac, (1930) I cite the following passage: "The growth of the use of transformation theory, as applied first to relativity and later to the quantum theory, is the essence of the new method in theoretical physics. Further progress lies in the direction of making our equations

count all quasi-localizational treatments of the psychic as effluvia of physically developed physiology and neurology. We inspect the realistic terms of structural psychology, such as concept, cognition, sensation, feeling, and emotion, as limiting expressions in the sense developed in previous sections of this paper. We develop then the technique of those operations and procedures which are commonly taken to be subjective-individual, regarding them as frames of expression primarily for social portrayals, but already with indications of their importance for physical portrayals.[21] Such a psychology will be operational in a sense analogous to that in which the term operational has been used for mathematics and for physics. The difficulties in its development are enormously increased by the problem of inter-communication between languages. Whereas mathematical terms remain precise in removal from one nation to another: and physical terms have secured a close approximation to precision through the power of their mathematical formulations; psychological terms are wholly un-

---

invariant under wider and still wider transformations. This state of affairs is very satisfactory from a philosophical point of view, as implying an increasing recognition of the part played by the observer in himself introducing the regularities that appear in his observations, and a lack of arbitrariness in the ways of nature, but it makes things less easy for the learner of physics. The new theories, if one looks apart from their mathematical setting, are built up from physical concepts which cannot be explained in terms of things previously known to the student, which cannot even be explained adequately in words at all. Like the fundamental concepts (e.g., proximity, identity) which everyone must learn on his arrival into the world, the newer concepts of physics can be mastered only by long familiarity with their properties and uses.'']

[21]The exigencies of the quantum have already led to various suggestions from writers of widely different viewpoints that interpretation will require some combination of radiant neurological construction with radiant factual physical construction.

translatable in any exact sense. The background clottings of implication for these terms as between French, German and English, and even within English as between England and America, are such that progress will hardly be possible until a thoroughly cold-blooded attempt is made in terms of all three languages at once, and perhaps of several other types of language as well, to secure specifications of meaning interchangeable between them.[22]

### 17. *The Paradox of One-to-One Correspondences.*

For final emphasis upon an issue between facts and language that is characteristic for the development of semantic analysis, we may make use of a form of reasoning in L-Prop and F′rel.L′.

Let us place before our consideration mathematical

---

[22] ''Gestalt-psychologie'' makes advance over older introspective and naturalistic psychologies in the specialized attention it gives to structures, but it is defective in that it still sees its phenomena as ''inner'' or ''psychic'' in dichotomic, logical split from the world of the ''outer'' and ''material'': it is also hampered by the fact that it has made no thorough analysis of the ''individual-social'' and ''actor-action'' phases of its subject-matter. The ''organismic'' psychology of Professor J. R. Kantor has long seemed to me the most advanced construction that we possess in the direct line of growth of psychology as a science. Professor Kantor fully rejects all specialized description of his materials as ''psychic'' or ''inner,'' and he takes the ''organism as a whole'' as the locus of the behaviors he studies, envisioning this organism, however, as functioning in an objectively given physical space and physical time, rather than in a space-time in which it is itself analytically participant. Freud and his co-workers made researches of the highest importance into the conduct of men, and established the life-long durational frame as that in which conduct must be appraised: but they made no theoretical constructions of value, and the jargon of the ''sub-conscious'' which so many Freudians employ is worse than worthless. Expanding greatly from the Freudian base, Korzybski has secured an extensive development in his Generalized Semantics and psycho-logics, to which attention will be directed in connection with the discussion of his more specialized interpretations in the mathematical and semantic fields in the next succeeding chapter.

induction, considering it primarily with the vision of Poincaré rather than with that of Russell or of the realists of the German idiom. This rests on a postulatory presentation of "one," and indeed in such form that the "one" is taken as involving "another one," the two together permitting mathematical substitution without precedence in postulatory authority of the one over the other one. The postulation therefore includes the one-to-one.

Many systems, indeed, exist which take these elements apart, value them in one way or another, and attempt thereby to gain interpretations. Characteristic of all of these systems is their inability to find basis of agreement. I present here, not the systems, but the situation in which they arise.

Inspecting all of the formulations of the one-to-one correspondence, we may distinguish two typical cases, which we may differentiate as follows:[23]

a) that in which we have the "one" as operational in one-to-one, and as specialized component of the system. We may call this case the *one*.

b) that in which we have the "one" as actuality or entity, mathematical, philosophical or practical: it being taken in its own right, so that with respect to it the one-to-one correspondence appears as relational. We may call this case the ONE.

The ONE has thus the values of outer to the one-to-one, while the *one* has the values of inner to it.

---

[23] [This presentation of the situation was made prior to the special differentiation of two forms of postulation, x-to-X and x-to-x, for purposes of research in Part II of this book, but it manifestly leads directly to those postulations.]

Inspect any instance of a split between reality and knowledge: letting the first member of the split have any of the values of actuality, fact or objectivity: and the second member have any of the values of subjectivity, theory, science, intelligence or formulated language-knowledge.

This split receives symbolization as a dichotomy between ONE and *one*.

But a dichotomy is a one-to-one in the form of one-to-(not-one), the *not-one* having values in the one-to-one just as the *one* has.

Hence any such distinction between *one* and ONE is an operation in one-to-one.

Hence in any application of the one-to-one, in the form of one-to-ONE, the ONE by that very application is transformed into *one,* and the split between the *one* and the ONE vanishes with the transformation.

The rule establishes itself: A one-to-one correspondence cannot be applied as between *one* and ONE, since it reduces the ONE to *one*.

To avoid this paradox it will be necessary to use some different technique by which to establish the ONE. But the condition of such technique would seem to be that it avoid the use of language, whether in words-common, terms or symbols: since words struggle to become terms, and terms to become symbols, and symbols turn out as above.

For mathematics in especial the one-to-one must remain within mathematics, that is, within language. The L-Symb form has validity within symbolic language, but for interpretation as between language and fact the value $Lim_f L''$ must be taken. The discussions of the foundations of mathematics in the form of a one-to-ONE are thereby as a whole excluded.

18. *Conclusion.*

Semantic analysis is in form an extension of mathematical analysis over the full linguistic field: in that extension it removes the conflict of issues which arises in the attempt to interpret mathematical analysis in a setting of fixities of language and fixities of fact. The Aristotelian scientific discovery of logic was deified, especially in the Middle Ages, as a master of knowledge. The rise of modern science has brought into rivalry with it the inductive logics of discovery, but has allowed the implication of one-to ONE as between word and fact to remain. The further requirement is the complete destruction of this one-to-ONE by the establishment of analysis within the full field of knowledge. The value of such analysis will be found, not in any monumental aspects it may claim to possess as a theory, but in the ease with which it permits and itself furthers its own destruction, that better reconstruction may follow. The possibility of self-destructions is the test of values: and the speed of reconstructions is their measure.

# XIV

## RECONSTRUCTIONS OF LOGIC

The "logic" of Aristotle was the outcome of long investigations that may rightfully be described as of scientific type. A region of great confusion and difficulty in the use of words and sentences and arguments had been giving acute trouble to the Greek world for several generations: and this Aristotle explored as fully and fairly as he could by the best methods available to him. Throughout he exhibited much that same naturalness and objectivity that he gave to his studies of animal life and physical facts. His results he reported in terms of definitions, propositions, species, syllogisms and contradictions.[1]

In modern times the prevailing attitude towards logic has been that it is a mental discipline. In consequence those Aristotelian lines of guidance that had long been known as the "canons" of logic came to be styled "laws of thought." And in this mental garb logic proceeded to make the most emphatic claims to

[1]This description of "logic" in its earliest systematized form is broadly correct—no matter what "metaphysics" was involved in Aristotle's personal background of thought, no matter how sharply divergent have been the lines of evolution in this or that later school of Aristotelian logic, and no matter what specialized interpretation it may be possible to put upon Aristotle's treatises by inspecting them under the influence of some of these later schools. It is broadly correct, even though Aristotle's analysis was still very imperfect and incomplete as between the conflicting verbal implications of such presentations as "minds," "facts" and "words": imperfections of analysis which still remain and give rise to the worst of our difficulties in the appraisal of knowledge.

authority and power for the establishment and control of truth: claims that in one prominent construction or another are still prevalent today.

In our own generation we have witnessed a unique development. This is Logistic which seeks to combine all the generality of language with all the high prerogative of the mental logic. Its aim is an absolute verbal precision which will yield the final and perfect organization of formal knowledge. Though its suggestions reach back to Leibnitz it was not until the sharpened tools of symbolic calculus were secured that its construction could be attempted.

Logistic, however, endeavored too much: or, if not that, at least it made its claims too soon. Its earlier projects had gone little beyond the organization of the logical symbols and the mathematical symbols in a common system. From this it advanced to its more imposing constructions. But these led to new and unexpected difficulties. Logistic found itself facing problems of radical importance which it could not avoid, but which would not yield themselves to the clear and perfect solutions of its ambition. It resorted then to devices which seemed to its critics to fall short of that high sincerity which it professed. And the result of this has been that all the procedures and standards of the ancient inherited Aristotelian logic, and of all of the members of the Aristotelian logical family, have been opened up to new analysis and to searching tests.

In the present chapter I wish to offer a brief survey of the more notable of these recent experiments with the techniques of logic. This chapter, like the preceding, should be taken as supplemental to the main purpose of the book, which was the examination of mathematics as language, as presented in Part II. In that main investigation the whole issue of "logic" was set to one side, and we proceeded by the use of linguistic postulations, one of which corresponded in the rough to a most important central characteristic of all Aristotelian procedures, while the other split sharply away from it. Now we shall inspect the efforts that are under way to make progress in a similar field of inquiry by experiments arising directly within the logical framework itself.

I shall attempt no detailed analysis of any of these new systems, and I shall make no use of the specialized forms of postulations previously employed. I shall aim, however, to appraise certain of the typical distinctions among these lines of development with a view to pointing out that their total result seems to be the requirement of a new and deeper analysis of the organization of language, logic and mathematics, and of the phenomena of "word," "mind" and "fact" which they imply.

Let it be understood that no issue whatever is raised as to the continued utility and power of logic in those fields of its application which are by postulation, or by fiat, taken as "closed" for the purposes of its work. It is only where such "closed" fields overlap; where the indications appear that the analysis of these "fields is itself imperfect and the "closing" of them precarious: and where logical attitudes have themselves participated in the "closing": that the difficulties appear.

Let it be recognized further that the problems involved have been discussed extensively, though tentatively, by the many philosophical and psychological books on logic which have sought wide orientation over the general field of knowledge. In especial the instrumental and experimental logics have raised perhaps all of these issues. There is a great practical difference, however, between such generalized discussion, and the close analysis which is necessary where logic-at-work—its actual tools and procedures—are in difficulty. I shall take for granted the former type of study as a stimulant to research, but I shall give it no direct attention. Instead I shall confine myself to the actual working experiments that have been found necessary where mathematical and physical problems are so pressing that they cannot be set aside, and where the older logical techniques have failed of success even in their most powerful modern expansions.

As a guide for the presentation and discussion of these recent constructions I shall employ the three Aristotelian canons, those of identity, of non-contradiction and of the excluded middle, or "third." This is not for a moment to imply that these canons offer an adequate frame for all logical discussion. They have had their very prominent place in the older logical history, but their consideration has been greatly subordinated in the more recent philosophical discussions, from which indeed they have at times disappeared entirely. Nevertheless, in the latest technical developments, and ever more prominently, it is exactly these three canons, how they help or how they hinder, how their hampering effects can be evaded, or what postulatory substitutions can be made for them, or for some of them, that give us the best guide to our description. To characterize these three canons we may say that the first has to do with precision of word (and/or "fact"): the others with precision of sentence and syllogism (and/or "truth"). Since there are so many ways of expressing them, for the uses of one philosophical construction or another, whether in terms of existence or of truth, of language or of thought: and since every person who is at all interested in these problems is acquainted with them in various of their formulations; I shall not attempt to analyze them further here.[2] Our sole interest in them will be as we find them at work; and any attempt to expound them dialectically would be very apt to interfere with that direct vision which is required of us, if we are to observe at all accurately the developments that are now under way with respect to them.

With respect to the third canon, that of the excluded middle, one remark is, however, necessary. The requirement it makes of "either this, or that, and no alternative" was not set up by Aristotle himself in the

---

[2]Jevons' formulation of the canons is well known, as follows: "(1) Whatever is, is. (2) Nothing can both be, and not be. (3) Everything must either be, or not be." Keynes, after a long discussion of them (See Appendix B of his Studies and Exercises in Formal Logic, 4th ed. 1906) expresses them in the following formulas: "(1) I affirm what I affirm, and deny what I deny. (2) If I make any affirmation, I thereby deny its contradictory. (3) If I make any denial, I thereby affirm its contradictory." The earlier pages of Keynes' book may profitably be examined to illustrate the loosely general manner of discussion current in his day for those vital underlying issues which are now in course of being brought to sharp test.

rigid form which it later came to have. As scientist Aristotle was eminently practical, and since he saw the world and the men in it as involved in a process of development and growth, he made allowance for the situations of a contingent future, which he regarded as lying beyond the range of applicability for the canon.[3] This procedure was far from satisfactory to the Stoics; and, especially by Chrysippus, the canon was sharpened so as to yield a rigidly two-valued logic. It was this sharpened logic that, in due time, became the dominant logic of mathematics. Following the suggestion of Lukasiewicz we may call it Chrysippian in order to distinguish it within the more general frame of the Aristotelian logical system.

When the Cantorian construction appeared with its synthesis of mathematical procedures, it was this Chrysippian logic which harvested a crop of paradox. As investigation continued, the issue became ever more sharply drawn. If Chrysippian logic is to prevail, then much important mathematical work seems to lie under a threat of permanent logical insecurity. If, on the contrary, the mathematical procedure is to remain firmly established by right of its own power—and that, by the way, is just what mathematics most commonly achieves—then the Chrysippian logic is itself in a state of insecurity. Hence inevitably the compulsion to the many intricate investigations that are under way.

---

[3]Lukasiewicz discusses this point and cites from Aristotle, De interpr. 4. 17a 2, and 9. 19a 36: also from the Hermeneutik, Chap. IX. See Philosophische Bemerkungen zu mehrwertigen Systemen des Aussagenkalküls, Comptes Rendus des séances de la Société des Sciences et des Lettres de Varsovie, XXIII, 1930, Classe III, p. 75.

Before proceeding to description of the new systems let us first recall the historical conditions under which the Aristotelian logic was produced; and let us then observe the great technical expansion of this logic in symbolic form which preceded, and made possible, the precise formulation of the present issues. We may commence by reminding ourselves of that early chaos of words, implications, meanings and references, historically "pre-logical" which extends backwards towards what we commonly regard as the dawn of the "human" in the world. We may surmise a slowly increasing efficiency in the use of words across the ages, finally developing into a precision, spectacular in its day, in the verbal procedures of counting and measuring. The history of this development we know in Egypt and Asia Minor and along the Euphrates and in China prior to the great flower of Athenian culture. Here it is that we may see the birth of mathematics as a specialization within the great linguistic activity and behavior of men. We may pass on next to observe the Sophists harshly displaying the inadequacies of language in its more general uses: and after them Socrates, earnestly searching for a new efficiency of speech in the analysis of human relations and in the service of human behavior. We come, finally, to Aristotle, investigating words and their uses as systematically, as objectively, as "naturally," as he investigated, through his own observation and through travelers' tales and reports, the animals of known, of unknown, and even, most regrettably—though at times most amusingly—of non-existent regions. It is in Aristotle, thus, that we have the formal differentiation of logic out of language under the stimulus of mathematical precision: and, since the modern "mental" power plant had not yet been introduced, the Aristotelian logic was primarily and openly a technique of linguistic precision.

The Aristotelian syllogism furnished a framework for the display of logical ingenuity which seemed adequate to men for a matter of two thousand years. Leibnitz made suggestions and various tentative sketches for a universal scientific language and calculus, and minor attempts at development followed:[4] but it was not until the work of Boole in the middle of the last century, that a new and greatly expanded system of logical calculation was introduced, that, namely, which has led to all the procedure now known as Symbolic Logic. Here again it was the precision of mathematics which led the way to precisions for logic, since in Boole's development algebraic forms of expression were directly employed: but mathematics had even more to do with the innovation than this, for it was almost wholly to secure a logical technique that would give more satisfactory forms of expression to mathematical proofs that the work was needed. Peirce made many contributions to the symbolism of classes, of propositions, and especially of relations: and Schröder, using his results, proceeded to a new systematization which was so successful that the technique is now most commonly known as the Boole-Schröder Algebra of Logic. It has been usefully employed, but

[4]For these earlier developments, and as well for appraisal of the contributions of Boole, Peirce and Schröder, see Lewis, A Survey of Symbolic Logic, Chap. I.

its limitations have remained those of an algebra. Adopted by Peano and his collaborators, with some important changes and additions of symbolization, and incorporated in a common running transcription along with the symbols of mathematics, the procedure of this algebra yielded in the Formulaire one of the earlier types of Logistic.

It was Peirce who, in addition to his other great contributions, introduced the propositional function, though not as yet by that name, into symbolic logic, and here we have a further profound influence of mathematics upon logical development, much more important potentially, indeed, than the Boolean calculus; taking its rise, though it did, out of this latter. In the Principia Mathematica of Whitehead and Russell it became the central construction whereby propositions, propositional functions, classes and relations, entered into a great logical synthesis with a range all the way from the "entities" of its reference to the ideal validities and validity of its goal. Here finally upon the basis of a handful of primitive ideas, or notions, or postulates, all of a logical nature, was set up a construction much more imposing than a mere logical tool which mathematicians could use, or than a specialized logical language which could be incorporated along with the specialized mathematical language to form a common system of logistic expression. It was to be a dominating logical framework into which mathematics, and in anticipation much other knowledge, could be absorbed, and by means of which it was hoped these could be reorganized into a self-sanctioned and absolute validity.

In the Principia we have the apotheosis of Chrysippian logic. The three canons are all formally in authority, and in forms aspiring to maximum precision. But it is apotheosis like all other apotheosis of our experience in this world: life blood is drained away to secure it, and an act of fealty remains necessary to sustain it.

All of the remaining constructions which we shall have to describe depart radically from the method of the Principia in one or another important respect. These we may examine in three groups: first, those which, by insistence on the linguistic frame, seek their consistency apart from that "intellectual" or "mentalistic" authority which Principia maintains: second, those which by postulation or by dictum, deprive the third canon of its Chrysippian power: third, those which see the seat of all paradox in the first canon, whether in its material or formal uses. But before doing this, and in order to get sharper background for their consideration, some further characterization is necessary for the system of the Principia.

This system while "mentalistic" is not psychological: it has no interest in the workings of "individual minds," its procedure being that of a generalized mental frame.[5]

Thus, while it is "symbolic" it is not technically "linguistic," nor is it what is now beginnng to be known as "semantic." That is to say, while its "symbols" are elements of "language," their system

[5]It is to be understood that most of the terms which it is necessary to use in this characterization are crude and unreliable. See the list of current-reference descriptions in Chapter III and the accompanying comments of the text.

of meanings is not linguistically or semantically developed: but the "meanings" and the "system of meanings" are read into them under a mental (but not psychological) construction, with respect to which the language forms are merely conveniences or tools.

It seeks its generality, its validity and its separate validities through an "abstraction" which retains the sharpness of Aristotelian definition, though avoiding the mixed "verbal" and "factual" implications of the first canon in the form Aristotle gave it. The "discretenesses" of the meanings of its symbols have orientation to wraith-like "entities" without which the system would have no fixation whatever.

Given these "entities" the logic of the Principia is "functional." Here, in these two terms, we have the specification, both of its "abstraction" and of its "mental."

While its start is made with a theory of propositions,[6] these propositions are at once fitted into the construction of the "propositional function"; and upon this the construction of "relations" is built, so that the "relations" are "functional" themselves, while at the same time they both actualize and organize actualization of "entities."[7] The propositions

[6]Although he rests his whole procedure on the postulation of certain "primitive propositions," Russell holds that "a proposition is not a single entity but a relation of several": in agreement with the general position that the universe consists of objects having various qualities and standing in various relations. Principia Mathematica, Vol. I (1910) p. 51, p. 45.

[7]I remind the reader again that many of the words I have been using, and which I am compelled to use for lack of others for the purpose, are wholly unreliable. Take even the word "relation" which has been under microscopic examination in logical investigation ever since De Morgan announced the emergence of the "relation of relation"

have truth or falsehood. The propositional functions abstract from them, and so have neither truth nor falsehood themselves; but this always in such manner that they must be filled in with truth or falsehood. They abstract from the special case, but not from the principle of test: and it is thus that they themselves still proceed under Chrysippian control.[8] They take over from mathematics, therefore, not merely the enormously useful procedure of "function," but at the same time they take with it that very borderland

---

in logical symbolism. At the start we have relations as another way of speaking about classes, or as an alternative manner of expression, that is to say, of symbolic technique, for classes. We have then studies of relations running far beyond what could be expressed in an algebra of classes. We have efforts at the study of relations wholly in logical "intension." We have relations taken as primitive, as well as those offered as defined. Relations may be developed out of propositions or out of propositional functions. In this latter development they are derived from two-valued propositional functions, and are thus opposed to classes which are derived from one-valued functions. Here the relations may transform into a sort of "relational function." In the Whitehead-Russell construction, after all their functional development, they come back to "definition in extension." Indeed the problem of relations, so far as the issue runs in the old forms of distinction between "intension" and "extension" is as confused today as it ever has been. I do not list these differences with any implied reproach against the many manners of discussion and development. Quite to the contrary, it is just in that way that knowledge is advanced. I do mention them as exhibiting a great uncertainty as to whether the factual status of the word "relation" is properly brought before us in its Aristotelian constructions.

[8]With apologies to Russell for using one of his earlier remarks, but in the belief that early expressions often enable us to peer more clearly beneath the elaborate raiment of later device, I cite from his "Mathematical Logic as Based on the Theory of Types," Amer. J., vol. 30, p. 226, (1908): "The first difficulty that confronts us is as to the fundamental principles of logic known under the quaint name of 'laws of thought.' 'All propositions are either true or false,' for example, has become meaningless. If it were significant, it would be a proposition, and would come under its own scope. Nevertheless some substitute must be found, or all general accounts of deduction become impossible." As the development from primitive propositions is made in the Principia the "excluded middle" enters as proposition *2.11 and is provided with a form of proof.

vagueness of interpretation for the meaning of "function," which it should be the first duty of logic to clear away, if "logic" is to exert supreme rule.[9]

When contradiction arises in mathematical development, recourse is had to a doctrine of "types," resting on ranges of significance, and involving a special doctrine of "descriptions." Only thus is full consistency given its appearance of approach in this system: and it is just because of this procedure, which can hardly be regarded as other than a makeshift, that other lines of attack have been felt by other investigators to be compulsory. This doctrine of "types" may be regarded merely as a technical device for the handling of certain mathematical difficulties: or as the beginnings of reconstruction of Chrysippian logic: or as a forecast of the downfall of logic itself. In whichever view, it presents historically the first penetrating vision of the sharpest problem which logic has to face.[10]

We are now in a position to use these characteristics of the Principia—namely the withdrawal into the

---

[9]Russell's view is that "propositional functions are the more fundamental kind from which the more usual kinds of function, such as 'sin $x$,' or 'log $x$,' or 'the father of $x$' are derived." Principia, p. 15. He also tells us repeatedly that "a function is essentially an ambiguity," a remark which is made with restricted application, but which may nevertheless be taken as much more broadly valid than his intention.

[10]Russell, (Amer. J., vol. 30, p. 243) in introducing the Axiom of Reducibility, without which the construction of "types" would be wholly infertile, described it as containing the "essence of the usual assumption of classes," and hopefully added: "At any rate it retains as much of classes as we have any use for, and little enough to avoid the contradictions which a less grudging admission of classes is apt to entail." For his further discussion of the practical justification for the use of this axiom, see Principia, I, p. 25 and p. 62. For classes as incomplete symbols and for the opportunist reconciliation of extension and intension see Idem, p. 75.

region of mental abstraction or abstract mentality, the functional procedure which still involves "entities" as references of its functions, and the linkage to the language of factuality through the retention of the classical canons and particularly of the sharp definition of the first canon,—as a background against which to inspect the other recent lines of logical reconstruction. First we have to consider the transfer from the mental to the linguistic base. Here again we will disregard the more general studies of speculative or tentative nature, running from Hobbes, Locke and Bentham to Welby and Ogden and Richards in England, stimulated by Bréal in France, and copiously developed by Mauthner in Germany: and we shall confine ourselves to the working procedures of Hilbert and Chwistek in the active attack upon insistent problems of science.

Hilbert inspects the "mental" as individually "psychological," but by a specific, though not fully analyzed, postulation, he sets it "apart from," "outside," "beyond," his logical procedure. Its name is "Anschauung," and when that name is not broad enough for his advancing work, he adds another name or two to help it. His materials he takes as linguistic-symbolical, and regards them as "objects" before his "Anschauung"; the mathematical and the logical symbols entering alike as such "objects." We may take his work, in a sense, as a "return to Aristotle," though under conditions immensely more complex than any of which Aristotle could ever have dreamed. Explicitly Hilbert makes his search for a full consistency, a "Widerspruchsfreiheit,"[11] something more positive and immediate than the "non-contradiction" of the Aristotelian system: so that one may, if one wishes, classify him as giving a reconstruction in the region of the second canon. This, however, as is manifest, is rather an incident of his change of base away from the mentalistic logics. So far as the first canon is concerned, the "identity" is fixed by a direct consolidation of "word" and "object," "Zeichen als Objekt": a consolidation which first appeared to him as carrying "discreteness" in opposition to a world of "Tatsachen" to which he gave consideration, but which in growing measure came to appear to him rather as "concrete." Here again we see his sharp departure from the point of view of Russell, whose "abstraction" yielded rather a ghostly "entity." So also Hilbert's "relations," instead of being functionally dominant over the whole construction, are merely the incidental attributes of his "Objects." With this treatment, and in his widened linguistic base, he evades the "types." His technical development has proceeded to great lengths with the important issues of mathematical consistency, but it, like Russell's, still exhibits an unsolved problem, intimately connected with the basic postulation of his entire procedure.

In Chwistek we find a more explicit insistence on the linguistic frame than in Hilbert, although he does

---

[11]In his earlier stages of this work he spoke of "Widerspruchslosigkeit," thus still retaining the negative form of expression. His procedure has been repeatedly discussed in parts I and II of this book, especially in Chap. V.

not give us so steady and firm an employment of it. Where Hilbert combines logical and mathematical symbols in a simple linguistic form, Chwistek sees before him logical, mathematical and linguistic territories, and strives towards the organization of all three in his theoretical "Semantik," a "meta-mathematical method of analysis" which will dominate in the end everywhere. In his first essays of a "Semantik" the mental logic persists alongside, so that we have to deal both with systems of judgment and with systems of expressions. The mental postulate is reduced to a minimum of observation and of capacity to carry out directions. Nevertheless, we have the old arrogancy of the mental logic still showing itself in the ever-repeated insistence that once a full theoretical "Semantik" is attained, knowledge will be finally and absolutely established, and that this, that and the other pretender to the throne will have been driven out forever.[12] In his earlier studies Chwistek regarded "types" as inevitable in any theory on the ground that they were characteristic of the very nature

[12]Since my description of Chwistek's mathematical construction in Chap. V was put into type, I have been able to examine the two of his papers there listed which were not then available to me. The harshness of characterization in these earlier remarks was solely designed to illuminate the particular issues in question, and it should not be read over into an appraisal of Chwistek's procedure from the wider point of view of the logical problem. His work is brilliant and of great interest and concerns many of the most vital issues. Nevertheless, it still seems to me to remain true that, just as at the start his interest lay in Poincaré's formulation of decisions "in a finite number of words," so at the latest stage of his development, it is words "finitely taken" which compose his "Semantik." Realistic separations remain between his materials, and between the components of each group of materials: and the control which he has in view remains "mechanistic." For his views on the status of the Alephs in his perfected semantic system, see p. 255 of the last of the papers cited in Chap. V.

of human thought. As he continued in his search for pure semantic theory, the "types" of actual use in mathematics became more and more special practical devices, which he has endeavored to develop carefully in their provisional practical values. His perfected theory has no place left for the Cantorian Alephs, which he now regards as "little consonant with the methods of logic."

We have next to consider those proposed departures from the Chrysippian logic, designed to secure consistency in the interpretation of mathematics, which have proceeded by revisions or changes of the third canon, that of the excluded middle.

Among these the project of Brouwer is perhaps the earliest, and by far the most widely known. This is that the canon be cut down in range and restricted officially to issues which it can successfully handle. It is Brouwer's "Intuition"—his "Fundamental Intuition," the "oerintuitie"—upon which he relies to make the decision and issue the order. The critical point for Brouwer is the passage from the finite to the infinite, and here it is a solidly realistic attitude towards both finites and infinites which dominates all of his thought and development. Here it is that the "Intuition" makes its decision. It must be observed, however, that the "Intuition" will also be called upon, if it exerts authority to this extent—and whether this is explicitly stated in the construction or not—to furnish bail and bond for that part of the Chrysippian logic which it retains: and behind that, it will be called upon to decree likewise the basic certainty of the distinction between the finite and the infinite. Here we have issues which lie far beyond the range of our present limitation to logic itself "at work."[13]

Following upon Brouwer's development, Barzin and Errera made an effort to discover what would happen if propositions in the nature of "thirds" were permitted in a logic, and they concluded that the Brouwer project would lead to inconsistency. Given "third" propositions, then an "excluded fourth" was one of the prospects in sight, and this various writers have considered. Church widened the basis of examination by suggesting that a stage had now been reached with respect to the third canon in which free postulation had become permissible, and that various constructions (of which he suggested three) might be developed and tested: and he held that the choice as between such postulated canons would now depend, not upon the "truth" of the canon, but upon its efficiency and utility.[14]

As early as 1900 MacColl had developed a system of logic into which he introduced "impossibility" as one of his fundamental ideas conveying a logical value

---

[13]An essay by Brouwer giving special attention to logical construction is Intuitionistische Zerlegung mathematischer Grundbegriffe, Deutsche Math.-Ver., 33, p. 251. See also item (G) in the list of Brouwer's papers in Chap. IX. Of his development along logical lines Lukasiewicz writes: "Das sind nur Bruchstücke eines Systems, dessen Konstruktion und Bedeutung noch völlig im Unklaren liegt." Op. cit., pp. 74-75.

[14]M. Barzin et A. Errera, "Sur la logique de M. Brouwer," Académie Royale de Belgique, Bulletins de la classe des Sciences (5) vol. 13 (1927), pp. 56-71. A. Church, "On the Law of Excluded Middle," Amer. M. S. Bull., vol. 34, p. 75 (1928). See also Arnold Dresden, "Some Philosophical Aspects of Mathematics," Amer. M. S. Bull., July-August, 1928. O. Becker discusses extensively all of these situations in his book, "Die Mathematische Existenz."

distinct from that of "false" in the old two-valued opposition of truth and falsehood. As the "unit" of reasoning and as the "ultimate constituent" of symbolic logic he took the "statement," envisioning this in its genetic linguistic status, and treating the proposition as a specialized form of it. Characteristic is that he was able to deal with the null class, not as a class "contained in every class," but as one "excluded from every real class."[15] Lewis, later, in developing his system of "strict implication," which he organized in connection with a system of "material implication" used a somewhat similar approach, and obtained five "truth-values" in the general region of the canon of the excluded middle. There were "true," "false," "impossible," "the falsity of the impossible," and "the impossibility of the false," the two last being capable of being read as "possible" and "necessarily true": and with these he brought "consistency" into a specialized position in logical development.[15] Post produced a general scheme for the construction of "m-valued truth systems," but left his construction purely formal without specific logical development.[17]

Extensive further investigations with respect to

---

[15]La Logique symbolique et ses applications: Bibliothèque du Congrès international de Philosophie, III, pp. 135-183, 1901. Symbolic Logic and its Applications, London, 1906. His use of the "statement" as unit of reasoning gives a potential approach at oppositive poles from that of Russell. Later logico-mathematicians, and indeed Russell himself, have been inclined to see in it a mere imperfect expression of the propositional function. More probably the reverse is true, and MacColl's manner of attack will hold the greater promise for the developments of the future.

[16]A Survey of Symbolic Logic, Chap. V, 1918.

[17]Introduction to a General Theory of Elementary Propositions, Amer. J., vol. 43, p. 163, 1921.

the third canon have been carried on in the last decade by Lukasiewicz and Tarski, and by a group of enthusiastic younger men who have ranged themselves with them. Lukasiewicz began by a study designed to introduce modality—possibility—into the logical framework. Inspecting the classical logic as two-valued by the test of its canon of the excluded third, he called his new logic three-valued:[18] and styling the older logic Chrysippian he described his own development as non-Chrysippian. In the earlier stages of his work he analyzed the various presentations of modality, and experimented with a number of definitions for those which could stand logically constructive tests. From a three-valued logic to a many-valued logic was the next step: but he soon concluded that "many" values, when these values were any finite number above three, were of comparatively little import for the more essential aspects of logical development: and with Tarski he advanced to a program for an Aleph-valued logic, and to the beginnings of its construction. All of these

[18]For a simple illustration of a three-valued logic (one, however, for which the Polish mathematicians must not be held responsible) we may consider the parlor game of Yes, No and Maybe So, in which the actor is required to identify some unknown object by asking questions, in response to which he may receive answers in the above forms only. Now, supposing the "Maybe So" to involve uncertainty, not merely in the information of the answerer, but instead in the structural world; and supposing that three situations, corresponding to the three types of answer, and these three only, "exist," and "exist definitely" in such a world—assuming further that one can attach meaning to these phrases; and assuming an endeavor to give precision and efficiency to language with respect to it: then a three-valued logic would be required. One will think at once of modern statistical and probability theories in physics. The possibilities and impossibilities of such probability or possibility are interestingly discussed by Bridgman in his Gibbs lecture for 1931, published under the title, "Statistical Mechanics and the Second Law of Thermodynamics," Amer. M. S. Bull., April, 1932.

logics, though non-Chrysippian, the originators still regard as Aristotelian.[19]

Without analyzing or appraising any of the logics of the group that is now being described, I may nevertheless point to the further problems that they open up. When Church suggests free postulation with respect to the third canon, he opens the way for a similar suggestion with respect to the first. When he proposes tests of serviceability for the third he becomes subject to counter proposals of similar tests for the first. Indeed we may remark a growing frequency of comment in logical works to the effect that in the appraisal of logic, logic itself can hardly be expected to sit as judge; comments that we must inevitably refer back for their incentive to the first appearance

[19]In addition to the paper by Lukasiewicz previously cited, see Jan Lukasiewicz and Alfred Tarski, Untersuchungen über den Aussagenkalkül, in the same volume of the Comtes Rendus, Varsovie, p. 1: and Alfred Tarski, Fundamentale Begriffe der Methodologie der deduktiven Wissenschaften, Monatshefte für Mathematik und Physik, XXXVII, No. 2. Paralleling this development is the work of Lesniewski who has produced a logical system called "Protothetic" and carrying with it an associated "Ontologie," in which he proceeds by the use of variable logical "funktors," His work is described by Lukasiewicz and Tarski as in certain aspects "still more general" than their own "erweiterten Aussagenkalkül." For his papers see Fundamenta Mathematicae, XIII, p. 319 and XIV, p. 242; also the volume of the Comptes Rendus, Varsovie, above cited, p. 111. For opportunity to examine reprints of these articles I am indebted to Alfred Korzybski who has discussed them in a paper read before the Mathematical Section of the American Association for the Advancement of Science, New Orleans, 1931, under the title "A Non-Aristotelian System and Its Necessity for Rigor in Mathematics and Physics." It is of incidental interest to observe that on the basis of three-valued and infinite-valued logics Lukasiewicz is able to make tests of the validities of some of the common, but less securely established, methods of proof used by the two-valued logics: and he points out that in the procedure of the "Diagonalverfahren" which I have discussed in Chap. XI, certain proofs are employed which, by his tests, should be rejected. Thereupon he raises the question as one of considerable interest as to whether it will be possible to find sounder proofs for such mathematical theorems as are based on the "Diagonalverfahren": Op. cit., pp. 73-74.

of "types" upon the logical scene. Beyond this when Lukasiewicz and Tarski construct an infinite-valued logic, they at once raise the question as to what significance such a logic will have for the old first canon, with its strident finiteness of definition which they still retain. With Aristotle's "practical" allowance for contingencies of the future, the question as to the coherence of his first and third canons did not necessarily arise: and it could perhaps be avoided for many-valued logics, so long as the "many" remained finite. But with "infinite values" the issue seems to enter in much the same form that it assumes in the crudest discussions of the infinite in every-day language: and since it is exactly the problems of the infinite in their more complex forms which these logics are constructed to solve: and since the words finite and infinite are a pair for which each term has expressible meaning only in terms of the other: it seems evident that the discrete finiteness of the individual word or symbol as used in the canon of identity is now at the point of being drawn into question, and that the way is being prepared for a further and more radical transformation of the Aristotelian procedure.

It is possible, of course, to take the view that the Whitehead-Russell development of the Principia, in which the intellectual-functional treatment dominates, does itself surmount all the difficulties of precision with respect to the first canon. Should this system, indeed, ever attain a complete consistency, or appearance of consistency, without the resort to special supporting devices, and should it clear up the status of function and entity, then its success might be exactly that which we need. Even then, its "primitive notions" would continue as subjects for further analysis; and its hugely laborious procedure would be incentive for the search for simpler methods. As the case stands today, however, this system is rather a challenge to immediate work in the further analysis and exploration of the canons themselves.

Should we consider the philosophical treatises on logic, and those especially deriving from pragmatism, and yielding experimental or instrumental logics, we would find a vast amount of preliminary work already done with respect to the field of the first canon. Again, in Bridgman's Logic of Modern Physics, while the book contains no strictly logical discussion, we find that the very material of investigation is the precision of the language of science, and the inadequacy for science of the old verbal precisions set up by Aristotle and inherited by modern logic.[20] Such an experimental study of the organization of words in their mathematical uses has been offered in Part II of this book: and it also may be taken as lying within this general range of inquiry.

In the meantime a direct attack upon the Aristotelian "identity" is being made by Alfred Korzybski, parts of whose unpublished work I have been privileged to examine in manuscript while the present book was passing through the press.[21] His approach is not

---

[20]The paper by Dr. Alexis Carrel, "The New Cytology, Science," March 20, 1931, is also very much in point.

[21]The origins of Korzybski's system are to be found in his book, "The Manhood of Humanity," 1921, and in two papers published under the title, Time-binding, the General Theory, 1924 and 1925. I shall

specifically logical, though it involves an appraisal of logic, and proposes a broadening of the logical basis to a new form he calls "semantic." He undertakes an explicit study of the characteristics of the language we use, and of the constructions we give it in reasoning, in terms of the scientific work that is required of it in the world today. Under such a study he finds that the whole Aristotelian construction has become antiquated, and is a hindrance, rather than a help, to the expression, development and interpretation of science.

Korzybski's fundamental assertion we may take to be that the Aristotelian language and logic are "*not similar* to the structure of the world and our nervous system."[22] He therefore discards the "is" of identity in the Aristotelian system, and proceeds to the investigation of structures: on the one side the structures exhibited by modern scientific knowledge, and on the other side the structures of language. It is, therefore, not merely the Aristotelian "logic" that he discards,

---

depend here on his New Orleans address previously cited. His comprehensive work under the title, "Science and Sanity: A General Introduction to Non-Aristotelian Systems and General Semantics," will soon be issued by the International Non-Aristotelian Library which he is establishing. The New Orleans address will be published as an appendix to this work.

[22]Structure is defined by Korzybski "in terms of relations and ultimately many-dimensional order." It is presented as "the only possible link between the objective and verbal levels," and as "the only possible content of knowledge." "The empirical search for, and verbal formulation of, structure," is, he says, "the only aim of knowledge and science." See his New Orleans address, previously cited, Propositions Nos. 11, 12 and 13. Mathematics is given its preferred standing among language systems, not so much by right of its own semantic consistency, as because it is "the only language in the main similar in structure to the world around us *and* the nervous system." Idem, No. 17.

but also the entire Aristotelian "system"[23]—its metaphysics, its attitudes towards men and nature, and all of the psychological and epistemological interpretations and languages developed within it. The Aristotelian language he describes as "elementalistic," and his demand therefore is for a "non-elementalistic, non-Aristotelian language."[24]

Under the tests of this "non-elementalistic" language the old psychologies and logics with all of their "splits" of meaning are rejected, and in place of them a new "psycho-logics" is constructed.[25] Characteristic of the new language is multiordinality of terms, successive levels of meanings, with increments of power and range of abstraction at each level. This he exhibits for illustrative and educational purposes in his "Structural Differential." We may best understand this construction by bringing to mind the "types" of the original Russell theory, or the "Stufen" of later writers: except that whereas the "types" were primarily introduced to meet a special need, and the "Stufen" are held within con-

---

[23]Just as passage was made from Euclidean to non-Euclidean geometries in the narrower logical range; and from Newtonian physics to the non-Newtonian physics of Einstein, this time by the destruction of the verbal split of space from time: so now Korzybski presents his work as a non-elementalistic, non-Aristotelian system, with respect to which the older Aristotelian system stands as a special case. See the introductory pages of the New Orleans address.

[24]Special devices used by him for purposes of non-Aristotelian linguistic expression include subscripts to words, "to indicate individual names for individual objects, etc., or levels, or orders of abstraction for multiordinal terms": the dating of many words through the use of time coordinates; and a non-Aristotelian, or extensional system of punctuation.

[25]Korzybski finds important contributions in the work of Freud which he expects to embody in his construction through the formulation of a "Freudian system-function."

ventional logical lines, Korzybski's multiordinality has much broader range in terms of human behavior and of the modern expansion of scientific knowledge.

Into his semantic system, not as having contributed directly to its development, but as arising beside it, and capable of adaptation to it, he fits both the "Semantik" of Chwistek and the many-valued logics of Lukasiewicz and Tarski: though for them to be of use within his framework he proposes to strip from them the procedure of the first Aristotelian canon, and all of the "elementalism" which he finds they still employ. With respect to the special problems of mathematical consistency we obtain from Korzybski the assertions that mathematics is a language, that as such it is the best language the world possesses, and that, by taking it as a model and guide for the eventual reconstruction of all other language, the mathematical and physical paradoxes will find their solutions.[26] These assertions are similar to positions secured in the present book through the specialized use of a form of semantic postulation: and this is perhaps worthy of remark in view of the wide divergence of Korzybski's methods, points of approach and constructions from those herein employed.

We have now reached the end of the series of attempted reconstructions of logic which we have to display. Within a single generation we have seen the default of logic in the accomplishment of a necessary and important piece of scientific work lead to postulatory experiments with all of its age-old canons, and to

---

[26]See his New Orleans address.

projects for supplanting it entirely. Two comments are indicated. The first is that it will henceforth be difficult indeed for anyone at all conversant with the issue to speak of "logic" as a region of authority and certainty in a transforming world. The second is that before a new security is reached a vast amount of difficult analysis and construction will be necessary in those intricately connected regions which we have in the past much too glibly separated, one from another, under the names of language, logic and mathematics.

## XV

## CONCLUSION

The pleasantest aspect of investigations such as those that have engaged us is that they yield no formal "conclusions." They are work in progress. The phenomena we have been analyzing, whether linguistic, mathematical or logical, have throughout been taken as themselves processes, procedures, events. To take them so, is not merely to tolerate for them some historical discussion of incidental import. It is instead to regard them before us full-bodied in time, and as not otherwise to be known.

With materials and methods thus durational, the results of study must likewise be transitional, durational: Their merit, whatever it may be, must be found in such stepping stones as they lay down, not in a pretended capping of eternal arches.

For the field of our study, so described, we may claim that it is as direct, as vivid, as immediate, as that of any empirical science. Its processes in time, its durational events are man-in-action, man in the fullness of his function, man in his evolving behavior and power. The field is itself empirical: its most remote postulations are empirically derived: the sole purpose of its postulations is to aid further empirical advance.

Accepting, as scientifically presented to us, a world in evolution, life in evolution, man biologically in evolution, man socially in evolution, we proceed to inspect man expressionally, communicationally, reflectionally, speculatingly, scientifically in evolution.

We must, indeed, remark one peculiarity of this empirical field as compared with others. The language and meanings of men, thus durationally social, comprise all formulated knowledge: and thus all the knowledge that we can investigate: and thus all empirical science: so that within their frame stand the sun that, in knowledge once, went around the earth; the earth that, in later knowledge, went around the sun; the sun and earth that, in knowledge now, move in forward spiral; and whatever else of sun and earth the future may reveal. But this peculiarity is no more pronounced and no more repellant than that of ordinary words as they are daily used in conventional speech: those ordinary words that forever keep issuing their decisions upon earths and suns, and are forever finding their earths and suns transformed when other words arrive to report differently upon them. The two peculiarities may stand unhappily facing each other: and so drop out of observation as we proceed upon our empirical business.

Under such approach, and in the course of our study of the language of mathematics, we have found ourselves in sharp conflict with those constructions of logic which claim the power to dominate these fields of inquiry. That conflict should here arise has been inevitable. What logic asserts, wherever it assures itself of reign, are validities and truths, instantaneous and enduring. Submission to the flow of time, appraisal in the values of durations that must pass, are not of its acknowledged heritage. Once challenged in its claims, once required itself to take durational form, logic and its prerogatives must submit to empirical examination in fusion with whatever else of inquiry may appear. We have, it is true, raised no issue with logic in those regions of high generalization presided over by the philosophies and the epistemologies. With close restraint we have been content to make our study where logic directly is found in its durational organization with the symbols of mathematics and the expressions of the embedding language.

What the dogmatic logic presents to us where it enters scientific work is a certain anthropic self-conceit. Scientists have for the most part long since freed themselves from the immodesties of individual self-conceit: but the immodesties of the generation, or of the age, stand in hardly better case. As for the pretensions of the human race in whole, once we rise above our "local" viewpoint and inspect ourselves in full evolutionary setting, there is little indeed of arrogance we can retain. That we have arrived after some hundreds of thousands of years at our present intellectual status is no guarantee that that status is high: rather is it to be taken as indication that further thousands of years may bring such progress that our present achievements will disappear in the perspective.

Not for a moment does this attitude deprive us of firm footing as we proceed with our work. Rather it establishes us all the more firmly for the substantial work we have to do. Just as Bridgman, from his operational viewpoint, has listed many "meaningless questions'' in physics, so likewise many meaningless questions will still be asked in other fields of inquiry. They will be meaningless, at least for our present generation, for our present stage of progress, and in the terms in which they are at present framed. Those who persist in asking such questions will be given no satisfaction: but it does not matter: they fail of satisfaction anyway, once they take time to think their answers over. As for the rest of us we may take our certainties where we find them.

In the inquiries we have had under way for the durational field of language, logic and mathematics, such certainties have been present in the very body of the algorithmic, geometric and analytic procedures: and from them outwards we have sought to extend the ranges of coherence. We have been able to present the three great historic branches of mathematics as three semantic fields. By analysis of the consistencies of these fields in their full durational form, we have been able to expand and deepen them in union. To accomplish this has required not only a firm hand of control upon the logics and the logistics, but has involved as well the expulsion of the cruder linguistic realisms in which the logics rest. For their many practical uses in conventional acceptance, these cruder realisms remain unimpaired. So also logic itself retains all the authority it has ever effectively had, for all linguistic situations in which the precedent analysis has been adequate for its safe employment.

It is in this way that we have dealt with the specialized problems of the infinite in mathematics. We have been led to reject not merely the realisms, implicit or explicit, still clinging to the mathematical infinity, but also those that pertain to the mathematically finite and to mathematical unity. It has been found that in the realisms of the "one" lie the sources of the paradoxes of the "infinite." As for the "null" which apes, now the "one" and now the "infinite," in its construction, the "existence" or "existences" which it asserts must be confined within the consistent system, or systems, in which they are expressed. But if the "null" and the "infinite" have controls established for their meanings, it is only such controls as are asserted for the "one": and the freedom of constructive development stands secure.

The present book remains, in the view of its writer, a record of exploration, not an achieved formulation. This is true whether we regard the immediate development of its subject matter, or the manner of investigation it employs. If it provides even a preliminary sketch for a map, or for a single form of map, of these jungles of knowledge, it will have fulfilled its hope.

## Index of Names

# Index of Linguistic Usage